Native Bush, Rainbow Springs, Rotorua

*The fourth edition of "Bed & Breakfast in New Zealand"
is dedicated to the many hosts who continuously
provide New Zealand's charming, unique
style of Bed & Breakfast
hospitality.*

For all enquiries please contact Uli or Brian at Travelwise
Ph 0064-3-476 1515.   Fax 0064-3-4761514
e-mail: enquiries@travelwise.co.nz

Charming
BED & BREAKFAST
in
New Zealand

"Welcome"

year 2002 edition

travel*wise* publications

Waterfront, Russell, Northland.

Charming
BED & BREAKFAST
in
New Zealand

Presenting New Zealand's
Charming World of
Bed & Breakfast Hospitality

Published by TRAVEL*WISE* Ltd.
P.O.Box 6226, Great King Street, Dunedin, New Zealand.
Production and design by TRAVELwise Ltd.

Printed by GP Print, Wellington, New Zealand.

Distributed by Nationwide Distributors, Christchurch.
Front Cover Photo:
Photography, **Bill Nichol**.
Furnished by '**MacKenzie & Willis**' Dunedin.
Accessories provided by the following Dunedin businesses:
Acquisitions, Dimensions, MacKenzie & Willis, The Victorian Room.

Table of Contents

Visit our Web site http://www.bnbnz.com

"*Experience the real New Zealand – its people*"

Welcome to the charming world
of
Hosted Accommodation in New Zealand.

And what a rich choice it is – from cottages to castles, from budget accommodation to luxurious lodges. You will stay with hosts ranging from those who simply love meeting people to those who have taken hospitality to great entrepreneurial heights. Under the umbrella of Bed & Breakfast you will find: Homestays, Farmstays, Guest Houses, Inns, Lodges, Boutique Accommodation, Countrystays. Bed & Breakfast in New Zealand, where you can get to know the real New Zealand – its people. Stay with teachers, farmers, retired professionals, orchardists,

artists, healers and writers. Share the same interests, hobbies or professional background as your hosts. Enjoy unique Bed & Breakfast experiences at a fishing lodge or a high country sheep farm, or at a riding or weaving school, or just find a "home away from home" in town or country. While both hosts and styles of accommodation vary widely, they all reflect the genuine warmth and friendly hospitality that New Zealanders are known for. Wherever you stay, you will be a welcome guest and your stay a pleasant and memorable one. Enjoy the world's finest hospitality.

WHAT TO EXPECT

Bed & Breakfast in New Zealand has a fine reputation for its standard of services. Guests can expect cleanliness, comfortable beds, a good substantial breakfast and warm, generous hospitality. In addition, your hosts can provide you with first-hand in-depth information about their area. They take pleasure in helping you with your pursuits and travel plans. Their invaluable knowledge can enrich your stay immensely.

WHAT IS EXPECTED
OF YOU

Your hosts will do everything in their power to make your stay an enjoyable and memorable one. However, it is important to remember that in most cases you are a guest in a private home. So please consider the little things, like arranging to have a house-key if returning late at night, or asking about the tariffs for toll calls prior to using the telephone. Please let your hosts know in time if you will be late. Thoughtfulness on your part will contribute to a satisfying experience for both host and guest.

WHAT TO DO – HINTS

You will avoid any disappointment by booking ahead, especially during the high summer season. It is also advisable to call your hosts one day in advance to confirm your booking and let them know about your expected time of arrival. Some hosts offer a complimentary pick-up service from coach, plane or train if guests don't have their own transport. Please give your hosts one day's notice if you would like to have an evening meal.

Most holiday memories are mere snapshots – images we treasure, but that fade with any passing year. But the people we meet – they become a part of us. They live in us. They travel with us.

PAM BROWN, b 1928

Bed & Breakfast Categories

Bed & Breakfast

Bed & Breakfast is the umbrella term for the variety of hosted accommodations that include a comfortable bed for the night and a substantial breakfast in the morning. The hosts offer warm and generous hospitality throughout your stay.

Homestay

Homestay is the popular Bed & Breakfast accommodation that offers warm and friendly hospitality in a private home. The hosts love meeting people, they enjoy providing their guests with that "home away from home" feeling, knowing that they arrive as strangers but will leave as friends.

Countrystay

Countrystays are often like Homestays. They offer accommodation in a private home. Being in a rural setting, they are associated with all the features and attractions of the countryside. Many Countrystays are close to popular country attractions which offer you the chance to experience rural New Zealand life.

Farmstay

Farmstays are an ideal way to experience real farm life in New Zealand. An opportunity for you to have hands-on contact with the animals and daily life on a farm. A farm tour may be included. Breakfast is usually taken with the family. Many Farmstays offer lunch and evening meals, as restaurants are often not close by.

Guesthouse/Inn

Guest Houses and Inns are usually larger establishments that cater for more guests, but still offer that personalised style of hospitality. They might have several lounge areas and a breakfast room. Guest Houses do not usually offer an evening meal.

Boutique Accommodation

Within the Bed & Breakfast world Boutique Accommodation has been adopted by those hosts whose unique property features reflect a special ambience - period elegance, grace and charm, romance, art, etc. These features are usually enhanced by the hosts' flair for entertainment and hospitality.

Luxury Accommodation

Luxury Accommodation symbolizes superb facilities, excellent food and an exceptional level of service. Many properties within this category have spectacular settings and offer various additional top class attractions. They represent outstanding accommodation and hospitality.

Self-contained Accommodation

Self-contained accommodation usually includes a separate entrance, own bathroom facilities and an independent lounge area. Kitchen and laundry facilities may be included. It can be a self-contained part of the family home or a separate cottage. Breakfast is either served in the hosts' home, delivered to the doorstep or breakfast provisions provided on the premises.

How to use this guide – "at a glance"

"at a glance"
Easy Contact Panel
Your hosts: who they are, where they are, and how to make quick contact.

"at a glance"
Tariff Panel
Each tariff indicates the nightly rate. **Double** *indicates the cost for two people sharing one room.* **Single** *indicates the cost for one person occupying a room. A deposit may be required when booking. Tariffs include breakfast unless otherwise stated.* **All prices quoted are in NZ$ – GST inclusive.** *Please confirm details with your host.*

"at a glance"
Category Symbols
These quick-to-spot symbols are designed to make selecting your preferred accommodation easy. Particularly helpful for travellers with a limited knowledge of the English language.

"at a glance"
Category Panel
Your hosts' personal description of their category.

"at a glance"
Features & Attractions
Highlighting the main features and attractions in and around this accommodation and locality.

"at a glance"
Location Map
Your hosts' property is indicated by a red dot. Property name is displayed in white box. Maps may be accompanied by a direction panel outlining easy directions.

Clear Address Details
Clear address panel displays essential information, including property address, telephone and fax numbers, e-mail and Internet address. **NOTE:** *When calling from overseas dial New Zealand's international code, 0064, then drop the 0 off the area code (03), for example "Whispering Pines"* **0064-3-443-1448.**

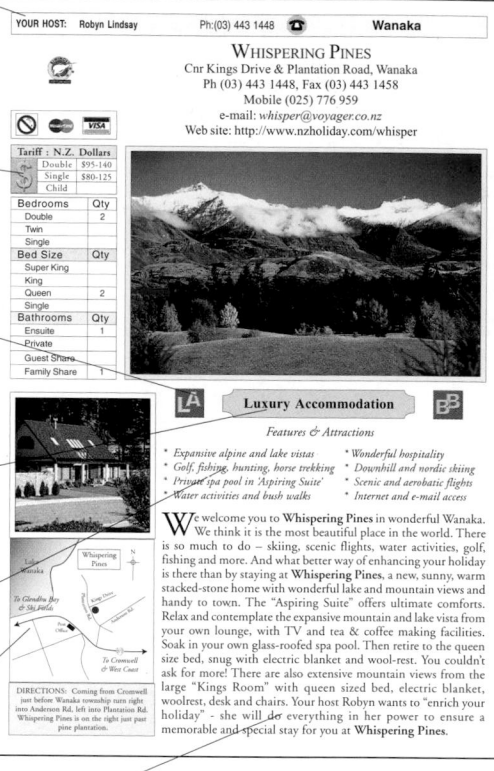

YOUR HOST:	Robyn Lindsay	Ph:(03) 443 1448		Wanaka

WHISPERING PINES
Cnr Kings Drive & Plantation Road, Wanaka
Ph (03) 443 1448, Fax (03) 443 1458
Mobile (025) 776 959
e-mail: *whisper@voyager.co.nz*
Web site: http://www.nzholiday.com/whisper

Tariff : N.Z. Dollars	
Double	$95-140
Single	$80-125
Child	

Bedrooms	Qty
Double	2
Twin	
Single	

Bed Size	Qty
Super King	
King	
Queen	2
Single	

Bathrooms	Qty
Ensuite	1
Private	
Guest Share	
Family Share	1

Luxury Accommodation

Features & Attractions

* Expansive alpine and lake vistas
* Golf, fishing, hunting, horse trekking
* Private spa pool in 'Aspiring Suite'
* Water activities and bush walks
* Wonderful hospitality
* Downhill and nordic skiing
* Scenic and aerobatic flights
* Internet and e-mail access

We welcome you to **Whispering Pines** in wonderful Wanaka. We think it is the most beautiful place in the world. There is so much to do – skiing, scenic flights, water activities, golf, fishing and more. And what better way of enhancing your holiday is there than by staying at **Whispering Pines**, a new, sunny, warm stacked-stone home with wonderful lake and mountain views and handy to town. The "Aspiring Suite" offers ultimate comforts. Relax and contemplate the expansive mountain and lake vista from your own lounge, with TV and tea & coffee making facilities. Soak in your own glass-roofed spa pool. Then retire to the queen size bed, snug with electric blanket and wool-rest. You couldn't ask for more! There are also extensive mountain views from the large "Kings Room" with queen sized bed, electric blanket, woolrest, desk and chairs. Your host Robyn wants to "enrich your holiday" - she will do everything in her power to ensure a memorable and special stay for you at **Whispering Pines**.

DIRECTIONS: Coming from Cromwell just before Wanaka township turn right into Anderson Rd, left into Plantation Rd. Whispering Pines is on the right just past pine plantation.

"A Personal Warm Welcome"
These words of welcome have been written personally by your hosts. They describe the features of the accommodation and portray their personality and lifestyle.

🚭 No Smoking

Abbreviations
SH   –   State Highway
h.p.   –   half price
N.A.   –   not applicable
neg.   –   negotiable
Qty   –   Quantity
Tce   –   Terrace

Book direct – Reduce costs

By booking direct with your Bed & Breakfast host in New Zealand, you make the personal connection right from the start and avoid many additional costs.

How to use this guide – Guest room details

Bedrooms

Double = Room with bed for two people
Twin = Room with two beds for two people
Single = Room with bed for one person

Bathrooms

Ensuite = Bathroom adjoining bedroom
Private = Separate bathroom for your use only
Guest Share/Family Share = Bathroom shared with other guests or host family

Bedrooms	Qty
Double	
Twin	
Single	
Bed Size	**Qty**
Super King	
King	
Queen/Double	
(King-) Single	
Bathrooms	**Qty**
Ensuite	
Private	
Guest Share	
Family Share	

Bed Size	
Super King	*180 x 200cm*
King	*165 x 200cm*
Queen	*150 x 200cm*
Double	*135 x 190cm*
Single	*90 x 190cm*
King Single	*90 x 200cm*

How to use this guide – Category Symbols

 Bed & Breakfast

 Boutique Accommodation

 Countrystay

 Farmstay

 Guest House / Lodges / Inns

 Homestay

 Luxury Accommodation

 Self-contained Accom. & Cottages

How to use this guide – Credit Cards Accepted by Hosts

 Amex – American Express

 Japanese Credit Card

 VISA

 Diners

 Bankcard

 MasterCard

 Maestro

 Eftpos

How to use this guide – Hosts' Associations & Affiliations

 Kiwihost

 New Zealand Association Farm & Home Hosts

 A network of Fine Hosts

 Historic Places Trust

The logo of the **New Zealand Farm and Home Host Association** assures you of a warm welcome in a private home, where guests are treated as friends of the family and given personal care and time by the hosts. Members' homes are inspected on a regular basis.

Dairies and Supermarkets

Dairies, a long-established feature of the New Zealand landscape, are usually open 7 days a week, from early to late. Like the old general country stores, dairies stock a wide variety of goods. You can normally expect to obtain basic foods and commodities, such as bread, milk, newspapers, confectionery and grocery items.

Because of the extended trading hours, and the benefits of convenient locations, prices are normally slightly higher than those at the supermarket. Some dairies, especially in small communities, also offer Post Shop services.

Supermarkets

Nearly all New Zealand towns and cities have supermarkets.

Supermarkets provide a wider range of goods for one-stop grocery shopping, and have more competitive prices.

Free parking is normally provided, but only for genuine customers - you may be asked to show your receipt. Some supermarkets now have extended trading hours, and most are open 7 days a week.

The Corner Dairy – so much a part of New Zealand's daily life.

Petrol Stations

Also known as 'Service Stations', provide basic commodities for motor vehicles: fuel, oil, air, water, and general motoring accessories. Although petrol stations do not normally provide repair or maintenance services - these are provided by 'Garages' - those that do may have a sign saying 'Mechanic on duty' or 'Repairs carried out'.

Tourist Radio

Tourist Information FM is a service established to provide information to visitors to New Zealand 24 hours a day, and is available in most tourist areas. For English-language broadcasts, tune to 88.2 FM on your radio. For German-language broadcasts, tune to 100.4 FM, and for Japanese-language broadcasts, tune to 100.8 FM on your radio.

Visitor Information Network

Visitor Information Centres are identified by the distinctive green italic *i* logo in conjunction with the Visitor Information logo.

Over 80 of them are located throughout New Zealand. They offer a wide range of services. including travel bookings, tours and accommodation.

The staff, who have unparalleled local and national knowledge are trained and committed to providing accurate and approriate information to visitors.

Emergency Services

**If you require the police, ambulance or fire service, dial 111.
There is no charge for making a 111 call from a public phone box.**

Posting a Letter

New Zealand's main postal operator is New Zealand Post with a network of 1000 Post Shops and Post Centres covering the whole country, and 5,000 post boxes where you can post letters. Some outlets combine their normal retail activities with providing New Zealand Post services, especially in smaller towns. Look for the red New Zealand Post logo displayed outside shops.

New Zealand Post Shop

If you need help and cannot get to a Post Shop, you can call New Zealand Post freephone 0800 NZPOST (0800 697 678), 8am to 7pm weekdays, or 9am to 1pm Saturdays.

Post Shops

Post Shops offer a wide range of products and services including:

- stamps
- protective packaging
- sending letters and parcels
- sending faxes and telegrams, couriering items overseas or around New Zealand
- stationery, greeting cards, phone cards, gifts (e.g. calendars) and more

Post Shop staff can help you decide which type of packaging will get your parcels delivered as cheaply as possible. A handy Parcel Packaging Guide is also available which contains advice on ways to ensure your parcel arrives safely. Post Shops accept cash, cheque, EFTPOS, MasterCard and VISA for most products and services.

Postal Costs

For Sending letters and packages within New Zealand,
A standard size letter (maximum 129mm x 235mm) costs 40 cents and takes 2-4 days to be delivered. If you want to get it there faster, FastPost costs 80 cents for a standard size letter which is then delivered by the next working day between major towns and cities. (Rural and remote areas may take a little longer.) You can send parcels from $3.40, depending on size and weight. Items can also be couriered from a Post Shop.

For sending letters and packages overseas. You can ask at the local Post Shop about the best way to package and send items overseas. Options include first class air mail, sea post, registered post and courier. By paying an additional $8 and sending your parcel as a customs parcel, New Zealand Post extends cover for loss or damage from NZ$250 to $1,500.

Packages for Japan

For sending packages to Japan, there is a special Kiwi Yu Pack for items up to 5kg, and for delivery within 2-4 working days.

The rural mailbox, a roadside feature throughout New Zealand's countryside.

Money and Banks

Currency

New Zealand has been operating on the decimal currency system with the NZ Dollar as its base since 10 July 1967. Coins in use are: 5c, 10c, 20c, 50c, $1 and $2. Bank notes are available in denominations of $5, $10, $20, $50 and $100.

Changing Money

Money exchange facilities exist at all banks and at most New Zealand international airports. New Zealand banks buy and sell all major currencies and offer competitive exchange rates which are updated daily.

Travellers' Cheques

Travellers' cheques can also be cashed at Bureaux de Change and hotels or large stores in resorts and larger cities.

Import or export of foreign currency is not subject to any restrictions.

All banks are listed in the Yellow Pages at the back of the local telephone directory.

Credit cards

Payment by any of the international credit cards, including Visa, Master Card, American Express, Diners Club and JCB (Japanese credit card) is widely accepted. Most shops display the card signs in their windows. If in doubt, please check with a sales person before you commence shopping.

**Automatic Teller Machine
24 hour access.**

Banks

All trading banks are open for business between the hours of 9:30am and 4:30pm. Monday to Friday inclusive, with the exception of public holidays. Automatic Teller Machines (ATMs), operate on a card and pin number system. Cash can be withdrawn 24 hours a day.

EFTPOS (Electronic Transfer of Funds at Point of Sale) is a highly used way of cash payments , which is being used all over New Zealand.

You will find operating EFTPOS machines in shops, museums, supermarkets, petrol stations, to name only a few. Instead of a cash payment, the cash amount is transferred directly from the customer's into the selling company's bank account. The transaction takes place at the counter or check out, where customers swipe their EFTPOS card through the machine and type in their pin number. This convenient way of cash payment can be very handy in remote places or after hours. Many stores with EFTPOS facilities also allow you to withdraw cash when making purchases.

Using the Telephone

The phone system in New Zealand is of a high technical standard and performs efficiently. There are two main service providers, **Telecom** and **Clear.** You will find public telephones throughout the entire country. The majority of public telephones in NZ operate the pre-paid phone card system. Telecom **PhoneCards** are available in NZ$5, NZ$10, NZ$20 and NZ$50 denominations. These can be purchased from many outlets including **NZ Post Shops,** supermarkets, dairies, newsagents, **Visi-**tor **Information Centres** and petrol stations. You may find it helpful to purchase a **PhoneCard** even if it is only for emergencies. Increasing numbers of credit card operated phones are now being established which accept major international credit cards. Some public telephones are still coin operated, using 10c, 20c, 50c, NZ$1 and NZ$2 coins. When dialling **Freephone** numbers (commencing with 0800) from public phones you will not require any cards or coins.

Typical public phone booths. Coloured for easy recognition, Yellow for Credit card, Green for PhoneCard, and Blue for Coin.

1 Lift handset, do not insert coins.

2 Dial the number you require. The price per minute or part minute will show on screen.

3 Insert coins. Usable coins:10c, 20c, 50c, NZ$1, and NZ$2.

4 Once call is finished replace handset.

5 Unused coins returned, partly used coins not returned.

Telecom PhoneCards available : NZ$5, NZ$10, NZ$20, and NZ$50. They can be easily obtained at many outlets such as Dairies, Post Offices, and Petrol Stations.

Using the PhoneCard
1. Lift handset. 2. Insert Card. 3. Dial number.
4. After call, replace handset. 5. Remove card (Don't forget!)

Coins acepted by Coin Phones:– 10c, 20c, 50c, NZ$1 and NZ$2.

e-Phone Maxi-Save Toll Card

The *e*-**Phone Toll Card** is an easy and convenient way to use almost any touch tone phone at your own expense. It can be used from a private phone, card phone, credit card phone, cellphone, **Your Yost's Phone,** etc.
Using these prepaid phone cards will make you and your host feel less apprehensive when you use their phone. *e*-**Phone Toll Cards** can be purchased in many dairies, super markets and shopping malls.
For detailed information, just call Free Phone 0800-437 4663.

EMERGENCY CALLS......111
Police, Fire, Ambulance
Useful Telephone Numbers

Operator 010
International Operator 0170
National Enquiries............ 018
International Enquiries 0172
International Access Code ... 00
Australia dialling code 0061
Germany dialling code 0049
Japan dialling code 008
USA dialling code 001

Driving in New Zealand can be a pleasure,
the ever changing scenery is superb.

On the Road

Driving in New Zealand is a pleasure; the scenery is superb, the roads are generally of a high standard and New Zealanders are helpful and courteous.

However, for your safety and that of other motorists, we urge you to take a little time (New Zealand is patient, it will wait for you) and read the following before you begin driving.

The *New Zealand Road Code* is the definitive guide to correct and lawful driving in New Zealand. It is available at a small cost from the Land Transport Safety Authority. Look in the local telephone directory for the nearest office. A useful leaflet, with English, German and Japanese sections, is *Driving Safely in New Zealand*, also available free of charge from the Land Transport Safety Authority.

Driving : Some Basic Points

Keep Left: In New Zealand we drive on the **left**.

Overseas vistors may find this difficult. – We suggest you take time to adjust and plan your journeys accordingly.

Speed Limit: In general, the maximum speed limit on the open road or motorway / freeway, identifiable by this sign, is 100 kilometres per hour.

In cities and towns, it is 50km per hour. There are exceptions, so watch out for signs (positioned on the left of the  road) which may indicate a lower specified speed limit.

Road Signs at Intersections:

Stop: Stop completely, then give way to all traffic.

Give way - Drive slowly. Stop if drivers are approaching from left or right, and give way to all traffic, including those opposite if you are turning left.

Seatbelts: The driver and all passengers (adults and children) - including those sitting in rear seats - must use seatbelts or approved child restraints.

The **New Zealand Automobile Association** (*AA*) offers an excellent service nationwide providing maps, guides and touring information. Freephone 0800 500 444 at any time.

Magnificent Contrasts and Colourful Variety

New Zealand's landscapes are as colourful and diverse as its people. No other country can offer such variety of magnificent scenery in such a comparatively small area. In both islands evergreen native bush abounds. In the North Island there are also exotic forests of huge Kauri trees. A wonderland of hot springs, geysers and boiling mud pools is situated near Rotorua in the centre of the North Island. Therapeutic hot springs are located in parts of both islands, and spectacularly beautiful National Parks with their unspoiled scenery and nature will delight the traveller. The South Island offers scenery on the grand scale: mountains, glaciers, lakes and sweeping coastal beaches. Deep-water fiords slice into the south-west coast, with virgin mountain country in the background. One of the most famous fiords - Milford Sound - is accessible by road as well as by the famed Milford Track, the "most beautiful walk in the world". New Zealand has an abundance of aquatic scenery. Take your pick of spectacular waterfalls, raging torrents, broad rivers, lakes big and small, surfing beaches and rocky coast lines.

South Island West Coast - Native bush.

Waitangi Golf Course - *one of the many superb golf courses you will find in New Zealand.*

Most New Zealanders love sport and the outdoors. Their country's natural features support an abundance of outdoor activities: yachting, golf, rugby and mountaineering, to name only a few. All types of winter sports are practised in both islands and wild game and fish provide excellent hunting and fishing.

Tane Mahuta, Waipoua Forest, Northland.

North Island

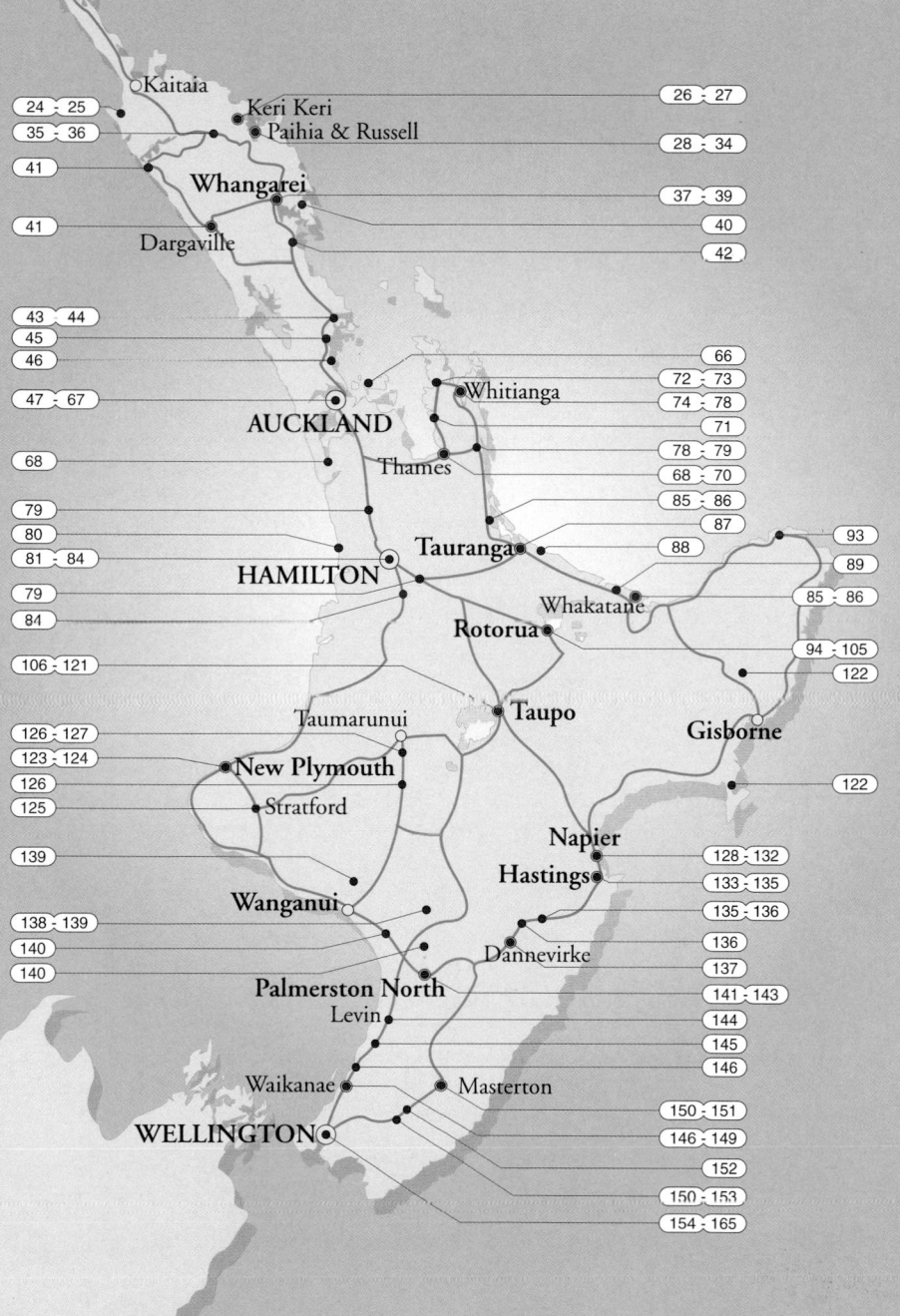

Kaitaia

24 - 25
35 - 36
41

26 - 27
28 - 34

Keri Keri
Paihia & Russell

41

Whangarei

37 - 39
40
42

Dargaville

43 - 44
45
46
47 - 67

Whitianga

66
72 - 73
74 - 78
71

AUCKLAND

68

Thames

78 - 79
68 - 70
85 - 86
87

79
80
81 - 84
79
84

Tauranga

88

93
89
85 - 86

HAMILTON

Whakatane

Rotorua

94 - 105
122

106 - 121

Taumarunui

Taupo

Gisborne

126 - 127
123 - 124
126
125

New Plymouth

Stratford

139

Wanganui

Napier

Hastings

122

128 - 132
133 - 135
135 - 136
136
137

138 - 139
140
140

Palmerston North

Dannevirke

Levin

141 - 143
144
145
146

Waikanae

Masterton

WELLINGTON

150 - 151
146 - 149
152
150 - 153
154 - 165

23

BEACH ABODE

11 Korora Street, P.O.Box 134, Ahipara, Northland
Ph/Fax: (09) 409 4070, Mobile: 025 574 963
e-mail:ned.susan@xtra.co.nz
http://www.beachabode.co.nz

Features & Attractions

- *Absolute beachfront*
- *Links golf course*
- *World class surfing*
- *Quad bike hire*
- *Horseback riding/fishing*
- *Breakfast/dinner available*

Double	$85-115
Single	$75-85
Child	$15

**Self-contained
Beachside Accommodation**

Bedrooms	Qty
Double	2
Twin	2
Single	
Bed Size	**Qty**
King	
Queen	2
Single	4
Bathrooms	**Qty**
Ensuite	
Private	2
Guest Share	
Family Share	

'Organic food available"

Ned and I were living in Tauranga and came to Ahipara for a holiday with friends from Hawaii. That was in November 1998. It was a rainy sub-tropical night when we arrived, reminiscent of Hawaii. The following day the weather became sunny and we spent our time in the warm sun, surfing and swimming in the Tasman Sea. What struck me was the stunning beauty of the green hills meeting the sea, the warm water and the expansiveness of 90 Mile Beach. After our holiday, we decided to make the move up north and build a new home and business. We found an ideal beach front property. The contemporary interior design of the purpose-built units in earth and sea tones reflects the natural environment. We love our **Beach Abode** and our little seaside village of Ahipara.

DIRECTIONS: Please phone for easy directions.

SURF VIEW

125 Foreshore Road, Ahipara, 90 Mile Beach
Ph (09) 408 1725.
e-mail: *Tjcurreen@hotmail.com*

Features & Attractions

- *Famous Ninety Mile Beach*
- *Beach 30 metres away*
- *Off street parking*
- *Privacy - owners live off site*
- *Fully self-contained, nice decor*
- *Courtesy pickup from airport/bus*

**Self-contained
Seaside Holiday Home**

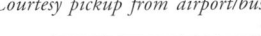

Double	$85
Single	$70
Child	neg.

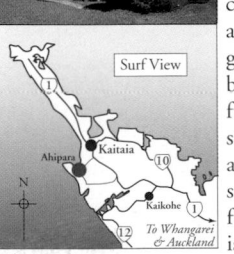

Surf View

S urf View holiday home is an excellent location to discover how scenic the Far North of New Zealand is. From here you can daily visit places of interest and historic significance. Situated at the southern end of the famous Ninety Mile Beach. We offer guests a place to relax in comfort just thirty metres from the beach. **Surf View** sleeps five with one queen bed, one double futon and one single bed. The kitchen is well equipped with stove, fridge-freezer, microwave, two TVs, washing machine and a monitored security system. Furnishings and decor are of a high standard. Ahipara has supply shops and offers golf, fish surf and fun activities. Kaitaia, the nearest town – ten minutes drive away, is the main shopping centre. *Extra adults $5 per person per day.*

Bedrooms	Qty
Double	1
Lounge Futon	1
Single	1
Bed Size	**Qty**
Queen	1
Double-Futon	1
Single	1
Bathrooms	**Qty**
Ensuite	
Private	1
Guest Share	
Family Share	

DIRECTIONS: Coming from Kaitaia on the main road, Ahipara is well signposted.

SHIPWRECK LODGE

70 Foreshore Road, Ahipara, 90 Mile Beach
(09) 409 4929, Fax (09) 409 4928
Mobile: 025 - 759 504
e-mail: *shipwrecklodge@xtra.co.nz*
http://www.shipwrecklodge.co.nz

Tariff : N.Z. Dollars	
Double	$145-225
Single	$115-155
Child	

Bedrooms	Qty
Double	2
Twin	
Single	
Bed Size	Qty
Super King	
King	1
Queen	1
Single	
Bathrooms	Qty
Ensuite	2
Private	
Guest Share	
Family Share	

**Beachfront
Spectacular Views**

Features & Attractions

- *Beachfront setting*
- *Spectacular views*
- *Beautifully appointed bedrooms*
- *Private balconies & ensuites*
- *Links golf course*
- *Fishing, swimming, walking*
- *Int. standard golf course close by*
- *Cape Reinga Tours*

The vast beautiful expanses of 90 Mile Beach form the backdrop for **Shipwreck Lodge**. **Shipwreck Lodge** was born out of our search for the perfect wave to surf. In '96 we came across the legendary surf breaks of Shipwreck Bay. My son and I surfed alone in this idyllic setting for hours. We purchased land and four years later set about building an architecturally designed masonry villa, which we could share with four guests. Guests have two upstairs rooms to choose from. Both, the spacious king and the queen size bedroom, have well appointed ensuite bathrooms. Furniture is made of recycled New Zealand timber. Natural fibres and cotton linen is used throughout. From your private balcony view the vast panorama of 90 Mile Beach: to the south the reefs of Shipwreck Bay, to the North the beach drifts off into the distant horizon with the giant sand hills of Te Paki and Cape Reinga - the tip of New Zealand. Your stay can encompass a wide range of activities: swimming, fishing, quad biking or playing the local golf courses. Enjoy the wines of our excellent winery, stroll the beach and delight in the romantic sunsets.

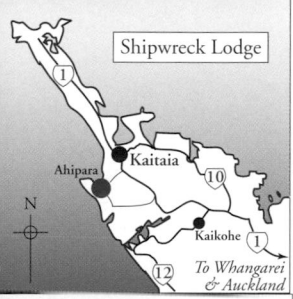

Shipwreck Lodge

Ahipara Kaitaia
Kaikohe
To Whangarei
& Auckland

DIRECTIONS: Take SH 1 north. From Auckland through Whangarei, KawaKawa to Kaitaia. As you enter the township of Kaitaia turn left at the town clock. The road is signposted to Ahipara. Enter Ahipara and turn left just past the school. **Shipwreck Lodge** is 600 m on the right.

THE SUMMER HOUSE
Kerikeri Road, Kerikeri
Ph (09) 407 4294, Fax(09) 407 4297
Mobile (025) 409 288
e-mail: *summerhouse@xtra.co.nz*
http://www.thesummerhouse.co.nz

Tariff : N.Z. Dollars	
Double	$165-185
Single	$135-145
Child	n/a

Bedrooms	Qty
Double	3
Twin	
Single	

Bed Size	Qty
Super King	
King	
Queen/Double	2
King/Single	1

Bathrooms	Qty
Ensuite	2
Private	1
Guest Share	
Family Share	

Self-contained
Boutique Accommodation

Special rates for off-season
and longer stays.

Features & Attractions
- *1.5 kms from Kerikeri village*
- *Cafés, craft shops, vineyards*
- *Historic sites*
- *Forests, beaches, Bay of Islands*
- *Striking design and decor*
- *Fruit and juice from orchard*
- *Tranquil garden and pond*
- *Kauri Cliffs golf course*

The setting is idyllic, the accommodation exquisite, and the company convivial at **The Summer House**, a French Provincial inspired Bed and Breakfast. This is the perfect retreat for relaxation, to experience Kerikeri's vineyards, cafés and craft shops and to explore the Bay of Islands and the beaches, Kauri forests and historic sites of the Far North.

This architecturally designed home is set in a tranquil hectare of citrus orchard and beautifully landscaped sub-tropical garden. Enjoy gourmet breakfasts, warm hospitality and inspiring surroundings. One self-contained, semi-detached suite and two double rooms in-house both with ensuites and guest lounge.

We can help with your itinerary and can arrange: sailing, diving, fishing, golf, bush walks, tours etc and even to see a kiwi in its habitat.

Friench and German spoken. Unsuitable for children.

DIRECTIONS: From State Highway 10, **The Summer House** is 1.7 km along Kerikeri Rd on the left, just two minutes drive from Kerikeri Village. Pick up from the airport would be a pleasure.

FERNBROOK

Kurapari Road, Rangitane
Kerikeri R.D.1.
Ph (09) 407 8570, Fax (09) 407 8572
e-mail: tfc@igrin.co.nz

Features & Attractions

- *Kiwi sanctuary*
- *Historic sites*
- *Magnificent views*
- *Bush walks*
- *Bay of Islands Tranquility*

Double	$175-200
Single	$85-100
Child	neg.

Boutique Holiday Accommodation

Bedrooms	Qty
Double	3
Twin	1
Single	
Bed Size	**Qty**
King	
Queen	3
Single	2
Bathrooms	**Qty**
Ensuite	2
Private	1
Guest Share	
Family Share	

 FERNBROOK

Fernbrook is a comfortable hillside country house, set in 27 hectares overlooking the Kerikeri Inlet - 12 minutes drive from the town of Kerikeri and 35 min. flying time from Auckland. It offers magnificent views, a secluded beach, bush walks and a wide variety of bird life including the rare North Island Brown Kiwi. The house has an extensive library, large garden, croquet lawn and petanque court. Dinner is by arrangement and comprises the best of New Zealand food and wine. Tariff includes laundry service and collection from the airport if required. The wide variety of recreational activities includes golf, horse riding, charter sailing, big game fishing and exploring ancient kauri forests and historic sites. In this idyllic rural setting you can enjoy New Zealand's northern region for its fascinating history and magnificent coastal scenery.

DIRECTIONS: From Stone Store, Kerikeri, toward Rangitane as signposted for 11 km. Turn right at end of Rangitane Rd., proceed 1 km, turn right into unsealed Kurapari Rd. **Fernbrook** is 2nd driveway on right.

YOUR HOSTS: **Jean and Ian Dunn**   Ph: (09) 407 9033   **Kerikeri - Bay of Islands**

WAI-TUI LODGE

Yacht Drive, Opito Bay RD 1, PO Box 256
Kerikeri, Bay of Islands
Ph (09) 407 9033. Fax (09) 407 7176
e-mail: waituilodge@actrix.co.nz

Features & Attractions

- *Tea/coffee, TV in rooms*
- *Sea and rural views*
- *Kiwi habitat*
- *Safe swimming beaches*
- *Bush walks*
- *Fishing*

A Relaxing Homestay In A Busy World

Double	$120
Single	$90
Child	NA

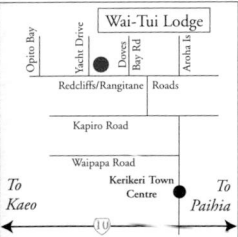

Bedrooms	Qty
Double	2
Twin	
Single	
Bed Size	**Qty**
King	
Queen	2
Single	
Bathrooms	**Qty**
Ensuite	2
Private	
Guest Share	
Family Share	

By day the gardens are alive with native birds. By night hear the call of the morepork and kiwi.

Wai-Tui Lodge is nestled in a peaceful bush-clad valley, overlooking the Kerikeri Inlet and twelve minutes from Kerikeri shops, restaurants and golf course. We are close to safe swimming beaches, Aroha Island Ecological Centre, bush walks, boat ramps and kayak hire.
Catering for a maximum of four guests, our priority is your comfort and relaxation. The spacious rooms have queen beds, luxurious ensuites with heated floors and towel rails. Enjoy our spa and swimming pool, private decks and gardens. Self catering available.
Ours is a stress-free environment – relax and enjoy!

PUKETONA LODGE

Puketona Road, RD 1, Paihia, Northland
Ph (09) 402 8152, Fax (09) 402 8152
Mobile 025-260 7058
e-mail: *puketonalodge@xtra.co.nz*

Tariff : N.Z. Dollars		
	Double	$115-120
	Single	$90
	Child	

Bedrooms	Qty
Double	1
Twin/King	1
Single	

Bed Size	Qty
Super King	
King/Twin	1
Queen	1
Single	

Bathrooms	Qty
Ensuite	1
Private	1
Guest Share	
Family Share	

**Relaxing
Country Homestay**

Features & Attractions

- *Tranquil setting*
- *Excellent golf courses*
- *Tours & cruises*
- *2 acres of gardens*
- *Historic sites*
- *Lovely walks & beaches*
- *Full breakfast available*
- *Bedrooms open onto verandah*

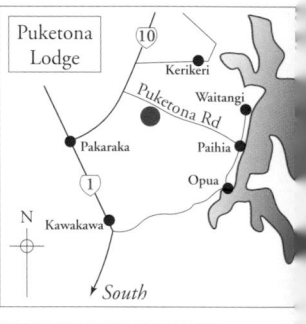

DIRECTIONS:
Please phone for simple directions,

Puketona Lodge is a modern country house, built by Maurice, set in two acres of landscaped gardens. It is located in the scenic Bay of Islands, handy to Kerikeri, Haruru Falls, Paihia and historic sites. Guests are encouraged to enjoy the garden and the native birds, including Tuis and Fantails. Tour buses pass the gate, and we can make bookings for tours and cruises. **Puketona Lodge** is close to walking tracks and golf courses.

The bedrooms are large and private. The king room has an ensuite, the double room has its own private bathroom with separate toilet. Both bedrooms open onto the verandah. Tariff includes full breakfast.

Heather and Maurice have lived in the UK and USA and still have family ties there. Heather enjoys showing guests her ceramic studio.

RiverPark

Puketona Road, RD 1, Paihia, Bay of Islands
e-mail: *RiverPark@xtra.co.nz*
http://www.riverpark.co.nz

Features & Attractions

- *Rural riverside setting*
- *Beaches & Golf 5 min. drive*
- *Two acres gardens/lawns*
- *Cruises/dolphin trips 5 min.*
- *Paihia 5 min. drive*
- *Wheelchair - friendly*

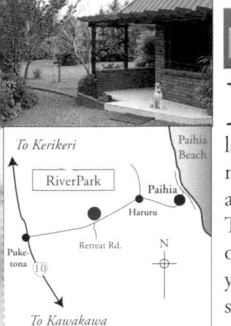

Bed & Breakfast Self-contained Unit		Double	$ 90-120
		Single	
		Child	

To Kerikeri — Paihia Beach — RiverPark — Paihia — Haruru — Retreat Rd. — Puketona (10) — To Kawakawa

DIRECTIONS: Opposite Retreat Rd. on Puketona Rd. 5.7 km from SH 10 on left. 6.5 km from Paihia Beach on right. Stone walls at entrance.

RiverPark is Noelle and Graham's modern riverside home with carefully landscaped gardens of trees, shrubs and evergreen lawns. **RiverPark's** self-contained unit is exclusively yours. Enjoy a microwave kitchen with fridge/freezer, fan oven, pantry, a TV lounge and a comfortably appointed bedroom with tiled bathroom ensuite. To freshen your wardrobe an electric steam iron is included in your own laundry with dryer. Noelle and Graham invite you to enjoy your generous continental breakfast in the sunny dining alcove. Or set your table outside on tiled verandah decks beside the tidy herb garden. A delightful idea! If you take pleasure from spacious gardens and lawns, lush sub-tropical growth, natural surroundings and sensible home comforts, neat and clean – welcome to **RiverPark!**

Bedrooms	Qty
Double	
Twin	2
Single	
Bed Size	**Qty**
King	
King - Single	2
Single	2
Bathrooms	**Qty**
Ensuite	2
Private	
Guest Share	
Family Share	

Villa Casablanca

18 Goffe Drive, Haruru Falls, Paihia
Postal: P.O. Box 73, Paihia, Bay of Islands
Ph/Fax (09) 402 6980, Mobile 021- 666 567
e-mail: *derek@bestprice.co.nz*
http://www.bestprice.co.nz

Features & Attractions

- *Spectacular bay views*
- *Viewing platform & sun deck*
- *Fine food - Happy hosts*
- *Walk to restaurants & water fall*
- *Dinner by arrangement*
- *Seasonal & weekly discounts*

	Double	$160-180
	Single	$130-150
	Child	neg

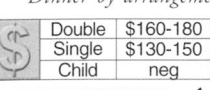

Luxury Bed & Breakfast Inn

Bedrooms	Qty
Double	4
Twin	3
Single	
Bed Size	**Qty**
Super King	1
Queen	3
King Single	6
Bathrooms	**Qty**
Ensuite	4
Private	2
Guest Share	
Family Share	

A romantic villa with spectacular views over the Bay of Islands and Waitangi golf course. Our unique house is modeled on a Spanish hacienda, surrounded by sub-tropical gardens of palm treees, ferns and flowering shrubs. The guest wing consists of three bedrooms, each with private or ensuite toilets, coffee or tea making facilities and a bar fridge. Our Champagne Room features a 2 person spa bath and the Roman Room a 2 person roman bath. There is a large guest lounge overlooking the Bay, a television lounge, library and breakfast room. The self-catering holiday apartments have two bedrooms, lounge and kitchen. **Villa Casablanca** makes an ideal base for your stay in Northland. It is within easy driving or coach distance from all the main sites and less than five minutes to Paihia's beach and shops.

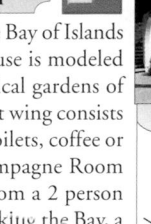

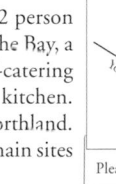

Waitangi — Villa Casablanca — Yorke Rd — Puketona Rd — Paihia — To Kerikeri

Please phone for easy directions

MARLIN HOUSE

15 Bayview Road, Paihia 1301, Northland
Ph (09) 402 8550, Fax (09) 402 6770
Mobile 025-487 937
e-mail: *chris.houry@xtra.co.nz*

Tariff : N.Z. Dollars	
Double	$90-130
Single	$80-100
Child	

Bedrooms	Qty
Double	3
Twin	1
Single	
Bed Size	**Qty**
Super King	
King	
Queen	2
King Single	2
Bathrooms	**Qty**
Ensuite	4
Private	
Guest Share	
Family Share	

 Luxury Ensuites

Features & Attractions

- *Luxury accommodation*
- *Big game fishing*
- *Close to sea and shops*
- *Stunning views*
- *Swimming with dolphins*
- *SKY TV in rooms*
- *Excursion discounts*
- *Special contin. breakfasts*

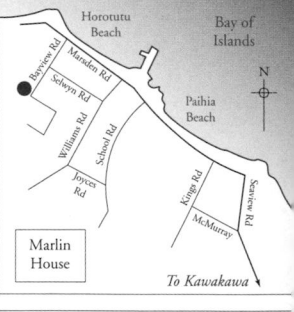

Marlin House is a classic modernised neo-colonial building (1996). It is set on a quiet tree-clad hillside just above Paihia.
The views of the Bay of Islands are wonderful.

Advance Booking Recommended.

The house offers safe off-road parking, four self-contained generous sized ensuites with fridge, sitting room, a deck and Sky TV all inclusive. It is close to the beachfront shops and restaurants.
We serve special continental breakfasts, but for a small extra charge you are welcome to something cooked and served in your suite or on the deck.
To help you enjoy your stay with us, we can arrange mini cruises, fishing, excursions, golf, kayaking restaurants and almost anything else our resort offers. In some cases we can get you a worthwhile discount.

"WINDERMERE"
168 Marsden Road (PO Box 289) Paihia
Ph (09) 402 8696 Fax (09) 402 5095
e-mail: *windermere@igrin.co.nz*
http://www.windermere.co.nz

Features & Attractions
- *Great views*
- *Spacious sunny units*
- *Own outside access*
- *Safe swimming beach*
- *Fishing and tours arranged*
- *Close to town & golf course*

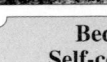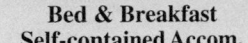

Double	$100-150
Single	$100
Child	$25

Bed & Breakfast Self-contained Accom.

Bedrooms	Qty
Double	2
Twin	
Single	
Bed Size	**Qty**
King	
Queen	2
Single	4
Bathrooms	**Qty**
Ensuite	2
Private	
Guest Share	
Family Share	

"**Windermere**" is a large modern family home set in a bush setting and yet located right on one of the best beaches in the Bay of Islands.

Superior accommodation is provided with suites having their own ensuite and kitchen facilities. For longer stays one suite has its own laundry, dryer and fully equipped kitchen. The other suite has microwave and fridge only. Each suite has its own decks (a BBQ is provided) where you can sit and relax and enjoy the view enhanced by spectacular sunsets.

Jill and Richard would welcome your company to enjoy our own little part of paradise.

ISLAND VIEW LODGE

1 Oromahoe Road, (PO Box 109, Paihia)
Opua, Bay of Islands
Ph/Fax (09) 402 7389, Mobile 025 - 366 360
e-mail: *view@bay-of-islands.co.nz*
http://www.bay-of-islands.co.nz/accomm/islandview.htm

Features & Attractions
- *Sea views from every room*
- *5 minutes Paihia Township*
- *Waitangi Golf Course 5 min.*
- *Tours & attractions arranged*
- *Walking distance to Opua*
- *Kauri and coastal bush walks*

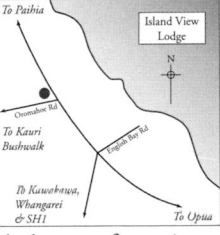

Self-contained Bed & Breakfast Accom.

Double	$120-160
Single	$90-110
Child	

Our large home is on a hilltop overlooking the Bay of Islands and Opua Harbour with fantastic sea and bush views and tropical gardens. We are within walking distance of the Opua Wharf store and marina. Once there, you can take the car ferry to Historic Russell, board the vintage steam train to Kawa Kawa return, or dine in a restaurant. There is a beautiful coastal walkway and magnificent kauri bush walk close by.

Three selfcontained studio units with ensuites, kitchenettes and balconies. A large four person self-contained cottage with the same fantastic sea views and tropical gardens. Generous continental breakfast can be provided either in your unit or to share with us in our dining room. Paihia township and tourist attractions 5 km away. No shoes in house please. Smoking outside only.

Bedrooms	Qty
Double	4
Twin	
Single	2
Bed Size	**Qty**
King	
Queen	4
Single	4
Bathrooms	**Qty**
Ensuite	4
Private	
Guest Share	
Family Share	

OUNUWHAO B & B HOMESTEAD

Matauwhi Bay, Russell, Bay of Islands
Ph (09) 403 7310, Fax (09) 403 8310
e-mail: ounuwhao@bay-of-islands.co.nz
http://www.bay-of-islands.co.nz/ounuwhao.

VISA
MasterCard

Tariff : N.Z. Dollars	
Double	$150-200
Single	$100-150
Child	$35 (u/12)

Bedrooms	Qty
Double	2
Twin	3
Single	
Bed Size	**Qty**
Super King	
King	1
Queen/Double	4
Single	4
Bathrooms	**Qty**
Ensuite	4
Private	2
Guest Share	
Family Share	

Boutique Accommodation & Self-contained Accommodation

Features & Attractions

- Detached garden suite
- Safe, sandy swimming beaches
- Swimming with the dolphins
- Hearty, healthy gourmet breakfasts
- Historic Russell Village
- Sea and island excursions
- Coastal and bush walks
- Historic homestead

DIRECTIONS:
We are on the main road from
the vehicular ferry, in Matauwhi Bay
1 km from Russell Village.

When visiting Historic Russell take a step back into a bygone era. Spend some time with us in our delightful nostalgic, immaculately restored villa (circa 1894). Enjoy wrap-around verandahs in summer and the large guest lounge with open fire in winter. Each room has traditional wallpapers and paint work with handmade patchwork quilts and fresh flowers to create a lovingly detailed, traditional romantic interior. Breakfast is served in our farmhouse kitchen around the large kauri dining table. It is an all homemade affair, from the fresh baked bread to the yummy daily special and the jam conserves. Our 1930's self-contained cottage is set in park-like grounds for your privacy and enjoyment. With two double bedrooms, large lounge and sunroom and fully self-contained kitchen, it is ideal for people wanting peace and time out. Breakfast is available if required. We look forward to meeting you soon. EXPERIENCE OUR HISTORIC BED & BREAKFAST, ENJOY A WORLD OF DIFFERENCE.

ARCADIA LODGE HISTORIC GUESTHOUSE
10 Florance Ave, Russell Village,
Bay of Islands (P.O.Box 23)
Ph (09) 403 7756, Fax (09) 403 7657
e-mail: *arcadialodge@xtra.co.nz*
http://www.bay-of-islands.co.nz/accomm/arcadia.html

Tariff : N.Z. Dollars	
Double	$155-200
Single	$125-135
Child	

Bedrooms	Qty
Double	6
Twin	1
Single	
Bed Size	**Qty**
Super King	
King	
Queen	2
Double	5
Bathrooms	**Qty**
Ensuite	4
Private	
Guest Share	1
Family Share	

**Boutique Accommodation
Bed & Breakfast**

DIRECTIONS:
By car: Find us on right just before Russell township or off extension of Brind Road for level access.
By bus/plane: All connect with passenger ferry from Paihia. Transport ex ferry is available.

Features & Attractions

- *Continental / cooked breakfast*
- *All tours/excursions arranged*
- *5 min. stroll to village*
- *Expansive gardens*

- *Circa 1899 Tudor*
- *Glorious bay views*
- *5 restaurants nearby*
- *Large guest lounge*

Victorian charm...
    This faithfully restored historic Russell landmark overlooking Matauwhi Bay has played host to world travellers for 100 years.
Arcadia Lodge is full of character, nooks, crannies and antiques. Set in a beautiful and expansive garden, Arcadia has 6 charming suites/bedrooms including decks and lounge areas all with magnificent views of the Bay.
The shops, cafés and wharf of Historic Russell are a mere 5 minute flat stroll away, and departure point for all tours, cruises and ferries.
Legendary breakfasts, hospitality and service from your hosts Jeanne and Curt, Christine and Gary.

33

YOUR HOSTS: **Janey and David Horrell**   Ph: (09) 403 8410

ANCHORAGE OF RUSSELL

43 Tapeka Road, Russell, Bay of Islands
Ph (09) 403 8410, Fax (09) 403 8410
Mobile 021-751 921
e-mail: *anchorage.boi@xtra.co.nz*
www.bay-of-islands.co.nz/accomm/anchorage.html

HOSTLINK
NEW ZEALAND

Features & Attractions

- *Beach front setting*
- *Great breakfasts*
- *Superb local restaurants*
- *Tours/excursions arranged*
- *Complimentary kayaks, mount.bikes*
- *Safe, sandy swimming beach*

Double	$150-180
Single	$120-140
Child	

H   Homestay Bed & Breakfast   **B**B

Bedrooms	Qty
Double	2
Twin	
Single	
Bed Size	**Qty**
King	
Queen	2
Single	
Bathrooms	**Qty**
Ensuite	2
Private	
Guest Share	
Family Share	

 VISA MasterCard 🚭

DIRECTIONS:
Travel through Russell
Village, up Flagstaff Hill to
Tapeka Point.

Step out of your new suite onto Tapeka Beach– the undiscovered gem of the Bay of Islands. Romantic Russell is a two minute drive, and here you may experience early European settlement, New Zealand's oldest church, Russell Museum or Flagstaff Hill. Russell offers a wide range of culinary experiences, the ambience of a small picturesque sea-side town, coastal walkways and from here all boat tours of the Bay depart. We, your hosts Janey, David and our dog Greta, have had a long involvement in the accommodation industry and offer the very best of Kiwi hospitality in our idyllic beachside location. Great breakfasts, served either on the deck or in the dining room, are only surpassed by the superb water views from either location. Your suite is complete with tea, coffee, fridge, TV, stereo and cane furniture. Please come and share our slice of heaven - make this your **Anchorage** where the only sound is the lap of waves.

Bay of Islands

YOUR HOSTS: **Beate and Thomas Lauterbach**   Ph: (09) 403 7095

GASTHAUS WAIPIRO BAY

Waipiro Bay, Rawhiti Road, PO Box 224, Russell
Ph (09) 403 7095. Fax (09) 403 7095
e-mail: *gasthaus@ihug.co.nz*
http://www.lauterbach.co.nz/guesthouse.html

Features & Attractions

- *Peace & harmony close to Russell*
- *Beach in walking distance*
- *Undisturbed seaviews*
- *Nature at your doorstep*
- *Artist's residence*
- *Gourmet food*

BA   Homestay Bed & Breakfast   **B**B   VISA MasterCard

Double	$165-150
Single	reduction
Child	negotiated

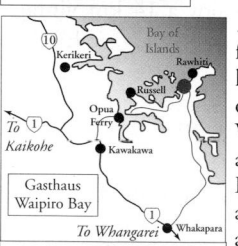

DIRECTIONS: Waipiro Bay
is located 19 km east of Russell
on the Coastal Scenic Drive.
Our driveway is signposted.

Dream of a place, an artist's home above a bay, the Pacific Ocean on the horizon, islands to explore, beaches, forests – nature at your doorstep. This world of space and light inspires artist Thomas Lauterbach to paint strong images of land, sea and the Maori people.
We offer our guests a warm and imaginative home of timber and stone, comfortable bedrooms with spectacular views. Enjoy your private living room with open fire and works of art. Relax on verandas amidst the beautiful garden or follow a romantic path to the beach.
We love to cook gourmet meals with flavours from Italy to the South Pacific. For a taste of heaven on earth - come along and let us spoil you a little.

Bedrooms	Qty
Double	2
Twin	
Single	
Bed Size	**Qty**
King	
Queen	2
Single	1
Bathrooms	**Qty**
Ensuite	1
Private	1
Guest Share	
Family Share	

TEN ON ONE HOME/FARMSTAY

Ludbrook Road, RD 2, Kaikohe, Bay of Islands
Ph (09) 405 9460, Fax (09) 405 9460
Mobile 025-886 618
e-mail: *farm.accommodation@xtra.co.nz*
www.hokiangatours.co.nz/homestay.html

Tariff : N.Z. Dollars	
Double	$80
Single	$50
Child	half price

Bedrooms	Qty
Double	4
Twin	1
Single	1
Bed Size	**Qty**
Super King	
Queen	4
Double	1
Single	7
Bathrooms	**Qty**
Ensuite	4
Private	1
Guest Share	1
Family Share	

 F | **Affordable & Relaxing**
Farm – Homestay Accommodation | **H**

Features & Attractions

- *Hearty breakfast*
- *Clean towels daily*
- *Complimentary tea/coffees*
- *Laundry service/iron avail.*
- *Evening meals available*
- *Laundry service,*
- *Courtesy airport and coach pick-up and return*

"Good morning" - to all our visitors a warm and friendly greeting. The Bay of Islands awaits you. Visit New Zealand's true sub-tropical region for that unforgettable and friendly experience. We have a shower of exciting things to keep you occupied, here are a few suggestions: Would you like to visit Cape Reinga (top of New Zealand), cruise to Cape Brett (*hole in the rock*), visit a 2000 year old kauri tree (*Tane Mahuta*) enjoy a 14 km vintage train ride, visit the famous Waitangi Treaty House, visit historic Russell Town, glow worm caves, chocolate factory, water falls, steam saw mill, visit hokianga to meet Louis (*the gentle giant*) in

DIRECTIONS:
At intersection of SH. 10 and SH.1 travel 80m north on SH.1. We are first house on left (use Ludbrook Rd. entrance).

his amazing craft shop, swimming, paragliding, tramping or milk a cow? Hey - the list goes on and on. **Why visit anywhere else?** Our modern farmstay is central to all activities with clean swimming pool and full Fire Safety Regulation standards. We have both been in the tourist business for many years, and our home meets all fire and safety regulations (1992). **Try us with our positive and caring attitude and you won't be disappointed.** Smoking area available.
Try a completely new tour experience, exclusive day Coach Tours to giant boulders, hot mud pools, petrified kauris.

JARVIS FAMILY FARMSTAY
Pakaraka, SH One, Ohaeawai, Bay of Islands
Ph (09) 405 9606 Fax (09) 405 9607
e-mail: *baystay@igrin.co.nz*
http://www.baystay.com

Tariff : N.Z. Dollars		
	Double	$90 -110
	Single	$45
	Child	neg

Bedrooms	Qty
Double	2
Twin	1
Triple	1
Bed Size	**Qty**
Super King/twin	
King	
Queen/Double	2
Single	5
Bathrooms	**Qty**
Ensuite	
Private	4
Spa Bath	1
Guest Share	

Countrystay
Boutique Accommodation

Features & Attractions

- *Unique accommodation*
- *Four poster bedroom suites*
- *English antiques & paintings*
- *Spa bath & swimming pool*

- *Landscaped subtropical & water gardens*
- *Horse and pony riding in orchard setting*
- *A bird lover's paradise*
- *Cross roads to Far North & Bay of Islands*

For a comfortable and relaxing break, look no further!
As you travel down our orchard road, emus and ostriches line the driveway paddocks. Closer to home family ponies and thoroughbred horses complete the picture.

Our four poster bedroom suite includes its own lounge with two single beds, tv/video, plus a private deck in the "wishing well" garden. Upstairs boasts the "Scottish Room" (3 singles) and an extra double overlooking the cascading water gardens.

Our home enjoys the choice of indoor and outdoor dining - either in the conservatory or on the spacious deck, with its many palms and comfortable outdoor furniture. Here guests can enjoy being hosted to a BBQ or self cater. Dinner parties can be arranged in advance.

Douglas and Fredi emigrated from the UK 10 years ago, where they ran one of England's Top Country Inns, so they are no strangers to hospitality. Guests may also wish to ride on the well-schooled horses and ponies at our adjoining Equestrian Centre - riding by arrangement.

We are centrally based for touring the Bay and West and North Coasts with all the popular tourist and marine activities.

We look forward to hearing from you - a warm welcome awaits you.

Directions:
Just off SH1 - 1.5 km past SH 10
T- junction travelling towards
Ohaeawai and the historical
Pakaraka Mission Church.
We are well signed with flag
poles on the right.

KARAMEA HOUSE

184 Apotu Road, RD 1, Kauri, Whangarei
Ph (09) 435 3401, Fax (09) 435 3495
e-mail: *snelgar@kcbbs.gen.nz*
http://www.karamea.co.nz

Tariff : N.Z. Dollars	
Double	$180
Single	$140
Child	$50

Bedrooms	Qty
Double	2
Twin	1
Single	
Bed Size	**Qty**
Super King	
King	
Queen	3
Single	1
Bathrooms	**Qty**
Ensuite	
Private	1
Guest Share	
Family Share	

 Boutique Accommodation
Homestay

Features & Attractions

- One hour to the Bay of Islands
- ½ hour to swimming & surf beaches
- Outdoor swimming and spa pool
- Gourmet dinner by arrangement
- Park-like grounds and gardens
- Generous hospitality
- Astroturf tennis court
- E-mail facilities available

Kia Ora and welcome to **Karamea House**. This is our home and we, your hosts Eliza and Denis Snelgar are delighted to share with you what we consider our "special place".

Set on 4.8 acres, **Karamea House** is built in colonial style fom native kauri, matai and rimu based on the historical design of Kemp House, the oldest wooden building in New Zealand. People had an opportunity recently to view our property on the "Garden Discovery and Gourmet & Design Tours". Features include a grand entrance, park-like grounds and gardens with doves, paddocks, one with sheep and groves of native trees, fish-ponds, astroturf tennis court, outdoor swimming and spa pools and comfortable elegant interior. Private and secluded, yet we are less than 2 km from the main State Highway, 12 minutes fom Whangarei, and one hour from the Bay of Islands. Our interests are wide, including travelling, wine tasting, fine food, gardening, our families and participating in projects around Northland. We will cook you a gourmet dinner by arrangement and assist you to have the ultimate Northland experience.

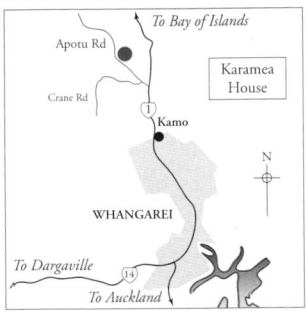

DIRECTIONS: Take SH 1 north of Whangarei and through Kamo for another 2km. Turn left into Apotu Road. Travel 1.8km to Karamea House on the right (12 minutes north of Whangarei.)

Whangarei

☎ YOUR HOSTS: **Cathy and Mel Clarke**   Free Ph: 0508 243 573

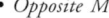

CHELSEA HOUSE
83 Hatea Drive, Whangarei
Free Ph: (0508) 243 573, Mobile 021 - 379 976
e-mail: *mel.clarke@clear.net.nz*

Features & Attractions

- *Central convenient location*
- *Double room with own kitchen*
- *Delicious breakfast menu*
- *Off-street parking*
- *1 km from city centre*
- *Opposite Mair Park*

	Double	$70-90
	Single	$40
	Child	$20

Chelsea House Bed & Breakfast

Bedrooms	Qty
Double	1
Twin	1
Single	
Bed Size	**Qty**
King	
Queen/Double	1
King/Single	2
Bathrooms	**Qty**
Ensuite	2
Private	
Guest Share	
Family Share	

Welcome to **Chelsea House**, the most convenient B & B in Whangarei. Our home is a double gable villa built in 1910 and close to the central city, Town Basin, restaurants and heated pools. Across the road is the entrance to Mair Park which features walkways through beautiful native bush to the summit of Parahaki, the site of the largest Maori Pa in New Zealand. Let us drive you to the top for spectacular views and a leisurely walk down to **Chelsea House**. Our double guest room has a fully equipped kitchen and ensuite, the twin room has tea and coffee making facilities and ensuite. A cooked breakfast of your choice can be served in our family kitchen or outside in the delightful cottage garden. Laundry available.

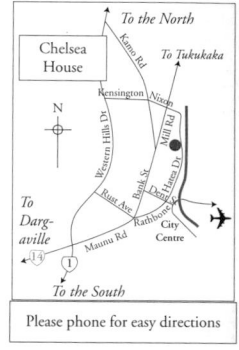

Please phone for easy directions

Whangarei

☎ YOUR HOSTS: **Linda and Grace**   Ph: (09) 437 7532

GRAELYN VILLA
166 Kiripaka Road, Whangarei
Ph (09) 437 7532. Fax (09) 437 7533
e-mail: graelyn@xtra.co.nz

Features & Attractions

- *Tranquil gardens*
- *Bush walks nearby*
- *Choice of golf courses*
- *Adjacent Whangarei Falls*
- *Close to city centre*
- *25 min. to Tutukaka Coast*

	Double	$80
	Single	$65
	Child	

Bed & Breakfast Boutique Accommodation

Bedrooms	Qty
Double	2
Twin	1
Single	
Bed Size	**Qty**
King	
Queen/Double	2
Single	2
Bathrooms	**Qty**
Ensuite	3
Private	
Guest Share	
Family Share	

DIRECTIONS:
5km from City Centre, north-east towards Whangarei Falls. Please call for further directions.

Come into our home and be our guest for a while. You'll receive a very warm welcome. Beautifully presented in a tranquil setting, **Graelyn** is a turn of the century villa, which has been lovingly restored to offer comfort and luxury. Three guest rooms all have ensuite bathrooms, superbly comfortable beds, TV, tea and coffee, electric blankets and heaters. Breakfast is continental, or for a small extra charge your choice of cooked breakfasts, other meals by arrangement. **Graelyn Villa** is only 25 min. from the Tutukaka Coast. Also handy to golf courses, horse riding, bush walks and the spectacular Whangarei Falls. The centre of Whangarei City is only 5 km, with many top class restaurants, cafés, shops, museums and the popular town basin marina. Courtesy transport available from bus or airport. Pets welcome. Mother and daughter team, Grace and Linda, look forward to offering you an escape from your everyday hustle and bustle to our haven of peace and tranquillity.

CHANNEL VISTA

254 Beach Road, Onerahi, Whangarei
Ph (09) 436 5529, Fax (09) 436 5529
Mobile 025 973 083
e-mail: *tancred@igrin.co.nz*

 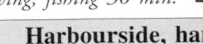

Features & Attractions

- *Only 1 hour to Bay of Islands*
- *Many golf courses handy*
- *Restaurants, shopping 5 min.*
- *Many interesting walks*
- *Sandy, safe beaches nearby*
- *Top diving, fishing 30 min.*

$	Double	$110-150
	Single	$90-100
	Child	

Harbourside, handy Luxury self-contained

Bedrooms	Qty
Double	2
Twin	
Single	
Bed Size	**Qty**
King	
Queen	2
Single	
Bathrooms	**Qty**
Ensuite	2
Private	
Guest Share	
Family Share	

Channel Vista is a modern purpose-built luxury self-contained Bed & Breakfast situated on the interesting Whangarei Harbour, 9 km from Whangarei Central and very handy to the Onerahi shopping complex and sports centres (golf, swimming, walks, pools) and only 5 min. walk along the waterfront to a top restaurant. Bay of Islands, Kerikeri and the West Coast are only one hour away. Poor Knight's Diving and deep sea fishing at Tutukaka is 30 minutes away and lovely Whangarei Heads beaches are so handy.

DIRECTIONS: Follow signs to Onerahi Airport, go past gates to Pah Road, go down Pah Road to roundabout and turn left into Beach Road - No 254.

You can see, we are a very handy base for your Northland Holiday. Both self-contained units have lovely decks where you can sit and relax or view the garden or watch superb sunsets. We have a cat called Pepi and a very friendly dog called Salty. We offer a smoke-free environment and a tantalising breakfast menu. Murray and Jenny look forward to hosting you in their home.

TIDE SONG

Beasley Road, RD 1, Onerahi,
Whangarei, Northland
Ph (09) 436 1959
e-mail: *stay@tidesong.co.nz*
http://www.tidesong.co.nz

Features & Attractions

- *Quiet privacy*
- *Bush setting*
- *Farm animals*
- *Spectacular walks*
- *Choice of ocean beaches*
- *Safe estuary for boating*

$	Double	$85
	Single	$60
	Child	

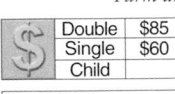

Countrystay Self-contained Accom.

Bedrooms	Qty
Double	2
Twin	
Single	
Bed Size	**Qty**
King	
Queen/Double	2
Single	1
Bathrooms	**Qty**
Ensuite	
Private	1
Guest Share	
Family Share	

From Whangarei drive east for 25 minutes to our 8 acres on the Taiharuru Estuary. With a bush and seaside setting, there is a small jetty, and a variety of small craft to use on the estuary. Spots for fishing and shellfish are close. There is a variety of wonderful walks, with Pacific views and peaks, available to differing levels of fitness. A choice of ocean and surf beaches 10 to 20 minutes away.

Our animals include sheep, dog and cattle. We have a farming and teaching background and are interested in sailing, cycling, conservation, gardening, home-cooking and music. We enjoy having company and looking after guests. Our accommodation is a separate upstairs flat with its own bathroom, kitchen and T.V. We can provide extra home-cooked meals if you wish, or there are restaurants 20 minutes away. We appreciate people not smoking indoors. Looking forward to showing you Northland hospitality.

PARUA HOUSE

Parua Bay, Whangarei Heads Road, RD 4
Postal: Parua Bay, RD 4, Whangarei, Northland
Ph (09) 436 5855, Fax (09) 436 5105
e-mail: paruahomestay@clear.net.nz
http://www.paruahomestay.homestead.com

Tariff : N.Z. Dollars	
Double	$100-110
Single	$70
Child	half price

Bedrooms	Qty
\ Double	2
Twin	1
Single	1
Bed Size	**Qty**
Super King	
King	
Queen	2
Single	3
Bathrooms	**Qty**
Ensuite	2
Private	1
Guest Share	
Family Share	

 Farmstay - Boutique Accommodation

Features & Attractions

- *Outstanding panoramic views*
- *Peaceful setting*
- *Homegrown fruit & produce*
- *Golf course nearby*
- *Superb swimming beaches*
- *Spa pool*
- *Featured on TV: "Ansett NZ-Time of Your Life" & "Corban's Taste NZ"*

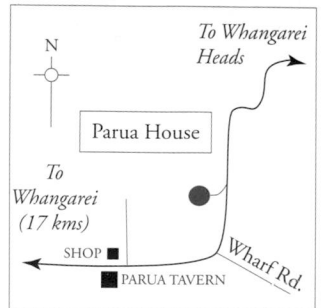

Parua House is a classical colonial house built in 1883, comfortably restored and occupying an elevated site with panoramic views of Parua Bay and Whangarei harbour. The property covers 29 hectares of farmland with lush valleys leading into steep slopes of native bush. Two protected reserves on the property are rich in a variety of native trees (including kauri) and native birds abound. Guests are welcome to explore the farm, milk the Jersey house cow, track through the bush beside the Kohinui stream, explore the olive grove and sub-tropical orchard or just relax in the spa-pool or on the verandah overlooking the marina. A safe swimming beach adjoins the farm with a short walk to a fishing jetty. Two marinas and an excellent golf course are nearby. We have travelled extensively and especially welcome overseas guests. Our interests are wide including travel, photography, patchwork-quilting and horticulture. The house is attractively appointed with antique furniture and a rare collection of spinning wheels. We enjoy good food, wine and conversation. Fresh home-grown produce is used where possible along with home-baked bread and freshly squeezed orange juice. Vegetarian food is provided if requested. A warm welcome awaits you.

N
To Whangarei Heads
Parua House
To Whangarei (17 kms)
SHOP
PARUA TAVERN
Wharf Rd.

Solitaire Historic Homestay

State Highway 12, Waimamaku, Hokianga
Ph (09) 405 4891. Fax (09) 405 4891
e-mail: *solitairehomestay@xtra.co.nz*

Features & Attractions

- *Closest to Waipoua Forest*
- *3½ hours from Auckland*
- *Great local bush walks*
- *Family room available*
- *Laundry and e-mail available*
- *Peace and quiet guaranteed*

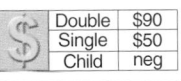

Double	$90
Single	$50
Child	neg

Homestay on "Twin Coast Discovery Route"

Bedrooms	Qty
Double	3
Twin	1
Single	
Bed Size	Qty
Queen	2
Double	1
Single	2
Bathrooms	Qty
Ensuite	2
Private	
Guest Share	1
Family Share	

Visit our restored Kauri Homestead just 6 km north of the enchanting Waipoua Kauri Forest. An ideal base to visit the giant kauri trees, the Hokianga Harbour and the West Coast beaches. **Solitaire Homestay**, on 30 acres of bush and farmland, is flanked by two rivers abounding with birdlife. Security doors with flyscreens are fitted to guest bedrooms, all opening out onto covered verandahs. We offer complimentary tea and coffee, advice on local sites and walks. Our bathrooms are newly built for the 2002 season with spacious showers. Waimamaku, a place of ancient Maori and European settlement is surrounded by splendid forest and coastal walks. Come and experience the hospitality of the Hokianga region. The perfect overnight stop between Auckland and the Bay of Islands, travelling the well signposted "Twin Coast Discovery Route". A stay at **Solitaire** will help you recharge the batteries and enjoy your holiday.

DIRECTIONS: 10 min. drive north from "the Big Tree" in Waipoua Forest or 1.5 hrs. west of the Bay of Islands. Well signposted on SH12 at Waimamaku.

Kauri House Lodge

Bowen Street, Dargaville, P.O.Box 382
Ph (09) 439 8082, Fax (09) 439 8082
Mobile 025-547 769
e-mail: *kauri@infomace.co.nz*

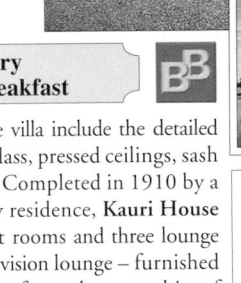

Features & Attractions

- *Kauri villa over 5000 sq"*
- *Farm bush walk included*
- *Set in private location*
- *Beach, lakes, bush walks*
- *Breakfast included*
- *Summer swimming pool*

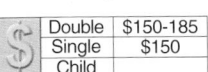

Double	$150-185
Single	$150
Child	

Luxury Bed & Breakfast

Bedrooms	Qty
Double	2
Twin	1
Single	
Bed Size	Qty
Super King	1
King	1
King/Single	1
Bathrooms	Qty
Ensuite	3
Private	
Guest Share	
Family Share	

Original features of this 1880s style villa include the detailed verandah balustrading, stained glass, pressed ceilings, sash windows and native Kauri panelling. Completed in 1910 by a leading bushman as a spacious family residence, **Kauri House** now offers three private ensuite guest rooms and three lounge rooms – a billiard room, library and television lounge – furnished with antiques. Only three kilometres from the township of Dargaville, with many nice restaurants.
Kauri House is set in three hectares of garden with abundant native birdlife including fantails, wood pigeons and seasonal tui. A swimming pool provides relaxation and exercise in summer only. Nearby is Doug's 40 hectare farm on which he runs steers and donkeys. This land includes 16 hectares of protected native bush.

FLOWER HAVEN

53 St Ann Road, Waipu Cove, Northland
Ph (09) 432 0421, Mobile 025-287 2418
e-mail: *flowerhaven@xtra.co.nz*

Features & Attractions

- Panoramic ocean view
- Garden retreat
- Surf patrol in summer
- Extensive beach walks
- Walk to bird sanctuary
- Golf courses & fishing

$	Double	$70-90
	Single	$45-65
	Child	neg.

Bed & Breakfast
Self-contained Accom.

Bedrooms	Qty
Double	2
Twin	
Single	
Bed Size	**Qty**
King	
Queen/Double	2
Single	
Bathrooms	**Qty**
Ensuite	
Private	1
Guest Share	
Family Share	

At **Flower Haven** we enjoy an elevated position with panoramic views of the sweep of Bream Bay and off-shore islands and are developing the quarter acre grounds as a garden retreat. We are retired with interests in gardening, genealogy and meeting people. Our accommodation is a self-contained downstairs two bedroom flat with separate access, fridge/freezer, stove, microwave, washing machine, radio and TV. Linen, duvets, blankets and bath towels are provided. Reduced tariff applies if continental breakfast not required. We are a 5 minute walk to shop, sandy surf beach and rocks – restaurants handy. We are near many places of interest such as bird sanctuary, museums, golf courses, horse riding treks, chartered fishing trips, limestone caves, walking tracks, Marsden Point Oil Refinery Visitors Centre. Auckland is 1 1/2 hours away.

DIRECTIONS: 8km south of Waipu on Cove Road, right into St Ann Road, Flower Haven is the last house on left.

MANGAWHAI LODGE "A ROOM WITH A VIEW"

4 Heather Street, Mangawhai Heads, Northland
Ph (09) 431 5311. Fax (09) 431 5312
e-mail: *mlodge@xtra.co.nz*
http://www.seaviewlodge.co.nz

Features & Attractions

- Golf course adjacent
- Close to shops & cafés
- 2 hours Auckland Airport
- Couples & groups welcome
- Beaches & walkways
- Guest kitchenettte

$	Double	$110-150
	Single	$80-130
	Child	

Boutique
Bed & Breakfast Lodge

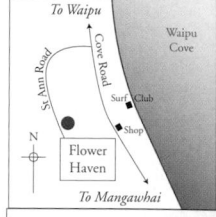

Indulge, escape to the tranquillity and magic of **Mangawhai Lodge**. Midway between Auckland Airport and the Bay of Islands, **Mangawhai Lodge** offers the perfect beach retreat for rest and relaxation or base to discover the treasures of Northland. Spectacular sea and island views of the Hauraki Gulf, Bream Bay, and white sandy beaches of Mangawhai make **Mangawhai Lodge** the ultimate "room with a view". Five individually styled guest rooms open onto wraparound verandahs. Spend your days on the championship golf course, explore beaches and walkways, curl up reading or watch the boats sail by. A licensed café and championship golf course are adjacent, harbour access 400 m. Sleep to the sound of the sea, awake to sumptuous cooked and continental breakfast. Having travelled extensively, we look forward to ensuring your stay is enjoyable and relaxing. Bookings and 2-day stay recommended.

Bedrooms	Qty
Double	5
Twin	
Single	
Bed Size	**Qty**
King	
Queen	2
King - Single	3
Bathrooms	**Qty**
Ensuite	3
Private	2
Guest Share	
Family Share	

DIRECTIONS: From Auckland turn right off SH1 past Te Hana, then right at Mangawhai village and next left, drive 3 km, then right at Naja Café. From north turn left at Waipu and follow coastal route, right at roundabout coming into Mangawhai Heads, then left past golf course entrance.

BELVEDERE HOMESTAY

38 Kanuka Road, RD 2, Sandspit, Warkworth
Ph/Fax (09) 425 7201, Mobile: 025 284 4771
e-mail:*belvederehomestay@xtra.co.nz*

Tariff : N.Z. Dollars	
Double	$100
Single	$65
Child	

Bedrooms	Qty
Double	2
Twin	1
Single	

Bed Size	Qty
Super King	
King	
Queen	2
Single	2

Bathrooms	Qty
Ensuite	1
Private	1
Guest Share	
Family Share	

 Quality Homestay Bed & Breakfast

Features & Attractions

- *Panoramic sea views*
- *Airconditioned home*
- *Dinner an occasion*
- *Warm, friendly hospitality*
- *Home produce for breakfast*
- *Glassed spa pool & games room*
- *"Goat Island" marine reserve*
- *Beaches, wineries, pottery*

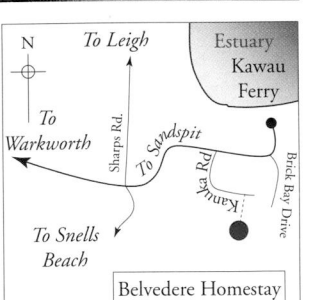

Map: To Leigh, To Warkworth, Sharps Rd., To Sandspit, Estuary Kawau Ferry, Kanuka Rd, Brick Bay Drive, To Snells Beach, Belvedere Homestay

Warkworth Sandspit is the perfect stop going to and from the Bay of Islands. **Belvedere Homestay** is sited on top of the hill with 360° views overlooking the spit where the ferries leave for Kawau Island and Governor Grey's restored mansion. The view is awesome which you will enjoy while relaxing on our spacious decks and terraces. Stroll around our 11 acre property with sunken barbecue, rose garden, orchards, lawns, native birds and bush and 2 lilly ponds and enjoy a friendly game of Petanque (boule).

Fishing off the beach or boat, golf, tennis, swimming etc. are all within 7 km. Our house is for your comfort and enjoyment and as "Roger Hall" (NZ/English stage and televison playwright) wrote about **Belvedere Homestay**: "It is no wonder people come for one day and stay a week." Margaret's flair with cooking is a great way to relax after an adventurous day - with pre-drinks, 3 course meal and wine.

Come and enjoy a stay with Margaret, Ron and our friendly dog "Nicky".

CASA ALEGRIA

180 Monarch-Downs Way, RD 2,
Warkworth
Ph (09) 422 7211 Fax (09) 422 7833
e-mail: *casaalegria@xtra.co.nz*

Tariff : N.Z. Dollars		
	Double	$120
	Single	$85

Bedrooms	Qty
Double	1
Twin	1
Single	

Bed Size	Qty
Super King	1
King - Single	2
Queen	
Single	

Bathrooms	Qty
Ensuite	1
Private	1
Guest Share	
Family Share	

Beauty Farm - Countrystay

Features & Attractions

- *Beauty farm - studio*
- *Wellness-holiday*
- *Golf course, wineries, beaches*
- *Magnificent views, peaceful*

- *Special breakfast*
- *International dinners*
- *German, French and Japanese spoken*
- *Diving-snorkeling/Goat Island*

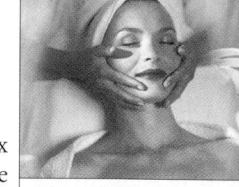

Advance booking essential.

As a happy family (Claudia, Alex and 10-year-old Julia) we welcome you to Casa Alegria, our brand new home. In a perfect mediterranean setting on the top of a hill you can enjoy breathtaking sunrises and sunsets and stunning views of Kawau Bay, vineyards, deer farm, Warkworth and the golf course.

The luxurious guest rooms are tastefully furnished, one with separate entrance, two king single beds (or alternatively one super king), TV, and own patio. The other guest room, with private bathroom, is in our main house. Our scrummy breakfast is served with freshly brewed coffee or tea and includes a variety of sweet and savoury homemade specialities. Ideas from all over the world inspire Claudia to create delicious 3-course dinners on request. We can arrange your outings to local top wineries, Kawau or Goat Island, horse-riding or fishing. Claudia, who used to run her own beauty salon in Germany, would love to pamper you in her beauty farm with many treatment options available (from a marvellous facial to a 3-day treatment package). Booking for accommodation and beauty treatment essential.

44

"OUR FARM-PARK"
Krippner Road, Puhoi
Ph (09) 422 0626, Fax (09) 422 0626
Mobile 021- 215 5165
e-mail: *ofp@friends.co.nz*
http://www.farmstaynz.com

Features & Attractions

- *Organic & GE free food*
- *Gentle treatment of animals*
- *"Conversation English Courses"*
- *Educational courses*
- *Wonderful meals*
- *Nobody smokes here*

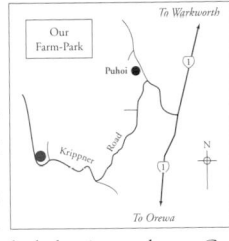

Double	$110-175*
Single	$95-130*
Child	$0-30*

Organic Farmstay
...the gentle way

Share with us our beautiful panoramic views, fresh air and clean water. *Tariff includes meals based on taste-filled, organic, fruit and vegetables; fresh baking (vegetarian if you ask). Very comfortable beds. We farm with kindness touchable sheep, spring lambs, beautiful Belted Galloway cows in family groupings with calves at foot, horses, ducks, poultry running free; providing farm milk, butter, yoghurt, ice-cream, cheeses. Sleep off 'jet-lag'. Share knowledge over dinner. Share our love for Taha Maori, environment, flora, fauna. Use our library and business facilities. Walk in the hills through trees streams, secluded private places. Go canoeing. Visit hot pools, beaches, bush walks, bird sanctuaries. Island trips, marine reserves, snorkelling, diving, fishing, Honey Centre, historic sites, crafts. Motorway provides easy Auckland shopping, zoo, evening events and more.

Bedrooms	Qty
Double	1
Twin	1
Single	
Bed Size	**Qty**
King	
Queen	1
Single	2
Bathrooms	**Qty**
Ensuite	1
Private	1
Guest Share	
Family Share	

Intensive sheep farming

BAYVIEW MANLY

1 Beach Road, Manly Village, Whangaparaoa Peninsula
Hibiscus Coast, North Auckland
Ph/Fax: (09) 428 0990, Mobile 025 - 280 8346
e-mail: *bayviewmanly@xtra.co.nz*
http://www.bayview-manly.co.nz

 Quality Bed & Breakfast Inn

Tariff : N.Z. Dollars		
	Double	$110-135
	Single	$95-120
	Child	n/a

Bedrooms	Qty
Double	2
Twin	1
Single	
Bed Size	**Qty**
King	
Queen	1
Double	1
Single	2
Bathrooms	**Qty**
Ensuite	2
Private	1
Guest Share	
Family Share	

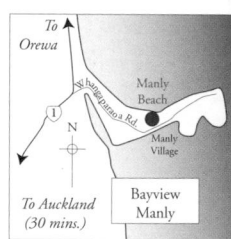

To Orewa

Manly Beach

Manly Village

To Auckland (30 mins.)

Bayview Manly

Features & Attractions

- *Panoramic seaviews*
- *Delicious full breakfasts*
- *Adjacent to 5 restaurants*
- *Guest lounge/tea, coffee*
- *Tiritiri Matangi Bird Island*
- *America's Cup course*
- *Gulf Harbour golf*
- *Stroll to warm sandy beach*

If you are looking for an exceptional B&B experience, stay with us at **Bayview Manly**. Facing the sun, our modern, comfortable, clean home is elevated with ever-changing seaviews and dramatic sunsets, yet only one minute walk to restaurants and shops. Upstairs bedrooms have comfortable beds, Queen and Twin rooms with balconies and panoramic sea views. Fresh flowers, sweeties and toiletries are provided. Tasteful table settings for generous breakfasts, freshly cooked to last you through the day. Laundry facilities, luggage stored and ample parking. The whole house is for guests to enjoy. Hosts have an attached apartment and are happy to join you, if you wish. Ideally situated for visiting Auckland or the many local attractions. Tourist information and bird books available. All year destination, great for a weekend break. Gulf Harbour 5 min. Auckland City 30 min. Airport 1hr Bay of Islands 2 hrs 30 min. Relax to the sound of the waves at **Bayview Manly** - your first choice for "**Quality, Hospitality and Value**". A place to stay for more than a day. Ideal arrival/departure point. Jet lagged? - we care!

DIRECTIONS:
From Auckland travel north,
exit motorway at Silverdale,
then turn right into
Whangaparaoa Road.
Continue to Manly
Village roundabout -
look for our signs.
Welcome to Bayview Manly.

46

VISA
MasterCard
AMERICAN EXPRESS
FARM & HOME HOSTS

ALBANY COUNTRY HOME

"Birethanti", 57 Ngarahana Avenue,
Albany 1331, Auckland
Ph (09) 413 9580, Fax (09) 413 9583
Mobile 025-745 898
e-mail: *patricia.fordham@xtra.co.nz*

Features & Attractions

- *Satisfaction guaranteed*
- *Tranquil retreat*
- *Special breakfasts included*
- *Ideal stopover going north or south*
- *Country walks*
- *Local restaurants in village*

	Countrystay Boutique Accommodation	C	🚭			
					Double	$100-130
					Single	$90-110
					Child	neg.

To Whangarei
Albany Country Home
The Avenue
Hudson Rd.
Albany
Paremoremo Rd.
At'woodhyll
Ngarahana Ave.
To Auckland City
Waitemata Harbour

DIRECTIONS:
Turn opposite Albany Inn,
7km, then left into
Attwood Road, 1km left into
Ngarahana Avenue.

When you arrive to awesome river views you will be greeted with a warm welcome, be offered refreshments with freshly baked muffins or slice. You will sleep in luxurious linen, have plenty of soft fluffy towels and all the little extras that will make your day special! You will awake to birdsong, the smell of freshly baked bread. You could amble down to the jetty before breakfasting on fresh tropical fruit, your choice of oaty pancakes, French toast with bacon, poached egg with smoked salmon, English or continental breakfast. "We never think of staying anywhere else" say Barry and Dorothy of Cambridge England (after their third stay). Bruce and I look forward to your call. 7 min. from Albany, North Harbour Stadium and University. 19 min. from Auckland.

Bedrooms	Qty
Double	2
Twin	
Single	
Bed Size	**Qty**
King	
Queen/Double	2
Single	
Bathrooms	**Qty**
Ensuite	1
Private	1
Guest Share	
Family Share	

TE HARINUI

102 Coatesville Highway, RD 3 Albany,
Auckland
Ph (09) 415 9295
e-mail: *sueblanchard@xtra.co.nz*
http://www.teharinui.f2s.com

FARM & HOME HOSTS

Features & Attractions

- *Pet "Coloured Sheep"*
- *Country views*
- *Close to many attractions*
- *Generous hospitality*
- *Full meals available*
- *Feel at home*

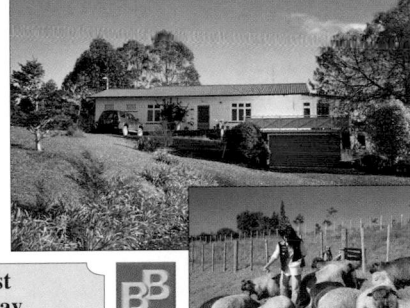

	Double	$80
	Single	$60
	Child	

Bed & Breakfast Country Homestay	

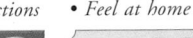

Bedrooms	Qty
Double	1
Twin	1
Single	
Bed Size	**Qty**
King	
Queen	1
Single	2
Bathrooms	**Qty**
Ensuite	
Private	
Guest Share	1
Family Share	

Te Harinui, a home away from home, only 15 minutes north of Auckland City, just off Highway 17. (We can meet you, if required). Stay for a night or enjoy an extended farmstay. Have your breakfast with views over the paddocks and bush. Feed our pet sheep and horse, meet our friendly dogs and cat, or learn to spin and make felt. Locally you can try horse-riding, visit ostriches, emus and beautiful gardens or walk in the bush. We have two guest rooms with a bathroom and lounge for guests' use. The swimming pool decking also has access from one guest room. The house has wheelchair access and a craft room with products for sale.
Mike and Sue have travelled extensively. Sue speaks French and is learning Chinese.

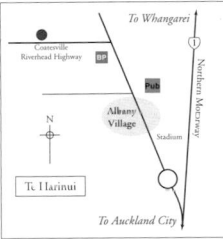

To Whangarei
Coatesville Riverhead Highway
BP
Pub
Albany Village
Stadium
N
Te Harinui
To Auckland City
Northern Motorway

PORT O CALL

12 Amelia Place, Coastal Beach Haven, Auckland
Ph (09) 483 4439 Fax (09) 483 4439
Mobile 025-227 2639
e-mail: *portocall.b&b@xtra.co.nz*

Tariff : N.Z. Dollars		
Double		$140-150
Single		$80-100
Child		

Bedrooms	Qty
Double	2
Twin	
Single	
Bed Size	**Qty**
Super King	1
King	
Queen	1
Single	
Bathrooms	**Qty**
Ensuite	2
Private	
Guest Share	
Family Share	

Quality Homestay
Bed & Breakfast

Features & Attractions

- *The ulitimate place to unwind*
- *Close-up water views*
- *Wine/craft/sightseeing tours*
- *Delicious breakfast*
- *20 minutes America's Cup Village*
- *Magnificent sunsets*
- *Charter fishing trips*
- *Lunch/dinner/BBQ by arrangement*

Welcome to **Port 'O' Call**, a secret hideaway overlooking the tranquil sparkling waters of the glorious Upper Waitemata Harbour. Enjoy watching the many water activities or partake in them yourselves. We can take you sailing on our 28 foot Catamaran "Akarana Express" or enjoy a leisurely paddle in a kayak around these calm waters, viewing the bird life that abounds.

Come and enjoy our warm and relaxed hospitality in one of two spacious private tastefully decorated bedrooms with ensuite, featuring hairdryer, toiletries, bathrobes, heated towel rail; all leading out to a large salt water pool and spa pool for your enjoyment, whilst still enjoying the relaxing views over the water and soak up the sunshine from the wide verandahs. Tea and coffee making facilities, fridge, laundry and ironing facilities, fresh flowers ...

To get away for a peaceful read or just to ponder, discover the "Secret Garden" amongst the tropical palms and watch the beautiful white doves nesting, or cuddle up in front of the log fire during winter with a complimentary glass of fine New Zealand wine.

PS: There are three resident cats.

Jill and Bernie look forward to making your stay totally enjoyable.

MILFORD HOUSE

34 Milford Road, Milford, Auckland
Ph/Fax (09) 486 6033, Mobile 025-287 7584
e-mail: *jimliz44@hotmail.com*
http://www.milfordbbnewzealand.com

Tariff : N.Z. Dollars	
Double	$125
Single	$95
Child	neg.

Bedrooms	Qty
Double	1
Twin	1
Single	

Bed Size	Qty
Super King	
King	
Queen	1
Single	2

Bathrooms	Qty
Ensuite	1
Private	1
Guest Share	
Family Share	

**Bed & Breakfast
Boutique Accommodation**

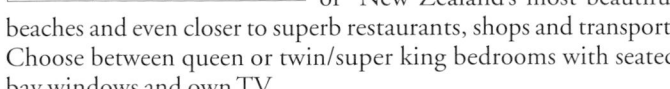

Features & Attractions

- *Milford Beach 400 metres*
- *Close to restaurants/shops*
- *Near golf course and boat trips*
- *Guest lounge*
- *Heated spa pool*
- *10 min. to Auckland City*

Milford House "is a very convenient place to stay". Situated in the centre of Milford it is only a level 400 metre stroll to one of New Zealand's most beautiful beaches and even closer to superb restaurants, shops and transport. Choose between queen or twin/super king bedrooms with seated bay windows and own TV.

Relax in the guest lounge. Delicious breakfasts are served in the dining room or private courtyard - tea and coffee are available all day. Enjoy time out in our heated spa pool.

Nearby available activities include golfing (4 courses within easy reach), boating, walking, safe swimming, plus much more!

It's all here for you on Auckland's North Shore.

Liz and Jim look forward to welcoming you to **Milford House**.

BUCHANAN'S OF DEVONPORT B&B INN

22 Buchanan Street, Devonport,
North Shore City, Auckland
Ph/Fax (09) 445 3333. Mobile 025-207 6738
e-mail:*info@buchanansofdevonport.co.nz*
http://www.buchanansofdevonport.co.nz

Tariff : N.Z. Dollars		
	Double	$170-230
	Single	$140-180
	Child	n/a

Bedrooms	Qty
Double	3
Twin	1
Single	

Bed Size	Qty
Super King	1
Queen	1
Double	2
King Single	2

Bathrooms	Qty
Ensuite	4
Private	
Guest Share	
Family Share	

Luxury Boutique
Bed & Breakfast

Features & Attractions

- *Elegant accommodation*
- *Perfect, quiet location*
- *Friendly, helpful host family*
- *24 hour security/safety deposit box*
- *Devonport tour by hosts*
- *Small conference venue*
- *Ample off-street parking*
- *Guests' spa-in-gazebo*

DIRECTIONS
Please phone for easy directions.

Welcome to Buchanan's of Devonport Inn, our gracious 2-storey Edwardian home in the heart of Devonport. Built in 1933 and immaculately restored in 1998 to its original era, it is furnished throughout with genuine New Zealand and colonial antiques and artworks. A private lounge with gas-log fireplace and complimentary tea/coffee/biscuits is available for guests' use. Upstairs we offer 4 colour-themed guestrooms, all with ensuite and balcony. Elegantly furnished with antiques, the rooms have the finest bed and bath linen, TV, CD player, alarm clock, hairdryer, ironing facilities, fresh flowers, and complimentary tea/coffee/biscuits/sherry. After a night's restful slumber, continental or full breakfast awaits for you to savour in the morning. Coffee of your choice is made from freshly ground beans. Only a short stroll to Devonport's attractions/amenities, like restaurants, shops, wedding venues and even a 18-hole golf course! A 10 minute ferry ride to Auckland City departs regularly from the Devonport wharf, which is only a 5 minute walk from our Inn.

AMBERLEY BED & BREAKFAST

3 Ewen Alison Avenue, Devonport, Auckland
Ph/Fax (09) 446 0506
Mobile 025-2880161
e-mail: *amberley@xtra.co.nz*

Features & Attractions

- *Quiet, peaceful surroundings*
- *Delicious breakfasts*
- *Cafés and antique shops*
- *Handy to golf course*
- *Safe swimming beaches*
- *Friendly helpful hosts*

Double	$100-130	
Single	$70-100	
Child	neg	

H   **Homestay Bed & Breakfast**   **BB**

Bedrooms	Qty
Double	3
Twin	1
Single	
Bed Size	**Qty**
King	
Queen/Double	3
Single	2
Bathrooms	**Qty**
Ensuite	
Private	
Guest Share	2
Family Share	

DIRECTIONS. Turn right at Mt Victoria roundabout, go 200m then first right at Superette Corner

Nestled at the base of Mt Victoria, our charming Edwardian Villa is within easy walking distance of Devonport's numerous cafés, shops, golf course, safe swimming beaches, and the ferry terminal (a 10 min. ride to downtown Auckland). It is the ideal base for Auckland and the Hauraki Gulf. Spectacular panoramic views are enjoyed from the summit of Mt. Victoria. Our spacious bedrooms are charmingly furnished with exceedingly comfortable beds! Double spa bath in one bathroom; bathrobes provided.

Early a.m. flight guests welcome. Door-to-door airport shuttle available. Large guest lounge with sky TV, complimentary tea/coffee making facilities, fridge and home baking. Laundry facilities available on request. Our delicious breakfasts are served in our spacious dining room with city views. We have travelled extensively both here and overseas. We look forward to meeting you and to making your stay with us in our beautiful country an enjoyable and unforgettable experience.

EASTVIEW

2 Parkside Road, Hobsonville, Auckland
Ph (09) 416 9254 Fax (09) 416 9254
e-mail: *djclarke@xtra.co.nz*

Features & Attractions

- *Guest lounge, TV, video, Sky*
- *Sunny spacious bedrooms*
- *Limited kitchen facilities*
- *Check your emails*
- *3 minutes motorway*
- *Shops, cinema nearby*

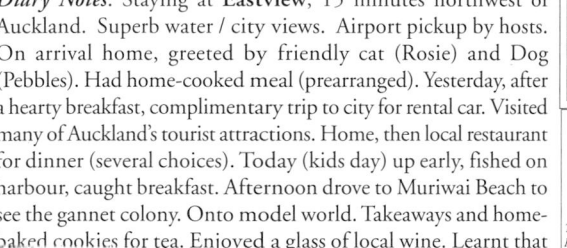

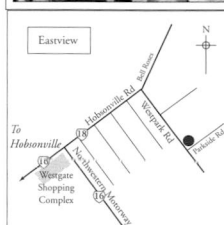

BB   **Bed & Breakfast Homestay**   **H**

Double	$85	
Single	$60	
Child	$30	

Bedrooms	Qty
Double	2
Twin	1
Single	
Bed Size	**Qty**
Queen	1
Double	1
Single	2
Bathrooms	**Qty**
Ensuite	
Private	1
Guest Share	1
Family Share	

Diary Notes: Staying at **Eastview**, 15 minutes northwest of Auckland. Superb water / city views. Airport pickup by hosts. On arrival home, greeted by friendly cat (Rosie) and Dog (Pebbles). Had home-cooked meal (prearranged). Yesterday, after a hearty breakfast, complimentary trip to city for rental car. Visited many of Auckland's tourist attractions. Home, then local restaurant for dinner (several choices). Today (kids day) up early, fished on harbour, caught breakfast. Afternoon drove to Muriwai Beach to see the gannet colony. Onto model world. Takeaways and home-baked cookies for tea. Enjoyed a glass of local wine. Learnt that Don and Joane sail, Don's interest is golf and Joane's is gardening and embroidery. Tomorrow a swim at thermal pools on way north, after Dad's golf and movie.

DIRECTIONS: From south, take SH 16 to intersection of SH 18 (turn right into Hobsonville Rd), fifth street on right, Westpark Drive, second left Parkside Rd. From north, take SH 18 (Upperharbour Highway). Hobsonville Rd left at Westpark Drive (opposite Bell Roses), second left Parkside Rd.

STAFFORD VILLA

2 Awanui Street, Birkenhead Point, Auckland
Ph:(09) 418 3022, Fax (09) 419 8197
e-mail: *rest@staffordvilla.co.nz*
http://www.staffordvilla.co.nz

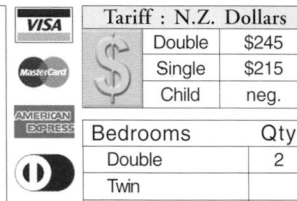

Tariff : N.Z. Dollars	
Double	$245
Single	$215
Child	neg.

Bedrooms	Qty
Double	2
Twin	
Single	
Bed Size	**Qty**
Super King	
King	2
Queen	
Single	2
Bathrooms	**Qty**
Ensuite	2
Private	
Guest Share	
Family Share	

Historic Elegant Luxury Boutique Accommodation

Features & Attractions

- *Heritage listed house*
- *Designer décor*
- *Perfect central location*
- *Warm and friendly hosts*
- *Private setting, gourmet food*
- *Bridal package*
- *Gateway to "Twin Coast Discovery Route"*

Children welcome if both rooms taken.

Welcome to **Stafford Villa**, located on the North Shore of Auckland City, in the historic harbour suburb of Birkenhead Point. Built in the late 1800's Stafford Villa is luxuriously interior designed in the grand elegance of yesteryear. Every effort is made so your stay is one to remember.

From the private and exquisitely furnished guest rooms – **China Blue**: with magnificent four poster bed, antique furniture, original paintings, luxurious ensuite facilities and dressing room with access to private verandah. **Tuscany Summer**: with large bay window, looking out onto the remaining Victorian orchard, furnishings in antique cream and terracotta, Victorian brass beds and armoire plus natural aromatheraphy fragrances and bath oils – to the fine food and wines New Zealand is famous for. Our family – 4th generation New Zealanders – can assist you with whatever you may wish to do from day trip fishing, the best golf courses or sailing on the harbour. As seasoned world travellers ourselves, Mark and I welcome you to our home and the beautiful harbour city of Auckland.

MOANA VISTA

60 Hamilton Road, Herne Bay/Ponsonby, Auckland
Free Phone: 0800 08VISTA
Mobile 021 376 150
e-mail: *info@moanavista.co.nz*
http://www.moanavista.co.nz

Tariff : N.Z. Dollars	
Double	$140-160
Single	$120
Child	

Bedrooms	Qty
Double	2
Twin	
Single	
Bed Size	**Qty**
Super King	
King	1
Queen	1
Single	
Bathrooms	**Qty**
Ensuite	
Private	1
Guest Share	1
Family Share	

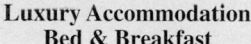

**Luxury Accommodation
Bed & Breakfast**

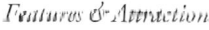

Features & Attractions

- *Central to city, restaurants, cafés and beaches*
- *Young, friendly hospitality*
- *Luxurious colonial charm*
- *Grand piano, open fire*
- *Views of harbour bridge, sky tower & Waitemata Harbour*
- *Cooked or continental breakfast*
- *TV, free internet*
- *Quiet and peaceful*

DIRECTIONS:
Please phone for very easy directions.
Advance reservation essential.

Relax and enjoy the hospitality of one of Auckland's grand old homes. Recently refurbished to include all modern amenities, but retaining its early colonial charm. Lovely water views. Stroll to the local Ponsonby cafés, restaurants and beaches with the city 15 minutes away. Continental or cooked breakfast supplied. Complimentary tea and coffee available. The entire upstairs floor is available for guests, with shower (high water pressure), bath, heated towel rail, dryer and toiletries. Gas and electric heating throughout and TV in both rooms with free Internet access in the adjoining library. Our in-house pianist delights in playing everything from Chopin to familiar show tunes. Tim and Matt are familiar with the local café scene. Matt is an international flight attendent of 12 years and delights in giving 1st class attention to all of his guests.

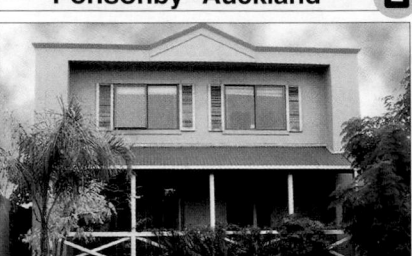

SUMMER STREET,

6 Summer Street, Ponsonby
Auckland
Ph (09) 361 3715, Fax (09) 361 3715
Mobile 021 - 535 635

Features & Attractions

- *Ponsonby one minute walk*
- *Close restaurants & shops*
- *Quiet location*
- *One minute walk buses*
- *Door to door airport shuttle*
- *Off-street parking*

Homestay
Bed & Breakfast

Double	$90-130
Single	$80-100
Child	neg.

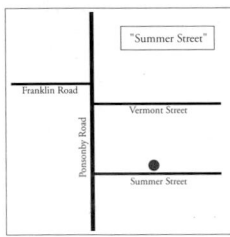

S ituated in a quiet street less than one minute's walk from the famous Ponsonby Road with all its exciting bistros, restaurants, cafés and excellent boutique shops. Public transport is close by and Auckland Airport shuttles come door to door on request.

There is off-street parking in front of the house. Quality queen-size beds, linen and towels are provided. In the morning a continental buffet breakfast is provided, either in the dining area or in our tropical landscaped garden at the rear of the house. Otherwise you have a huge choice and range of fantastic all day breakfast and coffee bars along the Ponsonby Road.

Bedrooms	Qty
Double	2
Twin	
Single	
Bed Size	**Qty**
King	
Queen	2
Single	
Bathrooms	**Qty**
Ensuite	
Private	
Guest Share	1
Family Share	1

VISA
MasterCard

VILLA 536

536 Mt Eden Road, Mt Eden, Auckland
Ph (09) 630 5258, Fax (09) 630 5258
e-mail: *annasvilla@hotmail.com*

Features & Attractions

- *"Quality" plus*
- *City bus at door. Parking*
- *Easy to find*
- *Close to city and airport*
- *Complimentary cookies, teas, coffees*
- *Stroll around village cafés/shops*

Superior Bed & Breakfast

DIRECTIONS:
On Mt Eden Road between
Windmill Road and Disraeli Street.

Double	$125-145
Single	$115-135
Child	

Villa 536 is a beautifully extended and restored early Auckland home situated in the heart of Mt Eden, a long-established central city suburb. The home is light and airy, comfortable and cheerful. Spacious bedrooms have excellent beds and bedding, a heater, cool-fan and television. The bathrooms boast high water-pressure showers, heated towel-rails, hair dryers and toiletries. Great breakfasts include fresh fruit, yoghurt and home-made muffins. You can relax in the pleasant lounge, casual living area or during summer on the wooden deck from where the view includes "One Tree Hill", Auckland's famous landmark. Guests like to stroll around popular Mt Eden Village with its many speciality shops and cafés. Downtown, motorways, airport, tourist attractions, Eden Park, Expo Centre, shopping centres, race courses, main hospitals and tertiary institutions are all easily and quickly reached. Guests say: "Excellent hospitality, conversation, breakfast and travel advice.", "Simply superb. Cheers!", "A truly relaxing stay.", "A great source of local knowledge."

Bedrooms	Qty
Double	1
Twin	1
Triple	1
Bed Size	**Qty**
King	
Queen	2
Single	3
Bathrooms	**Qty**
Ensuite	2
Private	1
Guest Share	
Family Share	

AMERSHAM HOUSE

Corner Gladstone Road & Canterbury Place,
Parnell, Auckland
Ph (09) 303 0321, Fax (09) 303 0621
e-mail: *info@amershamhouse.co.nz*
http://www.amershamhouse.co.nz

Tariff : N.Z. Dollars	
Double	$234-360
Single	
Child	

Bedrooms	Qty
Double	4
Twin	
Single	
Bed Size	**Qty**
Super King	1
King	1
Queen	1
Double	1
Bathrooms	**Qty**
Ensuite	4
Private	
Guest Share	
Family Share	

         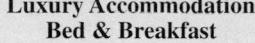

**Luxury Accommodation
Bed & Breakfast**

Features & Attractions

- *Spectacular views*
- *Five minutes to the city*
- *In-room spa or sauna*
- *"AT HOME" atmosphere*
- *Free in-room 24 hour*
- *internet and e-mail service*

Our guests like **Amersham House** as much as we do. "Felt just like home", "Absolutely exceeded all our expectations". Enjoy total privacy or relax with your NZ-born hosts in their luxury home in central Parnell. Our "oasis in the city" has a 10m gas-heated pool with illuminated palms and orchids and a private outdoor spa. Bedrooms are sunny and spacious with PC's with free fast internet and e-mail service, Sky TV, phone and office, original art and top quality beds and linen. All ensuites are unique and stylish, so select a room that has an ensuite with a spa bath and double shower or choose one with a private sauna. The bedrooms all have 180° views, some with city and harbour views as does our guest lounge/library. **Amersham House** is within safe and easy walking distance to shops, restaurants, malls, parks and historic homes. We are only a 5 min. drive to downtown Auckland. The hop-on hop-off city or tourist buses leave regularly.

In the evening relive the day with us and experience true "Kiwi" hospitality.

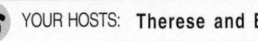 YOUR HOSTS: **Therese and Bart Blommaert**   Ph: (09) 309 9012

ASCOT PARNELL 'A SMALL HOTEL'

36 St Stephens Avenue, Parnell, Auckland 1
Ph (09) 309 9012, Fax (09) 309 3729
e-mail: *AscotParnell@compuserve.com*
http://www.AscotParnell.com

Tariff : N.Z. Dollars	
Double	$145-185
Single	$95-165
Child	$50

Bedrooms	Qty
Double	7
Twin	11
Single	2
Bed Size	**Qty**
King	
Queen	8
Double	1
Single	2
Bathrooms	**Qty**
Ensuite	10
Private	1
Guest Share	
Family Share	

   Bed & Breakfast in a charming atmosphere

Features & Attractions

- *Walk to all city attractions*
- *City-centre at 1 mile =1.5 km*
- *The airport bus stops at the door*
- *Historic house and garden*
- *Helpful and friendly hosts*
- *Private setting, gourmet food*
- *Free cookies, teas, coffee, juice*
- *Free parking in courtyard*

A warm welcome – Bienvenue – Herzlich Wilkommen – Benvenuto – Hartelijk Welkom. The **Ascot Parnell** is a charming b&b hotel in Auckland city. Centrally located but quiet this luxury bed and breakfast offers spacious accommodations, character and style. It is an easy 5 minute walk to the Rose-gardens, the Auckland Museum and Parnell Village with its many boutiques, craft-shops, art galleries, cafes and restaurants. Highly recommended by guidebooks such as Frommer, Fodor's, the Lonely Planet and the Maverick, **Ascot Parnell** provides top quality accommodations at reasonable rates. The friendly owners show real pleasure in caring for the comfort of their guests. Each room has an en-suite bathroom and is non-smoking. The rooms are private and secure, immaculate, tastefully decorated and all have hairdryer, clock-radio, individual heating, telephone and internet connection. A sumptuous breakfast is served in the morning room overlooking the subtropical garden. Complimentary refreshments are offered throughout the day, served either on the sunny verandah or in the shade of the trees.

DIRECTIONS: From airport: take road No. 20 motorway to Auckland city, exit at Queenstown Rd, follow Auckland centre. Follow Manukau Rd (Road No 12) to Parnell. Turn right at the Cathedral of the Holy Trinity into St. Stephens Ave. The **Ascot Parnell** is 300m down on your left.

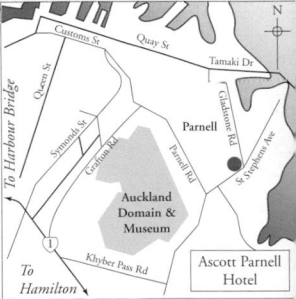

AUCKLAND OMAHU HOUSE

35 Omahu Road, Remuera, Auckland
Ph (09) 524 9697, Fax (09) 524 9997
e-mail: *omahu@voyager.co.nz*
http://www.aucklandOmahuHouse.com

Tariff : N.Z. Dollars	
Double	$165-185
Single	$140-165
Child	$30

Bedrooms	Qty
Double	3
Twin	3
Single	1
Bed Size	**Qty**
King	3
King/Single	3
Double	1
Single	
Bathrooms	**Qty**
Ensuite	3
Private	1
Guest Share	
Family Share	

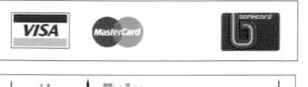

Boutique Accommodation
Bed & Breakfast

Features & Attractions

- *Easy to find - city location*
- *Off-street parking*
- *Frequent bus service - 200 m*
- *Fax - email - telephone*
- *Large, relaxing garden, big pool*
- *Quiet city living, country style*
- *10 min. - city, shops and attractions*
- *Walk to café, Remuera, Newmarket*

DIRECTIONS: Exit Market Road off ramp. Travel and right turn at Remuera Road, next right to 35 Omahu Road.

Whether you visit us on business, as an overseas visitor, on holiday or require an exclusive conference venue, we offer our guests hospitality and privacy in an atmosphere of absolute comfort. Relaxing in the guests' lounge by the fire, in the garden or by the pool, take time to enjoy casually elegant **Auckland Omahu House**. **Auckland Omahu House** provides country-style hospitality, set in peaceful surroundings, on a quiet street, within an easy walk to a selection of cafés, fine restaurants, retail therapy locations and a short distance from Auckland's main attractions. Offstreet parking available. City transport nearby. Spacious King Size or Twin Rooms with ensuites. Pleasant surprises await you at Omahu House, where small extra details provide for your comfort, including quality linen, feather duvets, electric blankets, bathrobes, hairdryers, fruit, flowers and magazines. Also ironing and laundry facilities available. Suggest a 2/3 day stopover, enjoy Auckland, City of Sails, and try a quick city tour with Keith by motorbike, fun! Evening meal by arrangement. We look forward to sharing our home with you at **Auckland Omahu House**, the quintessential Bed and Breakfast!

YOUR HOSTS: **Heather and Bill Nicholson**   Ph: (09) 522 2836

SEALLADH
2/9 Rewiti Street, Orakei, Auckland
Ph: (09) 522 2836, Fax:(09) 522 9666
Mobile 025-211 7186
e-mail: *sealladh@xtra.co.nz*

Features & Attractions

- *Spacious modern home*
- *City and sea views*
- *Near tourist attractions*
- *Exclusive guest lounge*
- *Secure parking*
- *Restaurants close by*

**Homestay
Bed & Breakfast**

	Double	$140-160
	Single	$100
	Child	

Bedrooms	Qty
Double	1
Twin	1
Single	
Bed Size	**Qty**
King	1
Queen/Double	
Single	2
Bathrooms	**Qty**
Ensuite	2
Private	
Guest Share	
Family Share	

Welcome to our modern sunny and spacious home. Enjoy the views from the king bedroom which has TV and a large ensuite. The exclusive guest lounge has views, stereo, TV, video, piano, library and mini kitchen including complimentary tea and coffee. A full breakfast is served in the sunny dining room or "al fresco". We have plenty of secure off street parking and laundry facilities are available. Close to amenities in a quiet residential area, we are five minutes to restaurants, cafés, theatres, CBD and casino. Five minutes to parks, beaches, Kelly Tarlton's Underwater World, harbour cruises, Viaduct Harbour and many other tourist attractions. Ten minutes to race courses and northern and southern motorways. Enjoy many local scenic walks. A short stroll to post office and bus stops.

We have travelled extensively in NZ and overseas and warm and friendly hospitality is assured. No smoking indoors please. From the airport, taxi or shuttle will deliver you to our door.

Auckland Central

YOUR HOSTS: **Jude and Roger Harwood**   Ph: (09) 524 6990

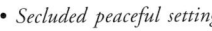

WOODLANDS
18 Waiatarua Road, Remuera
Auckland
Ph: (09) 524 6990, Fax:(09) 524 6993
e-mail: woodlands@ake.quik.co.nz

Features & Attractions

- *Secluded peaceful setting*
- *Woodland views*
- *Dinner by arrangement*
- *Wonderful full breakfasts*
- *Close to Ericsson Stadium*
- *Handy to Auckland Airport*

**Homestay
Bed & Breakfast**

	Double	$110-120
	Single	$90-100
	Child	n/a

Bedrooms	Qty
Double	2
Twin	
Single	
Bed Size	**Qty**
King	1
Double	1
Single	
Bathrooms	**Qty**
Ensuite	1
Private	1
Guest Share	
Family Share	

Our two guest bedrooms overlook the solar heated swimming pool and lush native greenery. The ensuite king-size bedroom is very large and has french windows opening out into a sunny private conservatory. The **Pink Room** has a double bed and private bathroom. Each room has coffee/tea making facilities, coloured TV and heated towel rails. Both rooms are very quiet and peaceful. There is safe off street undercover carparking. Our breakfasts are very special, starting with an individual platter of seasonal fruits, followed by a cooked breakfast of your choice, homemade preserves and jams, assorted teas or percolated coffee. In the evening, join us for a Advanced Cordon Bleu candlelit dinner. We delight in using fresh NZ produce and serving good NZ wines. Bookings essential. Guest Book comments - "super hospitality with delectable food" - "Divine breakfasts" - "Incredible dinner - wow" "we have found paradise". We are close to motorways - north and south, cafés and bistros, Ericsson Stadium, Expo Centre, Ellerslie Racecourse.

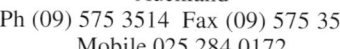

The Totara

1/17 Glover Road, St Heliers Bay,
Auckland
Ph (09) 575 3514 Fax (09) 575 3582
Mobile 025 284 0172
e-mail: *maxwell.totara@clear.net.nz*

Features & Attractions

- *St Heliers Bay 12 min. to CBD*
- *Short walk to beach and cafés*
- *Close to tourist attractions*
- *Hospitality 'plus'*
- *Modern multi-level home*
- *Great breakfasts*

Bed & Breakfast
Quality Homestay

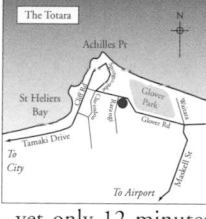
The Totara

Double	$120
Single	$90
Child	

Whether on holiday or business, relax in our home overlooking picturesque Glover Park. You are sure to enjoy our great breakfasts and hospitality. We are a short walk from the beach, cafés, shopping and banks, yet only 12 minutes drive to the central city. Start the day with a jog around the park or a walk along the beach. Visit Kelly Tarltons Underwater World, Sky City Tower or cruise on the Waitemata Harbour. Parking available - or good bus service from St Heliers Bay village. Tea and coffee always available in separate guest lounge. We are happy to assist with travel plans, dinner reservations etc. Catch an airport shuttle to the door. Peter and Jeanne with Sophie the cat welcome you.

Bedrooms	Qty
Double	1
Twin	1
Single	
Bed Size	**Qty**
King	
Queen	1
Single	2
Bathrooms	**Qty**
Ensuite	
Private	1
Guest Share	
Family Share	

Panorama Heights

42 Kitewaho Road, Swanson, Waitakere City
Ph (09) 832 4777 Fax (09) 833 7773
Mobile 025 272 8811
e-mail: *nzbnb4u@zfree.co.nz*
http://www.panoramaheights.co.nz

Features & Attractions

- *Panoramic views*
- *Dinner on request*
- *West Coast surf beaches*
- *Private and peaceful*
- *250 km walking tracks*
- *Wineries, golf courses*

VISA **MasterCard** **JCB**

Bed & Breakfast
With a Little Indulgence

Double	$110
Single	$75
Child	

The panoramic views are breathtaking from our 'free-standing' accommodation high in the Waitakere Ranges, 35 minutes from Auckland City Centre. Our private, peaceful spot on the 'Twin Coast Discovery Route' provides a unique base to explore; 250 km of walking and tramping tracks in 17,000 ha of native rainforest, the best West Coast surf beaches with black sands and unspoilt beauty renowned for the filming of movies and television ('The Piano', 'Xena' and 'Hercules'). Your hosts, who reside nextdoor, encourage full use of this beautiful 'home away from home'. Relax in comfort. Enjoy an evening meal (by request). Watch the sun rise across the city and we will serve you a delicious breakfast at your leisure. Airport pick-up available.

DIRECTIONS: Please phone for bookings and directions.

Bedrooms	Qty
Double	2
Twin	1
Single	1
Bed Size	**Qty**
King	
Queen	2
Single	3
Bathrooms	**Qty**
Ensuite	3
Private	1
Guest Share	
Family Share	

FERNDALE
2 Vineyard Road, Henderson Valley, Auckland
Ph (09) 837 4337
Mobile 025 262 2023
e-mail: *ferndale@titan.co.nz*

Features & Attractions

- 25 min downtown Auckland
- Heart of wine country
- Amidst the Waitakere Ranges
- Stunning beaches
- Superb bush & coastal walks
- 10 min West City Shops

	Double	$100-130
	Single	$70-100
	Child	$neg.

Bedrooms	Qty
Double	1
Twin	
Single	
Bed Size	**Qty**
King	
Queen	1
Single	1
Bathrooms	**Qty**
Ensuite	1
Private	
Guest Share	
Family Share	

Country Home with City Fun

A warm welcome awaits you at **Ferndale,** set on 10 acres of countryside in the foothills of the stunning Waitakere Ranges and yet only 25 minutes drive from the attractions of Auckland City. Kick back and relax or sample the varied outdoor pursuits West Auckland has to offer. Fine golf courses, fishing, bush walks for all abilities, world class surf beaches, visit the Gannet Colony or simply sample award winning wines in the home of New Zealand wine making. **Ferndale** itself was once a thriving vineyard and its position on the northern slopes provide our guests with a sunny relaxing vista. Your accommodation is a spacious self-contained ensuite bedroom with private terrace enjoying country views. It has a separate entrance, a kitchenette and covered parking. Our aim is to provide warm homely comforts and friendly help, so you can enjoy your stay to the full.

AUCKLAND HOMESTAY
37 Torrance Street, Epsom, Auckland
Ph (09) 624 3714
e-mail: *aucklandhomestay@xtra.co.nz*
http://www.aucklandhomestay.co.nz

Features & Attractions

- Friendly and helpful hosts
- 5 min. walk to Cornwall
- Antiques & shopping close
- Park/One Tree Hill/Restaurants
- Great location easy to find
- Adjacent to main bus route

	Double	$120
	Single	$60-90
	Child	

Bedrooms	Qty
Double	1
Twin	
Single	2
Bed Size	**Qty**
King	
Queen	1
Single	2
Bathrooms	**Qty**
Ensuite	1
Private	
Guest Share	1
Family Share	

Homestay Bed & Breakfast

Isobel and Ian would like to welcome you to our modern spacious home, and experience "our" special brand of friendly hospitality. Just five minutes from motorway and 15 minutes from city CBD and airport. Situated in quiet tree-lined street, we are ideally positioned to explore the many attractions that await you. These could include parks, beaches, harbour cruises, museums, art galleries, horse racing, trotting, Ericsson Stadium, Eden Park and several golf courses. Start your day with a fully cooked or continental breakfast (joining us if you choose). A lounge is available for you to use and full laundry facilities. Evening meals by arrangement as is telephone and e-mail services. Complimentary tea and coffee anytime.

AIRPORT BED & BREAKFAST

1 Westney Rd (cnr Kirkbride Rd),
Mangere, Auckland
Ph (09) 275 0533, Fax(09) 275 0533
e-mail: *airportbnb@paradise.net.nz*
www.quickpages.com.au/ad/593

Features & Attractions

- *TV lounge*
- *Car storage while away*
- *5 minutes to restaurants*
- *Nearest Bed & Breakfast*
  to Auckland Airport (5 min.)
- *Laundry & e-mail available*

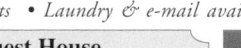

G Guest House
Bed & Breakfast

Double	$65-80
Single	$50-70
Child	neg

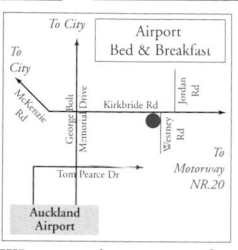

Friendly guest house, 5 minutes from Auckland Airport. Use Airport Free Phone dial 28 (located beside Information area at International, beside luggage terminal at Domestic) for courtesy transfers.
Dining room/lounge with TV, central heating. 10 quality rooms, 2 ensuites, family room. Tea, coffee, continental breakfast included. Kitchen, microwave, cot and disability facilities. City bus 100 metres.

We can advise you, if you need a rental car, restaurant or places to go and see in Auckland and the best ways to do this. If you are leaving Auckland and need to leave your car behind, we do have car storage available.
Please phone, e-mail or fax us for any futher information.

Bedrooms	Qty
Double	10
or Twin	10
or Single	10
Bed Size	**Qty**
King	
Queen	10
Single	10
Bathrooms	**Qty**
Ensuite	2
Private	
Guest Share	3
Family Share	-

MOUNTAIN VIEW BED & BREAKFAST

85A Wallace Road, Mangere Bridge, Auckland
Ph (09) 636 6535, Fax (09) 636 6126
e-mail: *mtviewbb@voyager.co.nz*

Features & Attractions

- *8 minutes from Airport*
- *10 min. Ericsson Stadium*
- *20 min. Auckland City*
- *Affordable 5 Star Service*
- *Quiet locality on ½ acre*
- *Friendly, helpful hosts*

H Homestay
Bed & Breakfast

Double	$75+
Single	$65+
Child	neg.

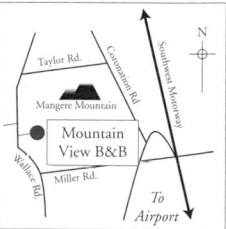

Situated on the lower slopes of historic Mangere Mountain, an extinct volcano with 2 craters, our restored kauri villa has stunning views of Manukau Harbour and Puketutu Island. Enjoy our quality décor and hearty cooked or continental breakfasts. Dinners by arrangement. Off-street parking available, public transport at gate. Helpful typed directions given to guests. The large, comfortable guest lounge has refreshment facilities, cosy fire and a wide range of literature about NZ. What our guests say: "Thanks for your friendly hospitality and insight into country affairs. Best bed in NZ." D & MB, South Australia. "10/10 for comfort and food, 11/10 for entertainment!!" P & A MacG., Scotland. Ian has two custom-built aircraft in progress. Jenny enjoys gardening, photography and travel. We both adore Oscar, our Burmese cat.

Bedrooms	Qty
Double	4
Twin	1
Single	
Bed Size	**Qty**
King	
Queen/Double	4
Single	3
Bathrooms	**Qty**
Ensuite	3
Private	
Guest Share	1
Family Share	

TOTARA LODGE

327 Redoubt Road, Manukau Heights
(RD 1, Papatoetoe) Auckland
Ph (09) 263 7777, Fax (09) 263 7777
Mobile 025 - 885 535
e-mail: totara-lodge@xtra.co.nz

Tariff : N.Z. Dollars	
Double	$90-160
Single	$75-110
Child	

Bedrooms	Qty
Double	2
Twin	1
Single	1
Bed Size	**Qty**
Super King	
King Single	2
Queen	2
Single	1
Bathrooms	**Qty**
Ensuite	2
Private	1
Guest Share	1
Family Share	

  Luxury Accommodation

Features & Attractions

- *Peace and quiet*
- *Bush walks*
- *10 minutes to Airport*
- *Auckland City 20 min.*
- *5 acres of gardens around the Lodge*
- *400 acres of Totora Park and Botanical Gardens adjacent*
- *Complimentary laundry*

Sited adjoining Totara Park, the Lodge is set in 5 acres of gardens with established trees and a pond. Extensive views, overlooking the 400 acres of Park Reserve with native bush and farmland to the harbour beyond, enhance the peace and quiet of this secluded location, yet Manukau City is only five minutes drive away, Auckland City 20 minutes away.

Built in 1988, **Totara Lodge** features French and old English interior style. Guests have tea and coffee facilities, refrigerator, TV, hair dryer and bathrobes. Breakfast is served in the dining room or alfresco on the deck looking out on to the pastoral scene beyond the harbour. Lunch and dinner with complimentary wine are also available at an extra charge.

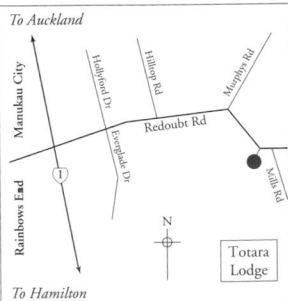

Staying at Totara Lodge is like staying in an oasis, no traffic noise, just peace and quiet. You will think you are miles away from the hustle and bustle, yet shops and restaurants are only minutes away.

ABOVE THE BEACH

141 Mellons Bay Road, Howick, Auckland
Ph (09) 534 2245. Fax (09) 534 2245
e-mail: *kea.nz@attglobal.net*

Tariff : N.Z. Dollars	
Double	$85-100
Single	$55
Child	

Bedrooms	Qty
Double	2
Twin	
Single	2
Bed Size	**Qty**
Super King	
King	
Queen	2
Single	2
Bathrooms	**Qty**
Ensuite	1
Private	1
Guest Share	1
Family Share	

**Bed & Breakfast
Homestay**

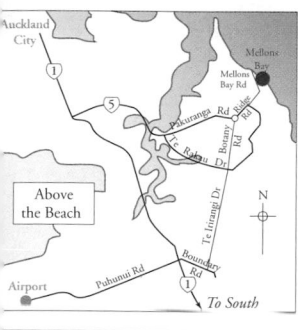

Features & Attractions

- *Lovely sea and bush views*
- *Beach 100 metres*
- *Close to delightful village*
- *Handy to Auckland Airport*
- *Six beaches, 2 golfcoursesnearby*
- *Auckland Ferry close by*

Welcome to our comfortable home – 100 yards **"Above the Beach"**, with kauri trees growing through our decks, lovely sea views to Waiheke Island, Rangitoto and Coromandel in the background. We are about 25 minutes from the International Airport, 16 kilometres to Auckland by road and just a 35 minute ferry ride to and from downtown Auckland.

Howick is a delightful village on the eastern side of Auckland. We have at least 14 restaurants, a historic church, colonial village and six beaches, two golf courses and the Auckland Ferry – all within a two mile radius. Our double rooms have feather duvets, electric blankets, heaters and individual decks looking onto bush and sea. Tea and coffee facilities, easy chairs, lounge suite, fridge and TVs for your convenience. We can advise you on places of interest.

We offer a "Home away from Home" and – super breakfasts. We look forward to meeting you. Come and relax with us. Marjorie and Max.

DIRECTIONS:
In Howick turn into Mellons Bay Road by Stockade Hill. We are well down Mellons Bay Road just 100 yards above the beach.

63

COCKLE BAY HOMESTAY

81 Pah Road, Cockle Bay, Howick, Auckland
Ph/Fax (09) 535 0120, Mobile (021) 685 638
e-mail: *cocklebay@bnbnz.co.nz*
http://www.bnbnz.co.nz

Tariff : N.Z. Dollars		
	Double	$115-135
	Single	$90-105
	Child	

Bedrooms	Qty
Double	1
Twin	1
Single	
Bed Size	**Qty**
Super King	
King	1
Queen	1
Single	2
Bathrooms	**Qty**
Ensuite	1
Private	1
Guest Share	
Family Share	

 Homestay Bed & Breakfast

Features & Attractions

- *Breathtaking sea views*
- *Warm welcome*
- *Quiet location*
- *Historical Village Museum*
- *Gateway to Pacific Coast Highway*
- *Walk to beach & historic restaurant*
- *Auckland Airport/City 20 min.*
- *Golf courses(4) within easy reach*

DIRECTIONS: Please phone for directions.

Jill and Richard welcome you to our elevated home above Cockle Bay Beach, and to join us for breakfast and share in some wonderfu conversations. Howick is one of the oldest settlements in N being one of the original four settlements established aroun 1847. Howick Village is 3 kilometres away with shops restaurants. A ferry (weekdays) ride to the city (35 minutes) is delightful way to see the harbour, or use the bus stop end of our driveway (45 minutes). Guest room are spacious and comfortable with sea views. The Taylor Suite is one large room with ensuite, tw comfortable chairs and private balcony. The Evan Room has a private bathroom, deck with chairs table close by for your use. Both have tea/fresh coffee making facilities. Off street parking. Laundr facilities.

Will help with rental car companies, cell phone requirements, and travel arrangements you ma require. Transport to/from the airport can be arranged. Feel relaxed with us and enjoy your holida We look forward to meeting you.

WHITFORDS COUNTRY VILLA
367 Whitford Road, Howick, Auckland
Ph (09) 530 8981, Fax (09) 530 8981
Mobile 025 - 657 3168
e-mail: *wendy39@attglobal.net*

Tariff : N.Z. Dollars	
Double	$120-140
Single	$90-100
Child	

Bedrooms	Qty
Double	1
Twin	1
Single	

Bed Size	Qty
Super King	
King	
Queen	1
Single	2

Bathrooms	Qty
Ensuite	
Private	1
Guest Share	
Family Share	

 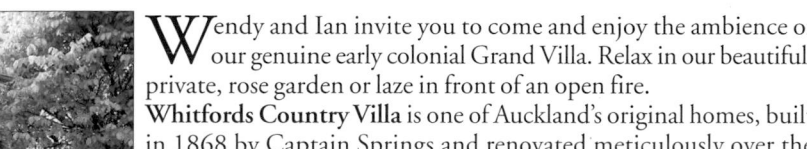

Boutique Accommodation Bed & Breakfast

DIRECTIONS:
On Whitford Road between Whitford and Howick. Howick is 20 minutes from Auckland Central.

Features & Attractions
- *Warm and friendly hosts*
- *Full silver service breakfast*
- *Private guest lounge*
- *Large English rose garden*
- *Historic Homestead with antiques*
- *On the Pacific Coast Highway*
- *Auckland Airport/City 20 minutes*
- *Restaurants, golf clubs, beaches close*

Wendy and Ian invite you to come and enjoy the ambience of our genuine early colonial Grand Villa. Relax in our beautiful, private, rose garden or laze in front of an open fire.
Whitfords Country Villa is one of Auckland's original homes, built in 1868 by Captain Springs and renovated meticulously over the last 20 years. Each bedroom has fresh flowers, tea and coffee making facilities, bathrobes, electric blankets, hairdryer etc.
Enjoy a scrumptious breakfast on our rose and wisteria clad verandah. We have 10 acres with sheep, a Border Collie named Jessie and a cat named Horse.
Our interests include boating, farming, travelling, skiing and golf. We love sharing our beautiful home and warmly welcome all our guests. Please phone for bookings and easy directions.

ARDERN'S FINE ACCOMMODATION

241 Church Bay Road, Oneroa, PO Box 193
Waiheke Island, Auckland
Ph (09) 372 5487, Fax(09) 372 5489
e-mail: *ardern@ihug.co.nz*
http://www.gotowaiheke.co.nz/arderns.htm

Tariff : N.Z. Dollars		
	Double	$180-250
	Single	$160-180
	Child	neg.

Bedrooms	Qty
Double	1
Twin	1
Single	
Bed Size	**Qty**
Super King	
King	
Queen	1
Single	2
Bathrooms	**Qty**
Ensuite	
Private	1
Guest Share	
Family Share	

 Self-contained Cottage

Features & Attractions

- *Tranquil, peaceful setting*
- *Local bush walks*
- *Warm, homely cottage*
- *Spectacular sea views*
- *Mudbrick Restaurant 3 min.*
- *Wharf and Oneroa 5 min.*

DIRECTIONS:
Please phone for easy directions
ADVANCE BOOKING
RECOMMENDED

Celebrating something special? Need a little pampering? Then **Ardern's** is the place for you! Our luxuriously appointed homestead offers a traditional friendly environment in a tranquil country setting. You are welcome to wander through the gardens and olive grove or explore the beautiful native bush abundant with birdlife. We encourage you to make **Ardern's** your home away from home. Hideaway in the reading room with a book, sip on a glass of wine in the lounge listening to your favourite music, snuggle up to one of the two open log fires, or just sit and marvel at the awe inspiring view - the choice is yours. We have three beautifully decorated rooms, each with fine linen, tea/coffee making facilities, TV, juliet balconies, fresh flowers and ensuites. In the morning you will be served the renowned **Ardern's** breakfast - a selection of cereals, nuts, fresh fruits, tea/coffee, toast and a sumptuous farmstyle cooked breakfast. Waiheke has many activities such as golf, vineyard/art tours, kayaking, bush walks and horse riding. The Mudbrick Restaurant is only 3 minutes away and Oneroa Village 5 minutes. Come and experience this Island Paradise - you will not be disappointed.

TOP OF THE HILL COUNTRY HOMESTAY

183 Fitzpatrick Road, Brookby, RD 1, Manurewa, Auckland
Ph/Fax (09) 530 8576, Mobile 025-288 0835
e-mail: *topofthehill@xtra.co.nz*
http://www.visions.co.nz/topofthehill.

Tariff : N.Z. Dollars	
Double	$110
Single	$75
Child	n/a

Bedrooms	Qty
Double	2
Twin	2
Single	

Bed Size	Qty
Super King	
King	
Queen	2
King Single	4

Bathrooms	Qty
Ensuite	4
Private	
Guest Share	
Family Share	

MasterCard VISA 🚭

 **Luxury Countrystay**

Features & Attractions
- Auckland Airport and City 25 min.
- Amazing expansive views
- Beautiful bush glow-worms
- Gateway to Pacific Coast Highway
- Tiled ensuite bathrooms
- Luxurious new home
- 42 acres to explore
- 10 minutes SH 1

A spacious newly built home, situated high on the Brookby-Clevedon Hills, overlooking beautiful picture-book fields dotted with sheep and cows, looking beyond to Auckland's eastern suburbs, bordered by the sparkling Waitemata waters. Our quaint country lane conveniently leads onto the scenic Pacific Coast Highway, gateway to the popular Coromandel Peninsula. The guest wing has four luxurious large bedrooms with guest lounge, each with their own ensuite bathroom, all with floor to ceiling landscape windows to take full advantage of the 360 ° spectacular views. Experience wonderful tranquility, clean air and a lifestyle only millions dream about! Meet friendly farm animals, or walk through pristine native bush with its colony of glow worms. Sample Pat's scrumptious home cooking and enjoy our warm hospitality. Dinner if required is $30 per person - wine included. We can help with any travel arrangements and provide a courtesy pick-up from Auckland Airport (25 minutes) or Manukau City bus stop. With much to see and do within Auckland City (only 25 minutes) and an area abounding with country attractions, we encourage longer stays with discounts available.

DIRECTIONS;
From Auckland take the Manurewaturn-off.
From Hamilton take the Takanini turn-off.

TATU ORCHARDS

McGowan Road, RD 3,
Waiuku, Franklin
Ph/Fax (09) 235 7924, Mobile 025-216 2301
e-mail: *tatu@zfree.co.nz*

Features & Attractions

- *Peaceful setting*
- *Beautiful scenery*
- *Garden tours*
- *Auckland Airport 45 min.*
- *Farmhouse breakfast*
- *Dinner by arrangement*

Double	$80-140
Single	$40-70
Child	$40-50

Farmstay
Bed & Breakfast

Bedrooms	Qty
Double	2
Twin	1
Single	
Bed Size	**Qty**
King	
Queen/Double	2
King/Single	2
Bathrooms	**Qty**
Ensuite	
Private	2
Guest Share	1
Family Share	

Enjoy the tranquility of a peaceful citrus orchard only 45 minutes from Auckland's international airport. A great place to start or end your New Zealand holiday or just take time out from the noisy metropolis. We offer traditional farm house accommodation with all modern conveniences. Three guest bedrooms with private bathrooms and all those little touches to make your stay comfortable. There are activities in the immediate area to suit all tastes. Sedate garden visits and bush walks, a stroll on a golden beach. For the more adventurous there is horse trekking, caving, abseiling and paragliding. Step back in time with a sail on the restored sailing scow 'Jane Gifford' or take a trip on the Glenbrook Vintage Steam Railway. We offer full farmhouse breakfast and our home-grown juice has been described by one visitor as "the best OJ in New Zealand"! A delicious three-course dinner is available with prior notice. We aim to make your stay relaxing and enjoyable. Why not come and have some fun in the country?

COTSWOLD COTTAGE

46 Maramarahi Road, PO Box 152
Totara, Thames
Ph (07) 868 6306, Fax (07)868 6306
e-mail: *NZH_COTSWOLD.COTTAGE@xtra.co.nz*

Features & Attractions

- *Picturesque view*
- *Quiet and comfortable*
- *5 minutes from Thames*
- *Gateway to Coromandel Penins.*
- *Cooked breakfast included*
- *Private entrance & ensuites*

Double	$80-100
Single	$50
Child	$12

Homestay
Bed & Breakfast

Bedrooms	Qty
Double	2
Twin	1
Single	
Bed Size	**Qty**
King/Single	2
Queen/Double	2
Single	1
Bathrooms	**Qty**
Ensuite	3
Private	
Guest Share	
Family Share	

Just one hour drive from Auckland and five minutes from Thames, **Cotswold Cottage** is the perfect place to stop over before seeing the Coromandel Peninsula. Shifted from Epsom in 1990, our gracious old villa was re-sited at Totara overlooking Thames and the Kauaeranga River/Valley. Initially a restaurant, the guest wing was added in 1995. Now, three sunny well appointed rooms with private ensuites, offer guests stunning views and a private entrance to come and go as they please. The lounge, conservatory and terrace offer a choice of places to read, write or simply relax. Tea and coffee making facilities. Sky Digital available. We offer dinner by arrangement.

ACORN LODGE

161 Kauaeranga Valley, RD 2, Thames
Ph (07) 868 8723, Fax (07) 868 8713
e-mail: *AcornLodge@xtra.co.nz*

Tariff : N.Z. Dollars	
Double	$95
Single	$55
Child	neg

Bedrooms	Qty
Double	2
Twin	
Single	1
Bed Size	**Qty**
King	
Queen	1
Double	1
Single	1
Bathrooms	**Qty**
Ensuite	
Private	2
Guest Share	
Family Share	

VISA   MasterCard

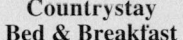
Countrystay
Bed & Breakfast

Features & Attractions

- *Glow-worms 2 min. walk*
- *Forest park nearby*
- *Rural and bush views*
- *4 km to Thames restaurants*
- *Home baking*
- *Warm, friendly hospitality*

Welcome to Thames – Gateway to the Coromandel. **Acorn Lodge** offers you the perfect base for exploring the many attractions the peninsula has to offer. We have extensive knowledge of the area and are happy to advise or arrange tours for you.

After a day's outing relax in our spacious, comfortable home with landscaped gardens. Enjoy a fresh pot of tea or coffee and home baking on your sunny patio, or sit in the guest lounge listening to the sound of the waterfall in the atrium. Dinner is by prior arrangement, with a woodfired barbecue being Dennis' speciality. Breakfast includes homemade muesli, fresh fruit, yummy bacon and mushrooms and more!

We enjoy tramping and mountain biking in the Kauaeranga Valley as well as fishing around the beautiful Coromandel Islands. We share our lifestyle with a friendly German shepherd, a cat, a goat and some sheep.

A warm welcome awaits you.

KAUAERANGA COUNTRY

33 Pakaraka Lane, 446 Kauaeranga Valley Rd,
RD 2, Thames
Ph (07) 868 6895 Fax (07) 868 6895
e-mail: *kauaeranga.country@voyager.co.nz*

Tariff : N.Z. Dollars	
Double	$110
Single	$60
Child	$20

Bedrooms	Qty
Double	1
Twin	1
Single	
Bed Size	**Qty**
Super King	
King	
Queen	1
Single	2
Bathrooms	**Qty**
Ensuite	
Private	1
Guest Share	
Family Share	

 Self-contained Accommodation Countrystay

Features & Attractions

- *Peaceful rural hideaway*
- *Tramping and bush walks*
- *Safe private swimming*
- *Laundry facilities*
- *Kayaks for river fun*
- *Restaurants and shops nearby*
- *Forest park visitors centre*
- *Gateway to forest park (horses)*

At **Kauaeranga Country** a warm welcome and comfortable bed await. Fluffy duvets and electric blankets for winter warmth and crisp cotton sheets for summer. To add to your comfort, your kitchen is complete with fridge, microwave and tea and coffee facilities. Guests can enjoy the privacy of their own apartment, while relaxing and enjoying the scenery close enough to touch. A large comfortable lounge area with books on New Zealand and local history overlooks the rambling bush garden.

The beautiful Kauaeranga River is literally on the doorstep with its 100% pure New Zealand water, great for swimming or kayaking. The valley offers hiking both easy and strenuous and we will happily recommend the walk to suit you.

Our 10 acre property is home to our horses, a passion we share. We also enjoy travelling and meeting people from other parts of the world. With only one party of guests at a time, we can ensure your stay with us is the very best it can be.

DIRECTIONS: Thames 6.2 km from the Toyota Plant. Pakaraka Lane is No 446 Kauaeranga Valley Road, we are first left down the lane.

TE MATA BAY COUNTRY HOMESTAY

29 Eames Crescent, Te Mata Bay
Thames Coast, Coromandel
Ph (07) 868 4754, Fax (07) 868 4757
Mobile (025) 233 0656
e-mail: *tematahomestay@xtra.co.nz*

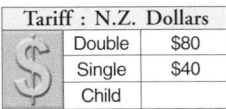

Tariff : N.Z. Dollars	
Double	$80
Single	$40
Child	

Bedrooms	Qty
Double	1
Twin	1
Single	1
Bed Size	**Qty**
Super King	
King	1
Queen	1
Single	2
Bathrooms	**Qty**
Ensuite	
Private	
Guest Share	1
Family Share	

 TE MATA BAY COUNTRY HOMESTAY

Country Homestay

Features & Attractions

- *Panoramic sea & mountain views*
- *Complimentary wine & juice*
- *Pianola, music for everyone*
- *Guest lounge with open fire*
- *Every room has superb views*
- *Peaceful - no traffic noise*
- *Excellent evening meal*
- *Bush or beach walks*

Come and stay with us at **Te Mata Bay**, any day of the year. You won't be disappointed!

Good beds, excellent home-cooked meals, great company too! Enjoy the peace and the wonderful sea and mountain views from the balcony, which surrounds our large comfortable home. Guest's bedrooms are pleasantly furnished and have sea and mountain views. We have a pianola and pool table for your enjoyment, also a comfortable lounge with a log fire.

Visit our local water garden and square kauri – 15 min. drive, or Coromandel's Driving Creek Railway – 35 min. away, or the famous Hot Water Beach – 50 min. by car, or enjoy good fishing at **Te Mata Bay.**

Hot bread, croissants, cappuccino and fresh percolated coffee along with fresh eggs from our chickens and a large choice of cereals and fruit are offered for breakfast. Complimentary wine with evening meals. Make our day – come and stay. **We are a non smoking family.**

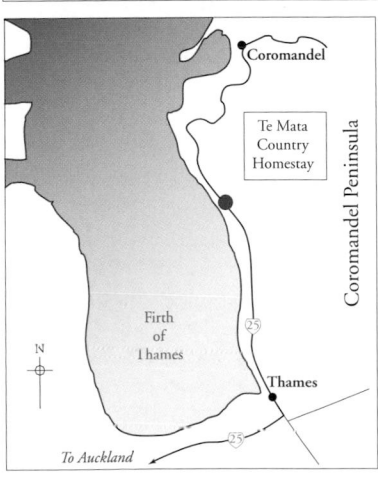

Directions: Please phone for easy directions

A WOODSY COTTAGE
2 Oxford Terrace, Coromandel Town,
Coromandel Peninsula
Ph (07) 866 8111
e-mail: *gaiacot@wave.co.nz*

Tariff : N.Z. Dollars	
Double	$80-140
Single	$70-90
Child	

Bedrooms	Qty
Double	4
Twin	
Single	
Bed Size	**Qty**
King	1
Queen	2
Double	2
Single	2
Bathrooms	**Qty**
Ensuite	3
Private	1
Guest Share	
Family Share	

 Unique Accommodation

  VISA MasterCard

Features & Attractions
- *Therapy spa, swimming pool*
- *"Driving Creek Railway", beaches*
- *Tours: 309 Rd. Hot Water Beach*
- *Bush, coastal and kauri walks*
- *Gardens, museums, fishing*
- *Fine restaurants, craft trail*

Welcome! Our unique pole house, set amidst lush sub-tropical gardens, is tastefully furnished with antiques, colonial furniture and ethnic works of art from your hosts extensive travels.
Wander through our orchard, have a drink in our tranquil zen-garden to the sound of running water and bird song. Wallow in our tree-fern lined plunge pool, relax in our special Therapy Spa under the stars. Enjoy breakfast of homemade fare: fruit, muesli, muffins, croissants, preserves, cheese, pungent freshly ground coffee or tea.

Directions given with bookings.

 Woodsy Cottage, charming, fully self-contained, spacious, made of native timbers (rimu & kauri), spiral fountain, pot-belly and north facing balcony, overlooking private gardens and tree-ferns. Sleeps 2-4.
The Pottery Studio (converted) fully self-contained, open plan, pot belly fireplace, with patio and private garden. Sleeps 3.
Self-catering $95-140 per night for two.
Extra person $15 per night.   Breakfast $10 per person per night.
Whether your goal is a private romantic retreat or an enriching social rapport, we wish to provide an harmonious and rewarding experience.

KARAMANA (1872) HOMESTEAD

84 Whangapoua Road, Coromandel
Ph (07) 866 7138, Fax (07) 866 7477
e-mail: karamana@xtra.co.nz

Tariff : N.Z. Dollars	
Double	$125
Single	$95
Child	

Bedrooms	Qty
Double	3
Twin	1
King Single	

Bed Size	Qty
Super King	1
King	
Queen/Double	2
Single	2

Bathrooms	Qty
Ensuite	4
Private	
Guest Share	
Family Share	

           Boutique Accommodation

DIRECTIONS:
Follow the coast road
from Thames to Coromandel. 200m
before the township turn right onto the
road to Whangapoua. Karamana is 1km
on the right at a right angle bend.

Features & Attractions

- *Spectacular coastal walks*
- *Driving Creek Railway*
- *Craft Trail*
- *Fishing and scenic tours*
- *Charming golf course*
- *Garden tours*
- *One hour from
  Cathedral Cove walk*

Karamana is one of New Zealand's unique Bed&Breakfast experiences. Set in a quiet rural valley in beautiful Coromandel, the Homestead is one of the oldest working buildings, built in 1872 for the well known Cadman family.

Karamana has been lovingly restored in keeping with the Victorian era. Turn back the clock as you rest comfortably in the king size oak canopy bed, the romantic queen size four poster bed, the twin sleigh beds, or for added privacy request the cottage with its queen size bed and own sitting room. All the rooms have ensuites.

Continental breakfast includes homemade baking and preserves. You will be welcomed with afternoon tea in the well-appointed dining room, or in the courtyard by the old well.

Your hosts, Margaret and Gerald Best, will ensure that you have a complete Coromandel experience and that you leave the region, having enjoyed its rugged beauty and hospitality.

Coromandel provides the visitor with the opportunity to relax and unwind in a different world only two hours by car or ferry from Auckland.

KUAOTUNU BAY LODGE

State Highway 25, Kuaotunu, RD 2, Whitianga
Ph (07) 866 4396, Fax (07) 866 4396
Mobile 025 - 601 3665
e-mail: *muir@kuaotunubay.co.nz*
http://www.kuaotunubay.co.nz

Features & Attractions

- *Purpose built*
- *Private decks*
- *Underfloor heating*
- *Golf course nearby*
- *2½ hrs to Auckland Airport*
- *Panoramic views*

Boutique Accomm. & Self-contained Accomm.

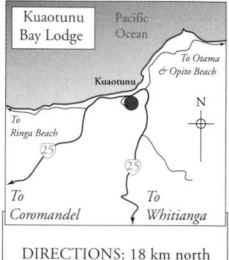

DIRECTIONS: 18 km north of Whitianga on SH 25. Please phone for bookings and easy directions.

	Double	$130-150
	Single	$95
	Child	n/a

Bedrooms	Qty
Double	3
Twin	1
Single	
Bed Size	**Qty**
King	
Queen	3
King Single	2
Bathrooms	**Qty**
Ensuite	3
Private	1
Guest Share	
Family Share	

Welcome to our elegant beachhouse set in 4 hectares of native bush and pasture, offering panoramic views of the Peninsula and Mercury Island. Enjoy the sunsets from your private deck. Breakfast is served in the sunny conservatory and dinner is by arrangement. The safe beach is just a short walk through the garden. Central to all activities on the peninsula, spend 2 or 3 days with us to give yourselves time for bush walks, kayaking, fishing, horseriding, or simply strolling the beach and enjoying some of the fine dining in Whitianga. Having enjoyed this property since 1972, we offer our experience in bushwalking, fishing and local attractions to help make your stay more enjoyable. A tastefully decorated S.C. Unit is also available.

AT PARKLAND PLACE

14 Parkland Place
Ph (07) 866 4987. Fax (07) 866 4946
e-mail: *parklandplace@wave.co.nz*

Features & Attractions

- *European hospitality*
- *Luxurious, romantic*
- *Sunny outdoor area*
- *Spa pool and barbecue*
- *Dinner by arrangement*
- *Quiet and peaceful*

Boutique Accommodation Luxurious Bed & Breakfast

	Double	$125-150
	Single	$100
	Child	neg.

Bedrooms	Qty
Double	4
Twin	1
Single	
Bed Size	**Qty**
Super King	2
Queen	3
King Single	2
Single	1
Bathrooms	**Qty**
Ensuite	3
Private	
Guest Share	1

Enjoy European hospitality in Whitianga's most luxurious 5 star Boutique Bed & Breakfast. Maria, a ship's chef from Poland and her New Zealand husband Guy, a Master Mariner, will make your stay a memorable experience with hospitality that has become renown around the world. Large luxuriously appointed rooms with TV, radio, writing desk and comfortable beds. Take your time over a magnificent breakfast and let Maria surprise you with a superb dinner or barbecue. Relax in the large guest lounge, watching Sky TV, reading a book or listening to music. Enjoy the sunny outdoors relaxing in the spa pool or take a quiet stroll along the reserve to popular Brophy's Beach. Being situated next to farmland and reserves ensures absolute peace and quiet. Laundry, fax and e-mail facilities are available. Privacy and discretion is assured.

DIRECTIONS: Take SH 25 to Whitianga. Drive through township along Buffalo Beach Road for 4 km. Turn left into Centennial Drive, then first into Parkland Place.

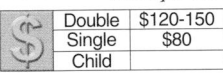

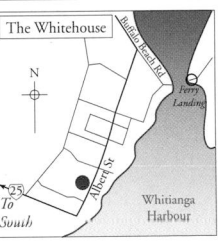

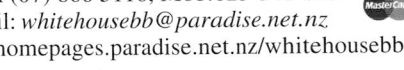

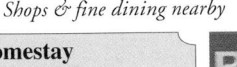

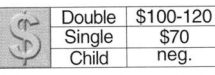

BEACHCOMBER

77 Buffalo Beach Road, Whitianga
Ph(07) 866 2123 Fax (07) 866 4165
Mobile - 021 212 2999
e-mail: *m.b.beachcomber@xtra.co.nz*

Features & Attractions

- *Outstanding 180° views*
- *Private guest lounge*
- *Barbeque area*
- *Dinner on request*
- *Safe off-street parking*
- *Internet/e-mail access*

Double	$120-150
Single	$80
Child	

**Homestay
Bed & Breakfast**

Bedrooms	Qty
Double	3
Twin	
Single	
Bed Size	**Qty**
King	
Queen	2
Double	1
Bathrooms	**Qty**
Ensuite	
Private	1
Guest Share	1
Family Share	

DIRECTIONS:
Travel along SH 25 to Whitianga,
along Buffalo Beach Road 2 km,
second home past Marlin Street.

Our home is situated along the Beach and takes in spectacular views of Mercury Bay with the setting sun glistening off the white face of Shakespeare's cliff. The private guest lounge on third floor with refreshments, ensuite and decks gives our home a unique and relaxing place to put your feet up. With Penny's knowledge gained from working in the Information Centre, it is the perfect location for planning your adventures on the Coromandel Peninsula, and we are able to pass on to our guests many interesting facts and facets about our area. Both of us are volunteers in the Emergency Services and in our spare time enjoy fishing, diving and travel and would love to share with you many anecdotes of these times.

We look forward to meeting you and sharing our home and hospitality with you.

THE WHITEHOUSE B&B

129 Albert Street
Whitianga, Coromandel Peninsula
Ph/Fax (07) 866 5116, Mob.025-341 029
e-mail: *whitehousebb@paradise.net.nz*
http://homepages.paradise.net.nz/whitehousebb/

Features & Attractions

- *Tasty, hearty breakfast*
- *Central to beaches*
- *Golf course nearby*
- *2¼ hrs from Auckland Airport*
- *Complimentary tour of area*
- *Shops & fine dining nearby*

**Homestay
Bed & Breakfast**

Double	$100-120
Single	$70
Child	neg.

Bedrooms	Qty
Double	2
Twin	1
Single	
Bed Size	**Qty**
King	
Queen/Double	2
Single	2
Bathrooms	**Qty**
Ensuite	1
Private	
Guest Share	1
Family Share	

"When only the best will do".

Welcome to **The White House** which overlooks the inner harbour. We offer a friendly comfortable stay in our modern purpose built home. We are happy to share local knowledge and folklore with you over breakfast. Feast on a continental, traditional or Murray's special of pan-fried fish and Pipi fritters. Whitianga is an excellent base to explore the Coromandel Peninsula. It is the closest town to the internationally recognised Cathedral Cove and Hot Water Beach. Try some of the many activities such as bone carving, deep sea fishing, watch the dolphins play, visit a kauri grove, or just enjoy our beautiful beaches. We can even arrange an intimate wedding for couples on holiday in New Zealand. We aim to make your stay memorable.

75

HARBOUR LIGHTS GUESTHOUSE
9 Harbour Lights Terrace, Whitianga
Coromandel Peninsula
Ph (07) 866 2408, Fax (07) 866 2108
e-mail: *harbourlights@xtra.co.nz*

Features & Attractions
- Spa pool for 4 people
- Sea views from all rooms
- BBQ area
- Big decks
- Candlelit dinner available
- German & French spoken

**Boutique Accom.
Bed & Breakfast**

DIRECTIONS: Take SH 25 to Whitianga. Through township along Buffalo Beach Rd, for 5km. At top of hill turn left into Harbour Lights Tce. We are at the end on the left.

	Double	$145-160
	Single	$100
	Child	half price

Bedrooms	Qty
Double	2
Twin	2
Single	
Bed Size	**Qty**
King	1
Queen	1
King Single	2
Bathrooms	**Qty**
Ensuite	2
Private	2
Guest Share	2
Family Share	

Harbour Lights Guesthouse was designed to look like an old New Zealand Villa, but has all the modern features that a top quality Bed & Breakfast needs. Nestled into a tree-covered hill, it has fabulous views of Mercury Bay and its deck is a vantage point for connoisseurs of fine sunsets! Inside, Lisa's good taste is reflected in the décor. Four charming double rooms are available for guests. All have sea views and ensuites or private bathrooms. A spacious lounge opens onto the balcony and there is a well-equipped kitchen. A spa pool and barbecue complete the facilities. The property is in a private residential area. Lisa and Brian live in a separate house of similar standard, where homestay accommodation is also available. We assure you that you will feel welcome and at "home" in this very comfortable house. Nothing is very far away.It is a short drive to the town with its restaurants and shops and **Harbour Lights** is within easy reach of many of Coromandel's fantastic beaches.

COSY CAT COTTAGE
41 South Highway, Whitianga, Mercury Bay
Coromandel Peninsula
Ph (07) 866 4488, Fax (07) 866 4488
e-mail: *cosycat@whitianga.co.nz*

Features & Attractions
- Picturesque cottage
- Amusing catty decor
- A-la-carte breakfast
- Large shaded verandah
- Comfortable guest lounge
- Helpful, friendly service

**Bed & Breakfast
Self-contained Cottage**

	Double	$80-95
	Single	$50-60
	Child	

Bedrooms	Qty
Double	2
Twin	1
Single	1
Bed Size	**Qty**
King	
Queen	2
Single	2
Bathrooms	**Qty**
Ensuite	2
Private	1
Guest Share	
Family Share	

DIRECTIONS:
1 km south of the town centre on Highway 25.

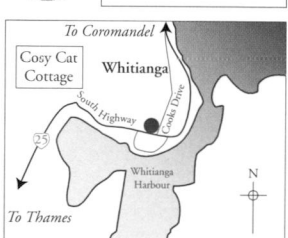

Welcome to our picturesque cottage and enjoy the amusing catty décor and unique feline ambience! Cosy queen/double/twin/single bedrooms with ensuite/private bathrooms are available all year. Delicious a-la-carte breakfasts are complimentary and teas or coffees can be served when required.
An easy drive may take you to "Hot Water Beach", "Cathedral Cove" and other fascinating places. Friendly and helpful service is assured and you will probably like to meet Sylvie the Tonkinese cat and perhaps visit the "cat hotel" in the garden.
A self-contained cottage is also available with two queen bedrooms, bathrooms and kitchen.

RIVERSIDE RETREAT

309 Road, RD 1, Whitianga, Coromandel Peninsula
Ph (07) 866 5155. Fax (07) 866 5155
e-mail: *retreat@xtra.co.nz*
http://www.riversideretreat.co.nz

Features & Attractions

- *Rural riverside location*
- *Trout fishing*
- *Tranquil bush setting*
- *Privacy-you'll be our only guests*
- *3 acres of landscaped gardens*
- *Beaches & restaurants 10min.*

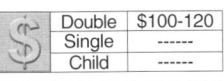

Double	$100-120
Single	------
Child	------

Self-contained Cottage
Bed & Breakfast

Bedrooms	Qty
Double	1
Twin	
Single	
Bed Size	**Qty**
King	
Queen	1
Single	
Bathrooms	**Qty**
Ensuite	
Private	1
Guest Share	
Family Share	

You are invited to share our **Riverside Retreat** on the edge of the waters which meander through the Mahikarau Valley. Your accommodation is at the end of the maple-lined driveway, nestled amongst mature native trees.

Built entirely of timbers, the cottage has a full kitchen, sunny lounge and private bathroom. The bedroom, upstairs on a mezzanine floor, has a queen size bed with views over the river and gardens. Separate laundry facilities are available. We invite

DIRECTIONS: 7 min. south of Whitianga turn off SH 25 onto 309 Road. 200 yards past bridge we are on the left. Look for cross-saw on gate.

you to enjoy a generous continental breakfast on your deck overlooking the gardens, after which you can flyfish for trout in the river, take a fresh water swim, or relax by the river with a good book. Or you can discover Whitianga's beautiful beaches, craftshops and local seafood restaurants - just a short 10 minutes drive. At the **Riverside Retreat** you can be assured of peace and tranquillity - we cater for one party at a time.

YOUR HOSTS: **Hisae and David Lynch**   Ph: (07) 866 0166 ☎   **Whitianga**

HALCYON HEIGHTS

365 Mill Creek Road, RD 1, Whitianga
Ph (07) 866 0166, Fax (07) 866 5399
Mobile 025-846 873
e-mail: *hisae@aikido.co.nz*
http://www.aikido.co.nz/farmstay

Features & Attractions

- *Tranquil setting*
- *65 acres of bush*
- *Large kauri*
- *Beautiful gardens*
- *Glow-worms*
- *Waterfalls*

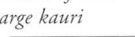

Countrystay
Bed & Breakfast

Double	$100
Single	$60
Child	$40

Set in a beautiful valley, **Halcyon Heights** is the dream of David Lynch, who lived in Tokyo for many years as Manager, Japan of New Zealand Tourist & Publicity Dept., and his Japanese wife Hisae. They wanted something somewhere far from the pressures of the big city, that had the essence of the Real New Zealand, and found it in this magic spot.

Familiar with the needs of international visitors, David and Hisae delight in sharing their piece of Paradise. Hisae's delicious meals have an international appeal. (Dinner by arrangement for $35 p.p.). Plan on staying more than one night and using **Halcyon Heights** as your base for exploring the fantastic Coromandel Peninsula.

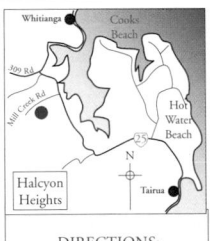

DIRECTIONS:
3.6 km along
Mill Creek Road off
State Highway 25.
Just south of Whitianga.

Bedrooms	Qty
Double	
Twin	3
Single	
Bed Size	**Qty**
King/Single	2
Queen/Double	
Single	4
Bathrooms	**Qty**
Ensuite	
Private	
Guest Share	1
Family Share	1

HOT WATER BEACH BED & BREAKFAST

48 Pye Place, Hot Water Beach, Whitianga
Ph (07) 866 3991. Fax (07) 866 3291
Mobile 025 - 799 620
e-mail: *TKnight@xtra.co.nz*
http://www.hotwaterbedandbreakfast.co.nz

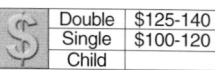

Features & Attractions

- *Wide sea/beach views*
- *Hot springs on beach*
- *Surf beach walks*
- *Spa pool, billiard table*
- *Spectacular night skies*
- *Sun-drenched decks*

Quality Homestay Bed & Breakfast

Double	$125-140
Single	$100-120
Child	

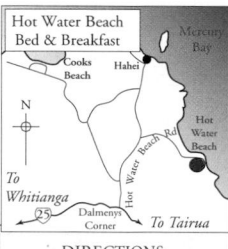

Hot Water Beach Bed & Breakfast

DIRECTIONS:
Follow Hot Water Beach Rd.
from SH 25. Travel past Beach
Shop and carpark. We are
50 m on right uphill.

Escape now to this premier Bed & Breakfast on the Coromandel Peninsula, situated approximately 2 hours drive from Auckland and Hamilton. Our modern home has been specifically designed for the comfort of our guests. On the beach you can dig your own natural hot pool, swim, surf and observe the native bird life.

Enjoy a generous breakfast on our extensive sun-drenched decks. Relax with a fresh coffee or cool drink and view the dolphins which often come to play in the bay, or observe the spectacular night skies. Nearby activities include Cathedral Cove, bush walks, kayaking, horsetreks, golf, diving, fishing and wineries. Proud to be members of the HOSTLINK network of quality homestays.

Bedrooms	Qty
Double	2
Twin	
Single	
Bed Size	**Qty**
King	
Queen	2
Single	
Bathrooms	**Qty**
Ensuite	2
Private	
Guest Share	
Family Share	

COPSEFIELD BED AND BREAKFAST

1055 SH 25, RD 1, Whangamata
Ph (07) 865 9555, Fax (07) 865 9555
Mobile 025-289 0131
e-mail:*copsefield@xtra.co.nz*
http://www.copsefield.co.nz

Features & Attractions

- *Stunning country scenery*
- *Canoes & mountain bikes available*
- *Peace and tranquility*
- *Hot tub*
- *3 acres of garden*
- *River, views*

Countrystay Bed & Breakfast

Double	$130
Single	$90
Child	

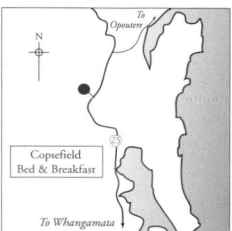

Copsefield Bed & Breakfast

Copsefield is situated at the Southern end of the stunning Coromandel Peninsula. Our home is close to exquisite native fauna and flora, magnificent beaches and walks. It has been architecturally designed for your comfort. Each bedroom has its own ensuite and adjoining verandah.

Relax in the private lounge with complimentary tea or coffee. We serve a glass of New Zealand wine before your evening meal. The nearest restaurant is some four minutes drive from our home. A full breakfast is served, either in the dining room, or outside.

We have bikes and canoes for your use, beaches are close by. Swimming in the river next to our property is an enjoyable experience. Trish and Richard offer you a warm and friendly welcome.

Bedrooms	Qty
Double	2
Twin	1
Single	
Bed Size	**Qty**
King	
Queen	2
Single	2
Bathrooms	**Qty**
Ensuite	3
Private	
Guest Share	
Family Share	

VISA
 MasterCard
bankcard
 KIWI HOST

IL CASA MORATTI HOMESTAY
313 Mary Road, Whangamata, Coromandel
Ph (07) 865 6164, Fax (07) 865 6164
e-mail: *ilcasamoratti@xtra.co.nz*
www.thepeninsula.co.nz/moratti

 FARM & HOME HOSTS

Features & Attractions
- *Beautiful safe surf beach*
- *Two golf courses 9 & 18 holes*
- *Guest lounge - tea/coffee*
- *Comfortable beds*
- *Seven day shopping*
- *Magnificent scenery*

H | **Homestay Bed & Breakfast** | **BB** | **$**

Double	$95
Single	$70
Child	

DIRECTIONS: Please phone for bookings and directions.

Experience genuine Kiwi hospitality with your friendly hosts George and Bev who welcome you to their comfortable, clean, modern smokefree home, where guests have their own TV, lounge, tea and coffee making facilities, microwave and fridge. Laundry facilities available for small charge. Dinner is available by prior arrangement - $25 pp. Our magnificent surf beach is only minutes away, handy to town, park, surf club and golf course. We have travelled extensively and enjoy swapping experiences with fellow travellers. Our other interests include gardening, sport, fishing, tramping and conservation. Whangamata has plenty to offer visitors - surfing, swimming, boating, fishing, and tramping through beautiful native bush. The area abounds with history of Kauri Gum Digging, gold mining and timber milling. Whangamata is known as the café capital of the Coromandel with many outdoor cafes and restaurants. Our aim is to ensure our guests have an enjoyable hassle free holiday.

Bedrooms	Qty
Double	1
Twin	1
Single	
Bed Size	**Qty**
King	
Double	1
Single	2
Bathrooms	**Qty**
Ensuite	
Private	
Guest Share	1
Family Share	

 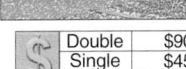

PARNASSUS FARM & GARDEN
191 Te Ohaki Road, Huntly
Ph/Fax (07) 828 8781, Mobile 021-458 525
e-mail: *parnassus@xtra.co.nz*

VISA
MasterCard
eftpos

Features & Attractions
- *Only minutes off SH1*
- *Auckland less than 1 hour*
- *Bush and farm walks*
- *Working farm*
- *Glorious gardens*
- *Families welcome*

F | **Bed & Breakfast Farmstay on "Real Working Farm"** | **BB** | | **$**

Double	$90
Single	$45
Child	neg.

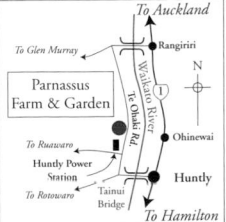

Parnassus offers you all the calm and beauty of the New Zealand countryside only minutes off SH1 and wonderful farmhouse meals using garden-fresh produce. We are a successful farming venture combining dairying, forestry, sheep and beef and have an extensive garden incorporating formal rose bed, woodland area, orchard, berry-fruit courtyard and kitchen gardens. Children enjoy our delightful range of birds and small animals.
Auckland, Raglan, Hamilton, the Coromandel, Waitomo, Rotorua and Taupo are all easy day trip destinations. Courtesy pick-up is available from Huntly, bus or rail. We offer a delicious cooked breakfast and picnics, luncheons and dinners are available by arrangement. Be assured of a warm country welcome at **Parnassus**.

DIRECTIONS: From south - cross Waikato River at Huntly turn right into Harris St, proceed 2km to Huntly power station, right into Te Ohaki Rd, we are 1.9km on left. From north - cross Waikato River at Rangiriri south along Te Ohaki Rd. 12km, we are on right.

Bedrooms	Qty
Double	2
Twin	1
Single	
Bed Size	**Qty**
King	
Double	2
Single	4
Bathrooms	**Qty**
Ensuite	
Private	1
Guest Share	1
Family Share	1

WATERS EDGE HOLIDAY HAVEN
100E Greenslade Road, Moonlight Bay, Raglan
Ph (07) 825 0567 Fax (07) 825 0562
Mobile 025-648 6803
e-mail: *watersedge.raglan@clear.net.nz*
http://www.raglan.net.nz/watersedge

New Zealand Association
FARM & HOME HOSTS

Tariff : N.Z. Dollars	
Double	$80-120
Single	$70-95
Child	

Bedrooms	Qty
Double	4
Twin	1
Single	2
Bed Size	**Qty**
King	2
Queen	2
Double	1
Single	3
Bathrooms	**Qty**
Ensuite	3
Private	3
Guest Share	
Family Share	

 Self-contained Seaside Bed & Breakfast

Features & Attractions

- *Stunning sea and bush views*
- *Peaceful gardens and beach*
- *Self-contained seclusion*
- *Great attractions nearby*
- *35 minutes Hamilton City*
- *90 minutes Auckland International Airport*

Discover Raglan with its wide range of outdoor activities and attractions and our unique seaside hideaway.

DIRECTIONS: Greenslade Road right hand turn off SH 23, 9 km past Te Uku. No 100E 1 km on right hand side.

Savour our peace, privacy and warm sheltered aspect, nestled in 2 acres of beautiful bush and gardens meandering down to the water's edge.

Choose between our charming Cottage, luxury Suite or cosy Chalet – all very appealing, well appointed, comfortable, self-contained and separate – exclusively yours. Enjoy magical harbour and native bush views, sunrises, sunsets and moonlight across our romantic, tranquil Moonlight Bay! Soak up the sun and views or laze on the beach or sundrenched decks.

Explore our beautiful harbour, waterfalls and birdlife by day or kayak up the gorgeous moonbeam at night! Great cafés, golf, swimming, world famous Raglan surf, bush walks, horse treks, harbour tours, jet boat safari, fishing charters, paragliding, skydiving and artisan and garden trails nearby. **Warm hospitality**, barbeques, kayaks, dinghies, and boat ramp at **Waters Edge**.

BEAUMERE LODGE

19 Riverlinks Lane, River Road North,
Horsham Downs, RD 1, Hamilton
Ph (07) 829 4556, Fax (07) 829 4556
e-mail: *beaumere@wave.co.nz*

Tariff : N.Z. Dollars	
Double	$80-120
Single	$70-95
Child	

Bedrooms	Qty
Double	1
Twin	2
Single	
Bed Size	**Qty**
King	
Queen	1
Double	
Single	4
Bathrooms	**Qty**
Ensuite	1
Private	1
Guest Share	1
Family Share	

**Countrystay
Bed & Breakfast**

Features & Attractions

- *Right on the edge of Golf Course*
- *Country setting on city boundary*
- *Brand new, purpose-built home*
- *Extensive native bush and gardens*
- *Opposite Equestrian Centre*
- *Spa Pool*
- *6 golf courses in the vicinity*
- *Dine with your hosts*

Beaumere Lodge is a golfer's dream, situated on 1¼ acres of native bush and water gardens adjacent to the lovely Horsham Downs Golf Course, on the Waikato River. Every room opens to fabulous views of the golf course - look right down on the fourth green and the fifth tee, against a backdrop of distant hills. Luxury accommodation provided in private guest wing, includes tea-making, fridge, microwave, TV, underfloor-heating, electric blankets, security surveillance, smoke alarm, security windows. Continental breakfast included. Dinner available on request ($25 pp). Isobel has had many years experience as an educator and is always delighted to help visitors with the English language.

We are a few minutes drive from Hamilton International Airport (we can pick you up), the city centre and many excellent shops, restaurants, river cruises, famous Museum of Art and History, the the world-renowned Clydesdale Museum and the Mystery Creek Events Centre. One hour from Auckland International Airport. We have home-hosted many overseas visitors and you can be assured of a wonderful overseas experience.

'PORT WILLIAMS'

Pencarrow Road, RD 3, Hamilton
Ph (07) 856 2499, Fax (07) 856 2499
Mobile 025-261 1959
e-mail: *port.williams@clear.net.nz*

Tariff : N.Z. Dollars	
Double	$105-110
Single	$55
Child	

Bedrooms	Qty
Double	1
Twin	1
Single	

Bed Size	Qty
Super King	
Queen	1
Double	1
Single	1

Bathrooms	Qty
Ensuite	2
Private	
Guest Share	
Family Share	

 Countrystay Bed & Breakfast   VISA MasterCard

Features & Attractions

- *5 acre farmlet*
- *Tranquil setting*
- *Extensive rural views*
- *Glorious sunsets*
- *3 km to Hamilton Airport*
- *6 km south of Hamilton off SH 1*

DIRECTIONS:
Please ring for directions and reservations.

Come and join us in our modern mediterranean style villa. In this rural setting of Tamahere, our tranquil views are over the Waikato River Valley with glorious sunsets and Mt Pirongia to the West. Being centrally sited between Hamilton, Cambridge, Te Awamutu, Hamilton Airport and Mystery Creek, we are also an ideal base for day trips to Auckland, Rotorua, Waitomo Caves, Tauranga, Taupo and National Park.

Enjoy the experience of our outstanding Waikato landscaped garden, which rises above a farmed gully, where our friendly sheep and goats graze. Having travelled the world extensively, we know the importance of hospitality, away from home and enjoy meeting guests from overseas countries. We are actively involved with arts and crafts, with much of our work on display in our home.

We serve continental breakfast and light refreshments. Dinners by arrangement. All rooms have ensuites - try our double spa bath!

MATANGI OAKS

634 Marychurch Road, Matangi RD 4, Hamilton
Ph (07) 829 5765, Fax (07) 829 5765
e-mail: *matangi.oaks@voyager.co.nz*

Tariff : N.Z. Dollars		
	Double	$120-130
	Single	$100
	Child	

Bedrooms	Qty
Double	2
Triple	1
Single	
Bed Size	**Qty**
Super King	
King	
Queen/Double	2
Single	3
Bathrooms	**Qty**
Ensuite	1
Private	
Guest Share	1
Family Share	

VISA MasterCard 🚭

 Countrystay - Bed & Breakfast

Features & Attractions

- *Midway Hamilton & Cambridge*
- *Stud tours available*
- *Sports memorabilia nearby*
- *Hamilton Gardens*
- *10 min. to Mystery Creek*
- *Peaceful and relaxing*
- *Waikato River Cruises*
- *Dinner by arrangement*

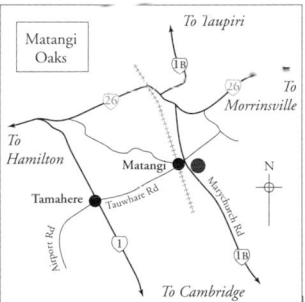

DIRECTIONS: 33 km from Taupiri along SH 1B towards Cambridge. From SH 1 at Tamahere turn onto Tauwhare Rd. to Matangi. Cross railway line, turn first right, SH 1B. We are 500m on left.

Matangi Oaks is situated midway between Hamilton and Cambridge on State Highway 1B in a delightful rural setting. Our American Colonial Home, built in 1997, offers peace and tranquillity while being only 12 minutes from the city. An ideal stopover for visits to the National Agricultural Field Days at Mystery Creek or for taking a tour of some of the famous thoroughbred horse studs in the district. Only 10 minutes from Hamilton Airport. For the golfing enthusiasts there are 12 golf courses within half an hour's drive. An hour's drive and you can be in Rotorua, Tauranga, Mt Maunganui and Waitomo Caves and only one and a half hours to Lake Taupo and Auckland International Airport. Cooked and continental breakfasts are provided and tea and coffee making facilities are available. Three-course evening meals are available with your hosts with great locally-grown vegetables. Pre-dinner drinks and dinner wines are all included at a cost of $40 per person. Complimentary laundry facilities are available. A separate guest lounge is available or visitors are welcome to join their hosts in the evening.

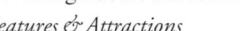

ROSEPARK

124 Matangi Road, RD 4, Hamilton
Ph (07) 859 0345 Fax (07) 859 0345
Mobile 025-839 930
http://www.nzguidedtours.co.nz

Features & Attractions

- *Warm, friendly hospitality*
- *Pleasant surroundings*
- *Spacious bedrooms*
- *Hamilton city boundary 1 km*
- *Tours by arrangement*
- *15 min. to local attractions*

 Countrystay Bed & Breakfast

DIRECTIONS: From Morrinsville Road turn south into Matangi Road. We are No.124 on right.

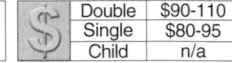

Double	$90-110
Single	$80-95
Child	n/a

Dave and Gail not only offer you a warm "kiwi" welcome, but you are given the opportunity of experiencing the best of both worlds – rural and city. Their modern comfortable home is situated on two and a half acres of parklike grounds, surrounded by roses and native bush and yet only eight minutes from the centre of town for retail therapy, or just a stroll along the banks of our famous Waikato River, where you can catch a ride on board the paddle steamer "Waipa Delta". To complete the rural picture, you can sit on the terrace sipping a glass of wine or maybe a coffee and listen to the waterfall cascading over the rocks, whilst keeping a watchful eye on the activities of a number of our native protected birds. You may even be lucky to get a glimpse of their adopted Pukeko as he wanders through the grounds. Enjoy a scrumptious continental or cooked breakfast prepared by Dave. Other meals by arrangement.

Bedrooms	Qty
Double	2
Twin	1
Single	
Bed Size	**Qty**
Queen	1
Double	1
Single	2
Bathrooms	**Qty**
Ensuite	1
Private	1
Guest Share	1
Family Share	

BLESKIE FARMSTAY

296 Storey Road, PO Box 527,
Te Awamutu, Waikato
Ph (07) 871 3301

Features & Attractions

- *5 min. to State Highway 1*
- *Dinner by arrangement*
- *Cooked breakfast*
- *Horseback riding*
- *Gig rides for children*
- *Tenniscourt/swimm.pool*

Double	$90
Single	$50
Child	$25

Farmstay Bed & Breakfast

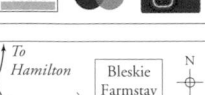

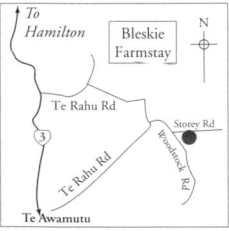

The 85 acres farm with cattle, horses, pigs, poultry, sheep, goats and pets, is situated in beautiful rolling countryside. We offer horseback riding and gig rides for children and adults. Guests have access to the milking of 500 dairy cows.

Our home is spacious with a large living area, swimming pool and tenniscourt(racquets available) – in a well-planned garden. It welcomes you in winter with underfloor heating and a huge open fireplace. Large guestrooms, all with doors to the garden, some with lofts.

We extend a warm country welcome to you.

Bedrooms	Qty
Double	1
Twin	4
Single	
Bed Size	**Qty**
King	
Double	1
Single	8
Bathrooms	**Qty**
Ensuite	1
Private	
Guest Share	1
Family Share	

GLENELG

6 Curnow Place, Cambridge
Ph (07) 823 0084. Fax (07) 823 4279
Mobile 025 - 275 8787
e-mail: *glenelgbedbreakfastnewzealand@hotmail.com*

Features & Attractions

- *Ensuite accommodation*
- *Warm hospitality*
- *Quiet, peaceful setting*
- *10 min. Hamilton Airport*
- *Spa and air bath*
- *5 min. to Lake Karapiro*

Double	$100
Single	$65
Child	$20

Bed & Breakfast Homestay

Map: To Cambridge, To Rotorua, To Te Awamutu, Leamington Medical Centre, To Karapiro, Browning St, To Te Awamutu, Mystery Creek, Lamb St, To Karapiro, Milton St, Cowley Drive, Cowley Drive, Glenelg, Curnow Place

Bedrooms	Qty
Double	4
Twin	1
Single	
Bed Size	**Qty**
Queen	3
Double	1
Single	2
Bathrooms	**Qty**
Ensuite	3
Private	1
Guest Share	
Family Share	

Cambridge – 15 km from Hamilton – is famous for its picturesque old English atmosphere and known as the "Town of Trees".

If you are looking for a "Home away from Home", restful and away from the hustle, bustle and traffic noise, **Glenelg** is the place for you to be. We have a new, modern home in a quiet, peaceful setting with 200 roses in our garden. Breakfast is either cooked or continental with a menu to choose from – evening meals by prior arrangement. Sky TV, guest laundry and off-street parking is available. We are in comfortable driving distance from the main tourist attractions: Mystery Creek Events Centre 10 min., Rotorua 30 min., Waitomo Caves 45 min., Auckland or Taupo 2 hours.

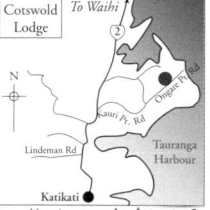

COTSWOLD LODGE

183 Ongare Point Road, RD 1, Katikati
Ph (07) 549 2110, Fax (07) 549 2109
Mobile 025-496 570
e-mail: *cotswold@ihug.co.nz*

HOSTLINK
VISA
MasterCard

FARM & HOME HOSTS

Features & Attractions

- *Ensuite bathrooms*
- *Large garden*
- *Dinner available*
- *Beaches, hot pools nearby*
- *4 golf courses nearby*
- *Murals & open air art*

Double	$115
Single	$80
Child	

Country Bed & Breakfast - with a little Luxury

Bedrooms	Qty
Double	2
Twin	1
Single	
Bed Size	**Qty**
King	
Double	2
Single	2
Bathrooms	**Qty**
Ensuite	3
Private	
Guest Share	
Family Share	

Map: Cotswold Lodge, To Waihi, Kauri Pt. Rd, Ongare Pt Rd, Lindeman Rd, Tauranga Harbour, Katikati

We welcome you to Cotwold Lodge. In a tranquil setting, Cotswold Lodge offers the best in Kiwi hospitality. Come and share our large colonial-style home that has been built with you in mind. Enjoy a sumptuous full breakfast to start your day. Wander around the gardens and enjoy the peaceful settings with lots of birds to entertain you. Sit on the deck and enjoy the views of the Kaimai Ranges or watch the beautiful sunsets while you relax with a cool drink. Take a stroll through kiwi fruit and avocado orchards. Close by are thermal hot pools, beautiful beaches, excellent bush walks, famous murals, bird gardens, potteries and open air art. Several picturesque golf courses, including Ballantynes, are a short distance away. Our interests are varied, we both enjoy golf, walking, gardening and travel. Boots, the Labrador, is people friendly.

GLEN SHEILING

27 Canon Road, RD 1
Katikati
Ph (07) 549 2559,
e-mail: *rchandl@xtra.co.nz*

Features & Attractions

- *Tranquil, rural surroundings*
- *Golf course 10 mins*
- *Bush or beach walks*
- *Friendly and comfortable*
- *Restaurants & winery nearby*
- *Dinner by arrangement*

Double	$70
Single	$40
Child	neg.

C   **Country Homestay**

Bedrooms	Qty
Double	1
Twin	1
Single	

DIRECTIONS:
Please phone for booking
and easy directions.

Bed Size	Qty
King	
Queen	1
Single	2

Bathrooms	Qty
Ensuite	
Private	
Guest Share	1
Family Share	

A warm welcome awaits you at **Glen Sheiling**, our modern comfortable home set on 3 tranquil acres with a backdrop of hills and bushland. Situated in the Western Bay of Plenty just off State Highway 2, we offer a pleasant stopover for your visit to this beautiful region.

Enjoy breakfast, served at your leisure, relax in one of our two lounges, stroll around the property, make yourself at home. The area is renowned for its arts and crafts, and offers a wide range of activities, from scenic bush walks, safe beaches, hot mineral pools, a winery, an excellent golf course to the Mural Town of Katikati, all within easy reach. The three of us are semi-retired, and between us enjoy a wide range of interests, including meeting people, walking, gardening, fishing, bridge, church activities.

We look forward to welcoming you to our little corner of paradise.

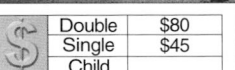

MIDDLE GABLE

51 Grammer Road, RD 1, Kati Kati
Ph (07) 549 1837, Fax (07) 549 1837
Mobile 021-632 842

Features & Attractions

- *Secluded and quiet*
- *Old fashioned rose gardens*
- *Golf courses nearby*
- *Excellent beaches*
- *Open air art*
- *Complimentary tea & coffee*

Double	$80
Single	$45
Child	

C   **Countrystay Bed & Breakfast**

Bedrooms	Qty
Double	2
Twin	
Single	

Bed Size	Qty
Double	1
Queen	1
Single	

Bathrooms	Qty
Ensuite	
Private	
Guest Share	1
Family Share	

Welcome to **Middle Gable**, our garden of old fashioned roses and avocado orchard nestled in the foothills of the Kaimai Ranges.

Wide views of Tauranga Harbour and surrounding farmland just 4½ km from Katikati noted for its murals and "Haiku" walkway along the Uretara River. Restaurants, cafés, wineries, 4 golf courses, ocean and harbour beaches and hot pools all close by. Tauranga City and airport only about 30 minutes away.

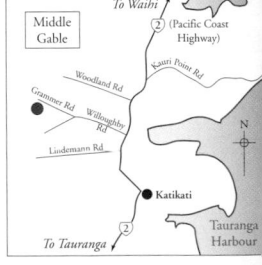

DIRECTIONS: Turn off SH 2, 2 km north of Katikati onto Willoughby Road. 1.8 km on, take the right fork into Grammer Road. We are first house on the left, 510 m up Grammer Road.

THE PALMS BED & BREAKFAST

241 Beach Road, Matua, Tauranga
Ph (07) 576 7687, Fax (07) 576 7627
e-mail: *donbrebs@xtra.co.nz*
www.angelfire.com/oh/thepalms

Tariff : N.Z. Dollars	
Double	$90-110
Single	$65-70
Child	

Bedrooms	Qty
Double	1
Twin	2
Single	1
Bed Size	**Qty**
Super King	
King	
Queen	1
Single	5
Bathrooms	**Qty**
Ensuite	1
Private	1
Guest Share	1
Family Share	

Bed & Breakfast
"to the sound of the waves"

Features & Attractions

- Every room has sea view
- Only 6 minutes from city
- Complimentary airport pickup
- Harbour fishing
- Wake to the lapping of waves
- On lovely harbour walkway
- Relax on sun-drenched balconies

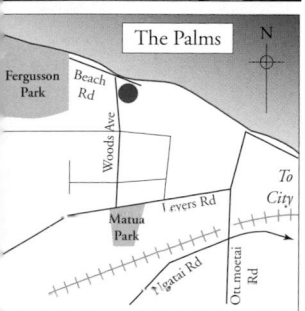

The Palms

Stay right on Tauranga's magnificent harbour! **The Palms** is situated at the end of a quiet cul-de-sac, with a lovely planted reserve as its eastern neighbour, and only the width of a roadway from the water.

All rooms have unobstructed views across the harbour to famous Mt Maunganui and Matakana Island.

Stroll Tauranga's favourite harbour walkway, which goes right past the front door and offers a peaceful relaxation in "another world".

You'll find the rooms comfortable and welcoming, with the guest wing separated from the host's.

Relax at night in the guest's TV lounge, and if you're feeling adventurous during the summer months, talk to Don: if the moon is right, an evening of shallow water harbour fishing could be on!

Papamoa - Tauranga

 YOUR HOSTS: **Verlie and Barry Yeager**   Ph: (07) 542 3459

Features & Attractions

- Short walk to ocean beach
- Off-street parking
- Pitch and drive golf nearby
- Complimentary fruit basket
- Dinner/packed lunches
  by arrangement

Double	$80
Single	$50
Child	$20

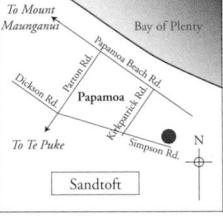

H — Homestay / Beachstay — **BB**

Bedrooms	Qty
Double	3
Twin	2
Single	1

Bed Size	Qty
King/Single	2
Queen/Double	3
Single	3

Bathrooms	Qty
Ensuite	
Private	
Guest Share	1
Family Share	

To Mount Maunganui — Bay of Plenty — Papamoa Beach Rd — Dickson Rd — Parton Rd — Papamoa — Kirkpatrick Rd — To Te Puke — Simpson Rd. — N — Sandtoft

DIRECTIONS: Turn off SH 2 at 'Wilson's Garden Centre' follow Domain Rd to round-about turn right onto Beach Rd. Proceed to Kirkpatrick right, then left into Simpson.

Sandtoft is a comfortable home, just 2 minutes walk from the beautiful Pacific Ocean. Enjoy a stroll along the sandy beach, sunbathe, swim, surfcast. Sample our local restaurants. We offer two spacious bedrooms with double/queen and single beds. These rooms each have their own wash basin, coffee table, and comfy chairs, plus a north facing balcony. Also available is a smaller double/single bedroom at a lower rate. Bath, shower, toilet facilities are each separate. A guest fridge, TV, tea/coffee are at your disposal. Continental only and/or cooked breakfast is offered. We are a semi-retired couple who enjoy travelling and meeting people. To meet you would be a pleasure.

Papamoa - Mt. Maunganui

YOUR HOSTS: **Joan and Jim Francis**   Free Ph: 0800 168 791

Markbeech

FARM & HOME HOSTS

Features & Attractions

- 10 min. walk to beach
- Off-street parking
- Relaxing and quiet
- Will meet public transport
- Dinner by arrangement $20
- Laundry facilities available

Double	$80-90
Single	$45
Child	half price

H — Homestay / Bed & Breakfast — **BB**

Bedrooms	Qty
Double	1
Twin	1
Single	

Bed Size	Qty
King	
Queen	1
Single	2

Bathrooms	Qty
Ensuite	1
Private	1
Guest Share	
Family Share	

We are retired, in our late late sixties and have been hosts for twelve years mostly in Dickson Road, Papamoa. Our hobbies are gardening, travel and entertaining guests. Our high level of personal service in quiet surroundings will, we hope, make you feel relaxed and comfortable. There are good restaurants close by. Laundry facilities are complimentary. From mid January 2002 we will be able to welcome guests in our newly built home. The queen room is a self-contained bed/sitting room with cooking facilities.

Markbeech Homestay — Papamoa Beach Rd — Maranui St. — Bay of Plenty — Gilvan Rd — Domain Rd — Dickson Rd — N — 29 — 2 — To Tauranga & Hamilton — To Te Puke & Rotorua

DIRECTIONS:
From SH2, the Rotorua - Tauranga highway, turn at Domain Road (sign posted Papamoa), then secon left at BP service station. Beachwater Drive is first left at roundabout. Pedrosa Court first cul de sac on right, Markbeech first house.

POHUTUKAWA FARMHOUSE B&B & COTTAGE

693 State Highway 2, RD 4 Whakatane, Pikowai/Matata
Ph (07) 322 2182, Fax (07) 322 2182
e-mail: bab@prinztours.co.nz
www.prinztours.co.nz

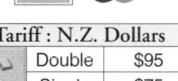

Tariff : N.Z. Dollars	
Double	$95
Single	$75
Child	

Bedrooms	Qty
Double	2
Twin	2
Single	
Bed Size	**Qty**
Super King	
King Single	2
Queen	2
Single	2
Bathrooms	**Qty**
Ensuite	2
Private	1
Guest Share	
Family Share	

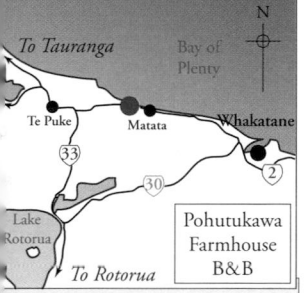

 Coastal Country Stay and Cottage

Features & Attractions

- *Cottage SC from $120*
- *Cottage B&B from $150*
- *Sauna, organic farm*
- *Guided tours arranged*
- *100 metres to the beach*
- *Out-door swimming pool*
- *Dinner on request*
- *German spoken*

Pohutukawa Farmhouse B&B and Te Moemoea Cottage is set in a picturesque location on the Pacific Coast Highway offering outstanding ocean views.

Glance up from the breakfast table and see active volcano White Island. Sometimes dolphins and even whales pass by.

The Farmhouse is the base of our tour company "Prinz Tours". We are specialists for guided tours and offer day tours in the area and personalised itineraries for New Zealand wide holidays.

We encourage visitors to stay several days (discounts available). There is so much to see and do in the Bay of Plenty region.

Or simply relax in our garden, by the pool at the beach or have a 'talk' to our many farm animals.

Dinners with ingredients from our organic farm on request.

We also speak German and are looking forward to meeting you.

DIRECTIONS:
Directly on State Highway 2, 8 km west of Matata, 34 km east of Te Puke.

LEABURN

237 Thornton Road (main Tauranga - Whakatane Highway)
RD 4, Whakatane
Ph (07) 308 7487 or 308 7955, Fax (07) 308 7487
e-mail: *kath.law@paradise.net.co.nz*

Tariff : N.Z. Dollars	
Double	$70
Single	$40
Child	

Bedrooms	Qty
Double	?
Twin	?
Single	?
Bed Size	**Qty**
Super King	
King	
Queen	1
Single	2
Bathrooms	**Qty**
Ensuite	
Private	1
Guest Share	1
Family Share	

Countrystay
Bed & Breakfast

Features & Attractions

- *Relaxed friendly hosts*
- *Dinner by arrangement*
- *Golf links nearby*
- *Hosts have wide interests*
- *Local knowledge - help given*
- *Spacious bedrooms*
- *On Pacific Coast Highway*
- *Rural surroundings handy to town*

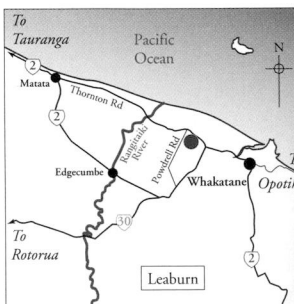

Fifty-one years on the same property and in the same house, we also love to travel. Fifty/Fifty sharemilkers manage our two dairy farms and we have a small citrus orchard. Rearing black and coloured sheep has been a hobby for nearly thirty years.

Currently we are involved in the management of The Red Barn Crafts and Country Kitchen, located on our property. Beside promoting the work of over 250 Bay of Plenty craftspeople, we cater for casual dinners and group functions.

We have home hosted for 18 years and enjoy the company of other travellers. This is the Sunshine town. If you get more than 12 hours of continuous rain, while you are with us, your accommodation is free.

Opportunities exist for you to be as busy as you like. We recommend a visit to White Island, jet boating, walks in the bush, swimming in hot pools, or just reading in our extensive personal library. Be as busy or as quiet as you like.

OCEANSPRAY HOMESTAY
283A Pohutukawa Avenue, Ohope, Bay of Plenty
Ph (07) 312 4112
Mobile 025-286 6824
e-mail: *frances@oceanspray.co.nz*
http://www.oceanspray.co.nz

Tariff : N.Z. Dollars		
	Double	$90-110
	Single	$55-75
	Child	neg.

Bedrooms	Qty
Double	2
Twin	1
Single	

Bed Size	Qty
Super King	
King	
Queen	2
Single	2

Bathrooms	Qty
Ensuite	
Private	1
Guest Share	
Family Share	

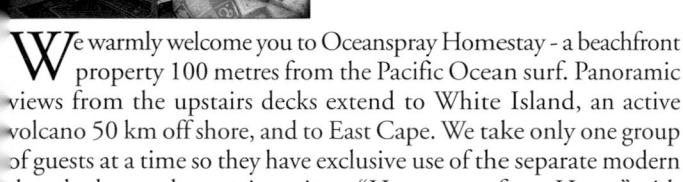
**Homestay
Bed & Breakfast**

Features & Attractions
- *Views to White Island and East Cape*
- *Beachfront*
- *Safe swimming beach*
- *Separate downstairs unit*
- *Deep-sea fishing nearby*
- *Swimming with dolphins*
- *Dinner on request*
- *Peaceful and relaxing*

We warmly welcome you to Oceanspray Homestay - a beachfront property 100 metres from the Pacific Ocean surf. Panoramic views from the upstairs decks extend to White Island, an active volcano 50 km off shore, and to East Cape. We take only one group of guests at a time so they have exclusive use of the separate modern three bedroom downstairs unit – a "Home away from Home" with comforts and luxuries of home baking, chocolates, complimentary wine on arrival, plus a good selection of books, videos, toys – children well catered for! John enjoys kayaking and towing the longline to catch your fish – snapper, gurnard. Frances enjoys gardening, cooking and crafts. We offer you an excellent standard of accommodation, comprehensive continental breakfast with home-made bread and home preserved fruits. Experience the tastes of fish and homegrown vegetables. For 3-course dinners – by prior arrangement, – $30 pp, in our dining room overlooking the sea. Our pets, Tessa, the Labrador and Benny, the cat, will also ensure your stay is a memorable one.

DIRECTIONS: From Whakatane, follow signs to Ohope. On reaching Ohope Beach turn right, proceed 3 km to 283A. From Gisborne/Opotiki, on reaching Ohope, proceed 1 km along Pohutukawa Avenue to 283A. Sign on street frontage.

YOUR HOSTS: **Marilyn and Em Turney**   Free Ph: 0800 266 269

TURNEYS BED & BREAKFAST
28 Pohutukawa Avenue (PO Box 3005) Ohope Beach
Ph (07) 312 5040, Fax (07) 312 5040
Mobile 025-960 894
e-mail:*turneys@xtra.co.nz*
http://www.businessonline.co.nz/turneys/

Tariff : N.Z. Dollars		
Double	$150
Single	
Child	

Bedrooms	Qty
Double	2
Twin	1
Single	
Bed Size	Qty
Super King	
King	1
Queen	1
Single	2
Bathrooms	Qty
Ensuite	2
Private	1
Guest Share	
Family Share	

   Coastal Bed & Breakfast   LA

Features & Attractions

- *Rotorua 1 hour away*
- *Safe swimming beach*
- *Bush walks/nearby golf*
- *White Island volcanic tours*
- *Business facilities*
- *Dolphin swimming*

If you are wanting a quality beachside holiday with friendly and comfortable surroundings, this is it, and Marilyn and Em will guarantee you a visit you will never forget. Treat yourselves to the "Blue" room with its private deck overlooking the Pacific Ocean, or the "Garden" room. Both are spacious and tasteful and with little extras which make it so special. Breakfast, with all the trimmings and as you like it, will set you up for the day to enjoy the excitement of the area; erupting White Island, dolphin swimming, fishing and golfing, to mention a few.

We are retired farmers and keen sports people with a love especially of tennis and golf. Come and share all we have to offer – you won't be disappointed.

DIRECTIONS:
On the Pacific Coast Highway
at Ohope Beach.

CLIFTON MANOR

5 Clifton Road, Whakatane
Ph (07) 307 2145 Fax (07) 307 2145
Mobile 025-448 702
e-mail: *cliftonmanor@xtra.co.nz*

Features & Attractions

- *200 metres to town centre*
- *Generous buffet breakfast*
- *Spacious modern units*
- *Stroll to wharf, restaurants*
- *Large swimming pool and garden*
- *Laundry facilities*

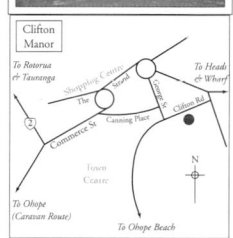

Double	$80-105
Single	$68-80
Child	$15

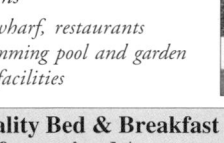

**Quality Bed & Breakfast
Self-contained Accomm.**

Bedrooms	Qty
Double	5
Twin	
Single	
Bed Size	**Qty**
King	1
Queen/Double	4
Single	3
Bathrooms	**Qty**
Ensuite	2
Private	1
Guest Share	1
Family Share	

Conveniently situated in a central location, **Clifton Manor** offers you warm, quiet and comfortable accommodation. Upstairs guest rooms are tastefully furnished with a large lounge exclusively for guests. Complimentary tea/coffee/biscuits supplied in a fully equipped kitchen. Downstairs we have two spacious units giving guests their own space and independence. These are well appointed with comfortable furnishings and large ensuites. Breakfast may be served in dining room upstairs or brought to your unit, whatever suits. Relax and enjoy our sunny climate in the sheltered gardens surrounding the pool. Nearby you will find a variety of restaurants, cafés and cinema, only two minutes walk to the wharf for the unique marine active White Island volcano or swim with dolphins. Bush walks with amazing views in close proximity.

OCEANSIDE APARTMENTS

SH 35, Oruaiti Beach 10932, (RD 3) Waihau Bay
Ph (07) 325 3699. Fax (07) 325 3689
Mobile 025-811 898
e-mail: *waihau@ihug.co.nz*
http://www.waihaubay.co.nz

Features & Attractions

- *Beachfront location*
- *Boat charters on site*
- *Swimming, fishing, diving*
- *Fully self contained apartments*
- *Seafood banquet our speciality*
- *Jet boating/horse trekking arranged*

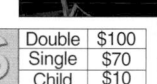

**Two Fully Self-contained
Beachfront Units**

Double	$100
Single	$70
Child	$10

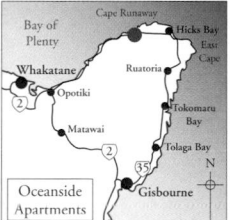

Located at beautiful Oruaiti Beach, a safe swimming and sandy beach at Waihau Bay, considered by many to be the best beach on the East Coast. The area offers excellent land based fishing and diving right on our doorstep, or charter Barry's licensed boating expertise for all game and bottom fishing, or the best diving locations. Experience the tranquility of this beautiful coast, take a stroll along the beach, a scenic boat trip, horse trekking or a jet boat trip up the Motu River, all these can be arranged for you. On arrival we will offer a complimentary beverage. All meals are provided on request with seafood our speciality. Our large apartments are smoke free, with glorious sea views, fully self contained, separate bedrooms, all the comforts of home and much more.

DIRECTIONS: Oruaiti Beach, Waihau Bay, East Coast, is located on State Highway 35, 109 km from Opotiki or 224 km from Gisborne.

Bedrooms	Qty
Double	2
Twin	1
Single	
Bed Size	**Qty**
King	
Queen	2
Single	2
Bathrooms	**Qty**
Ensuite	
Private	2
Guest Share	
Family Share	

Lake across the Lane

BUSH HAVEN COTTAGE
146 Okere Rd, Okere Falls, RD4
Ph (07) 362 4497. Fax (07) 362 4417
Mobile 021- 396709,
e-mail: *georgesheryll@xtra.co.nz*

FARM & HOME HOSTS

Features & Attractions
- Quiet, peaceful surroundings
- Ferns, native bush & native birds
- Across the lane to the lake
  - with boat mooring
- Swimming & trout fishing
- Okere Falls & bush walks
- Kayaking & white water rafting on the Kaituna River

Bed & Breakfast
Self- contained Accommodation

Double	$95
Single	$60
Child	neg.

Bedrooms	Qty
Double	2
Twin	
Single	1

Bed Size	Qty
King	
Queen	2
Single	2

Bathrooms	Qty
Ensuite	1
Private	1
Guest Share	
Family Share	

As the name suggests, our property is a restful, peaceful retreat surrounded by ferns, native bush and native birds. Awake to the sounds of the Tuis and have breakfast delivered to the door of our cosy, private, fully self-contained two bedroom cottage. We also have a separate studio with ensuite bathroom and cooking facilities. It has its own private deck overlooking the beautiful native bush. Laundry facilities and gas barbecue available. We have travelled extensively and enjoy meeting new people. George is available to assist in planning your itinerary and Oscar, the Persian cat, will keep you entertained. The lake and Okere Falls are within short walking distance. Rotorua, the leading tourist destination in the North Island, is only 15 min. drive away.

DIRECTIONS:
From Rotorua - follow SH 33, after Okere Falls Store, 1st right, Taheke Rd. then right Okere Rd., 146 is on left. From Tauranga - turn left Okere or Taheke Rd.

LAKESIDE BED & BREAKFAST
155G Okere Road, Okere Falls, RD 4,
Lake Rotoiti, Rotorua
Ph (07) 362 4288, Fax (07) 362 4288
Mobile 025-521 483
e-mail: tengae.physio@xtra.co.nz

Features & Attractions
- Spacious and comfortable
- Friendly hospitality
- Scenic walks
- Laundry facilities
- Barbecue and mooring
- Handy location

Double	$100
Single	$60
Child	$10-22

Bed & Breakfast
Homestay

Bedrooms	Qty
Double	3
Twin	
Single	

Bed Size	Qty
Super King	1
Queen	2
King/Single	2

Bathrooms	Qty
Ensuite	2
Private	1
Guest Share	
Family Share	

Our lakeside Bed & Breakfast is just 1 kilometre off the Taupo-**Rotorua**-**Tauranga**-Coromandel Highway. The house is centrally heated and each room has its own ensuite, TV, refrigerator and tea/coffee making facilities. You have the choice of either enjoying your own space or joining us in our living areas. Our homestay bedroom has a private bathroom and all bedrooms have a view of the lake and surrounding countryside. Within walking distance are the Okere Falls, trout pools, kayaking and white water rafting. Lake Rotoiti is renowned for trout fishing, sailing, hot pools and boating activities. Gardens, a 9 hole golf course, thermal attraction and airport are within 10 minutes drive from the house.

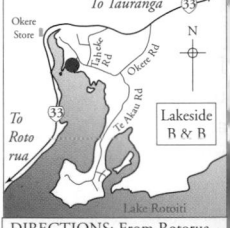

DIRECTIONS: From Rotorua - follow SH 33, after Okere Falls Store, 1st right, Taheke Rd., then right Okere Rd., 155 is on left. From Tauranga - turn left Okere or Taheke Rd., - proceed to 155

KOTARE LODGE

1000J Hamurana Road (PO Box 251, Ngongotaha)
Hamurana, Rotorua
Ph (07) 332 2679, Fax (07) 332 2678
Mobile 025 236 8468
e-mail: *pollards@kotarelodge.co.nz*

Tariff : N.Z. Dollars	
Double	$130-180
Single	$90-140
Child	

Bedrooms	Qty
Double	2
Twin	
Single	
Bed Size	**Qty**
Super King	
King Twin	1
Queen	1
Single	
Bathrooms	**Qty**
Ensuite	1
Private	1
Guest Share	
Family Share	

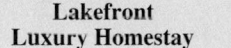
Lakefront Luxury Homestay

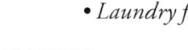

Features & Attractions

- *Absolute lake front*
- *Secluded tranquil beauty*
- *Delicious breakfasts*
- *Laundry facilities*
- *Glorious views and sunsets*
- *Luxurious private rooms*
- *Restaurants 20 minutes away*
- *Onsite kayak and sailing*

Welcome to the perfect retreat. **Kotare Lodge** is situated on the shores of Lake Rotorua, assuring you of exquisite views across to the city and surrounding hills. Set in beautiful park-like grounds, our Lodge offers every comfort that caring, well travelled hosts can provide. Relax alfresco with tea and cookies or with a complimentary aperitif and canapes in the summer or by the fire in winter. Guest accommodation, separate from hosts, offer bedrooms with their own entrances and lovely views of lake and garden. Bathrooms provide every comfort and there is a guest garden room and spacious lounge.

Separate from the main house, the secluded king/twin bedroom has tea and coffee making facilities, refrigerator and TV. After a delicious breakfast, we would be delighted to help you plan your day. **Kotare Lodge**, Rotorua, its tourist attractions, excellent restaurants and beautiful environs have so very much to offer you. We would love to welcome you to our home.

DIRECTIONS: **Kotare Lodge** is located on the northern shores of Lake Rotorua. Please ring/fax for simple directions.

ANCHORAGE ESTATE

48 Sharp Road, RD 2, Rotorua
Ph (07) 332 2996, Fax (07) 332 2997
Mobile 025-931 943
e-mail: *homestays@anchorage.co.nz*
http://www.anchorage.co.nz

Tariff : N.Z. Dollars	
Double	$150-180
Single	$130-150
Child	neg.

Bedrooms	Qty
Double	5
Twin	
Single	

Bed Size	Qty
Super King	3
King	
Queen	2
Single	

Bathrooms	Qty
Ensuite	5
Private	
Guest Share	
Family Share	

 Luxury Rural Bed & Breakfast Retreat

Features & Attractions

- *Private and peaceful*
- *Therapeutic spa pool*
- *Hand-feed farm animals*
- *Conference facilities*
- *Handy to tourist spots*
- *Close to golf courses*
- *Fishing trips organised*
- *Heli-pad on site*

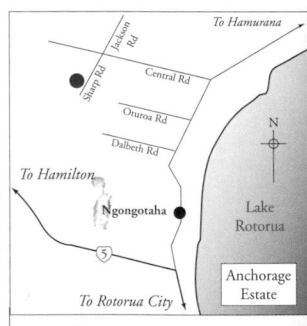

DIRECTIONS:
Take SH 5 to roundabout. Travel north through Ngongotaha approx. 3 km on Hamurana Rd. Take third left into Central Rd, then approx. 2 km, turn left into Sharp Rd.
Anchorage Estate is 480 m on right.

Anchorage Estate has all the requirements for a perfect holiday hideaway or a 'Romantic Retreat' and is highly recommended for its exclusive but relaxed ambience and friendly atmosphere. Why not base yourselves here for a few days and enjoy true Kiwi hospitality at this luxurious country homestay. It is ideally set on 15 acres of lush farmland within 15 minutes from Rotorua city centre, golf courses, lakes and many tourist attractions. The spacious suites, named after local lakes, boast magnificent views over the countryside, Lake Rotorua and the city beyond. They are equipped with super king/twin or queen beds, tea/coffee/snack making facilities, refrigerator, Sky digital TV system, a lounge/dining area and private outdoor patio. The downstairs suites have their own entry, enabling guests to come and go as they please. Guests are welcome to join Ra and Leon for a home-cooked meal by prior arrangement or there are many restaurants and Maori dinner shows nearby to choose from.

CLOVER DOWNS ESTATE

175 Jackson Road, RD 2, Ngongotaha, Rotorua
Ph (07) 332 2366, Fax (07) 332 2367
Mobile 027 471 2866
e-mail: *reservations@cloverdowns.co.nz*
http://www.cloverdowns.co.nz

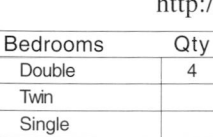

Bedrooms	Qty
Double	4
Twin	
Single	
Bed Size	**Qty**
Super King	3
King	1
Queen/Double	
King/Single	
Bathrooms	**Qty**
Ensuite	4
Private	
Guest Share	
Family Share	

Luxury Accommodation
Bed & Breakfast Countrystay

Tariff : N.Z. Dollars		
Double	$175-240
Single	$160-225
Child	neg.

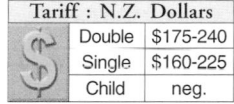

Features & Attractions

- *Secluded, peaceful rural retreat*
- *We offer peace and tranquility*
- *Spacious and relaxing décor*
- *Laundry facilities available*

- *Tourist attractions nearby*
- *Trout fishing guide available*
- *4 golf courses in Rotorua*
- *Deer and ostrich farm tour*

"A Unique Place to Stay"

So country yet so close to town... just 15 minutes drive north of the city centre. For the discerning traveller, we offer a place to unwind and rediscover the simple pleasures in life whilst having the best facilities available. Experience the tranquillity and style of our character home, situated on a secluded 35 acre deer and ostrich farm with magnificent rural and Lake Rotorua views.

We offer fine country accommodation with a choice of four beautifully appointed king-size suites, each equipped with tea and coffee making facilities, refrigerator, telephone, TV and video. Enjoy the privacy of an ensuite bathroom in each bedroom complete with toiletries, hairdryer and bathrobes.

After a sumptuous continental breakfast take a farm tour with Lloyd and the dogs, maybe try a game of petanque or just relax and enjoy the rural vistas from your own private deck. Major tourist attractions, trout fishing, golf and horse riding are all nearby.

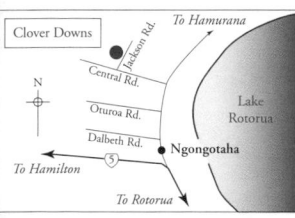

DIRECTIONS:
Take SH 5 to round about. Travel north around lake, through Ngongotaha on Hamurana Road. Take 3rd left into Central Road, then turn right into Jackson Road travel 1.75km to **Clover Downs** on left.

97

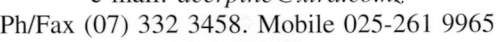

DEER PINE LODGE

255 Jackson Road, Ngongotaha
Postal: P.O. Box 22, Ngongotaha
Rotorua, Bay of Plenty
e-mail: *deerpine@xtra.co.nz*
Ph/Fax (07) 332 3458. Mobile 025-261 9965

Tariff : N.Z. Dollars	
Double	$85-100
Single	$70-85
Child	neg.

Bedrooms	Qty
Double	4
Twin	1
Single	

Bed Size	Qty
Super King	
King	3
Queen	1
Single	2

Bathrooms	Qty
Ensuite	5
Private	
Guest Share	
Family Share	

Farmstay Bed & Breakfast
Self-contained Accommodation

Features & Attractions

- *Quiet, peaceful surroundings*
- *Beach 30 minutes away*
- *Architect. designed units*
- *Beautiful views of lake*

- *Accredited deer farm*
- *Farm tours*
- *Horse riding close by*
- *No sulphur smells*

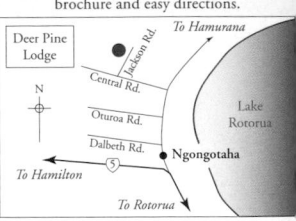

DIRECTIONS: Please phone or write for brochure and easy directions.

Welcome to **Deer Pine Lodge**. Enjoy the panoramic views of Lake Rotorua, Mt. Tarawera and Mokoia Island. We farm 260 deer on our accredited deer farm. Our property is surrounded with trees, planted by New Zealand Forest Research. We have a cat and a Boxer (Jake), who is very gentle. The nearby city of Rotorua is fast becoming New Zealand's most popular tourist destination. Our lunch/breakfast units are private with own bathroom, T.V., radio, fridge, microwave, heaters, electric blankets on all beds and tea/coffee making facilities. There are heaters and hair dryers in bathrooms. Our two-bedroom fully self-contained units, designed by prominent Rotorua architect Gerald Stock, each have a private balcony carport, sundeck, ensuite, spacious lounge, kitchen, also laundry facilities, T.V., radio, heaters etc. (cot/highchair available). Smoke detectors fitted in all bedrooms and lounges, fire extinguishers installed in all kitchens. We hold the N.Z. Certificate in Food Hygiene, which ensures high standards of food preparation and service. Please inform us on arrival if you are interested in a free conducted farm tour after breakfast. Observe the different species of deer and get first hand knowledge of all aspects of deer farming. An evening meal with pre-dinner drinks is available by prior arrangement. Hosts John and Betty, originally from Scotland, have travelled extensively overseas and have many years experience in hosting. We look forward to your stay with us. Budget accomm. available.

ALRAES LAKEVIEW HOMESTAY

124 Leonard Road, PO Box 14,
Ngongotaha, Rotorua
Ph (07) 357 4913, Fax (07) 357 4513
e-mail: *alraes@xtra.co.nz*

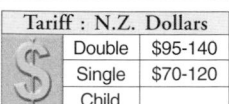

Tariff : N.Z. Dollars	
Double	$95-140
Single	$70-120
Child	

Bedrooms	Qty
Double	3
Twin	
Single	
Bed Size	**Qty**
Super King	
King	1
Queen	1
Single	2
Bathrooms	**Qty**
Ensuite	1
Private	1
Guest Share	1
Family Share	

Homestay
Bed & Breakfast

Features & Attractions

- *A Million Dollar View*
- *Handy major tourist attractions*
- *Dinner prior notice*
- *Ideal Homestay for relaxing*
- *Quiet, peaceful atmosphere*
- *Trout stream, lake, golf close by*
- *Laundry facilities available*
- *Transport available*

DIRECTIONS:
Drive through Ngongotaha towards Hamurana over railway line, turn 2nd right into Waiteti Rd. 1st left into Leonard Rd. ALRAES sign 180m on left.

Welcome to our HOMESTAY WITH THE MILLION DOLLAR VIEW and our two acre lifestyle block, with black sheep and friendly atmosphere. Your comfort is our priority. Just 10min. from Rotorua City, handy to Skyline Skyrides, Agrodrome, Rainbow Springs, Hangi and Maori Concerts, walking distance to Lake Rotorua and Waiteti Stream where you can flyfish then smoke your catch in our smoker. Breakfast on scrumptious home-made food in the conservatory while you enjoy the stunning 200°+ views of Lake Rotorua, Mounts Ngongotaha and Tarawera. Enjoy our company or the privacy of the guest lounge with its peaceful lake and garden views or listen to the bird life on the terrace. You will have the choice of king/twin ensuite with spa bath or queen bed with private bathroom. Tea/coffee, cookies and laundry are available.

We have travelled extensively and after hosting for twelve years our sense of humour and enthusiasm is still as strong as ever. OUR HOME IS YOUR HOME. Reduce your stress and relax. We hope to meet you soon.

🚫

ARIKI LODGE

2 Manuariki Ave, Ngongotoha, (PO Box 578) Rotorua
Ph (07) 357 5532, Fax (07) 357 5562

e-mail: *rgforgie@xtra.co.nz*
http://www.arikilodge.co.nz

Tariff : N.Z. Dollars		
	Double	$100-170
	Single	$80-150
	Child	neg.

Bedrooms	Qty
Double	3
Twin	
Single	

Bed Size	Qty
Super King	
Queen	2
Double	1
Single	

Bathrooms	Qty
Ensuite	2
Private	1
Guest Share	
Family Share	

 Bed & Breakfast
Luxury Accommodation

Features & Attractions

- *Lake Edge*
- *Close to major attractions*
- *Trout fishing*
- *Quiet and relaxing*

- *Warm and friendly hosts*
- *Generous breakfasts*
- *Quality bedding and furnishings*
- *Your comfort is our business*

Set on the edge of Lake Rotorua, **Ariki Lodge** offers luxury accommodation in a tranquil garden setting, where you can relax in comfort and style. Enjoy our friendly hospitality, or should you prefer total privacy, that's fine with us. Situated close to the Ngongotaha trout fishing stream and a short stroll along the beach to the Waiteti Stream and famous fly fishing spots. The bedrooms are beautifully appointed with quality linen, fresh flowers, toiletries and hairdryers. The suit has an Italian-tiled bathroom with spa bath, private sitting room with fridge and tea and coffee making facilities. **Ariki Lodge** is spacious and comfortable. All rooms can be converted to twin.

We can help you arrange your time to experience Rotorua's many sights and attractions: fishing, Maori cultural performances, thermal areas, lake cruises, scenic flights, golf, bush walks, Maori arts and crafts. Only ten minutes drive to the centre of Rotorua and many good restaurants.

DIRECTIONS: Drive to Ngongotaha. At shops turn right into Taui St., through "Give Way" sign towards Lake and right into Manuariki Avenue.

NGONGOTAHA LAKESIDE LODGE

41 Operiana Street, Ngongotaha, Rotorua
Ph (07) 357 4020, Fax (07) 357 4020
Mobile 025-200 7539
e-mail: lake.edge@xtra.co.nz

Tariff : N.Z. Dollars		
	Double	$115-150
	Single	$85-110
	Child	neg

Bedrooms	Qty
Double/Triple	2
Twin	1
Single	
Bed Size	**Qty**
Super King	
King	1
Queen	1
Single	4
Bathrooms	**Qty**
Ensuite	3
Private	
Guest Share	
Family Share	

Bed & Breakfast
Boutique Accomodation

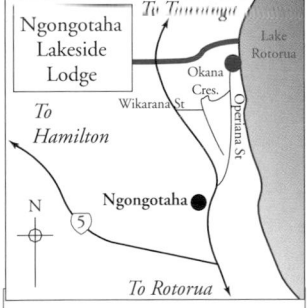

DIRECTIONS:
Take SH 5 to Ngongotaha. Drive through village, take 1st right after railway line turn right into Wikaraka St, left onto Okana Cresc., left onto Operiana St. We are on the right.

Features & Attractions

- *Trout fishing in lake & stream*
- *Bird watching*
- *Good restaurants 9-10 km away*
- *Laundry service available*
- *Volcanic sites to visit*
- *Separate guest lounge*
- *Rods, canoe, golf clubs to use*
- *Full breakfast*

Welcome to our friendly and comfortable Lodge on the shores of **Lake Rotorua**, where we have **panoramic views** of the lake and surrounding mountains. Our Lodge is central to all the major tourist attractions in the Rotorua area, but far enough away to be **sulphur-free**. The upper level of our two-storey home is exclusively for guests with three **ensuite** bedrooms, equipped with hairdryers, electric blanket and TV. The **guest lounge** opens onto a **conservatory**, which overlooks the lake.

We offer friendly service and excellent accommodation at affordable prices. We have **complimentary** tea and coffee facilities and a fridge. A full breakfast is served every morning while we help you plan your day, using our **complimentary** map and knowledge of the region. Gordon is an experienced fisherman and will happily share his knowledge with you, so you can try your luck for **fighting trout** just **metres** from the Lodge. We'll also cook your catch for you. A laundry service is available on request. **Free** use of the canoes, fishing rods and golf clubs to guests. We have ample parking.

KAHILANI B&B / FARMSTAY

691 Dansey Road, RD 2,
Rotorua, Bay of Plenty
Ph/Fax (07) 332 5662, Mobile 025-990 690
e-mail: *kahilani@wave.co.nz*

Tariff : N.Z. Dollars	
Double	$160-175
Single	$120-135
Child	neg.

Bedrooms	Qty
Double	2
Twin	1
Single	1
Bed Size	**Qty**
Super King	
King/Twin	1
Queen	2
Single	1
Bathrooms	**Qty**
Ensuite	1
Private	2
Guest Share	
Family Share	

 Farmstay Luxury Accommodation

Features & Attractions

- *100 ha Red Deer Farm*
- *Extensive gardens*
- *Tranquil surroundings*
- *Labrador breeding kennels*

- *Light or country cooked breakfasts*
- *Dinners by arrangement*
- *Farm tours & farm experiences*
- *Assistance with local sightseeing*

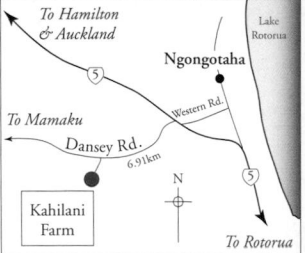

A fine accommodation, cuisine and real New Zealand country experience awaits you at **Kahilani**. The modern country house, built largely of native Kauri timber is set in the midst of a commercial **Red Deer and SheepFarm** - the peace and quiet of its setting is a feature of the homestead, an ambience of rural, forest and lake views can be enjoyed with a feeling of safe seclusion, far away from city hustle and bustle, yet only minutes from the thermal wonderland, Maori culture and many other world-famous attractions of Rotorua.

Upstairs guest accommodation, separate from hosts ensures complete privacy and comfort. Centrally heated in winter, cool in summer, the facilities provide all the amenities discerning guests may expect.

Classy comfort food is the house speciality! **Superb Breakfasts** can be as light or as hearty as desired, while the choice of pre-booked dinners can be either family meals of fresh, seasonal produce at $35 pp, or the famous **Kahilani Silver-Service 4-course Banquet**, featuring farm raised cervena (venison) and slected new Zealand wines $75 pp. Kiwi-Host Yvonne has been an airline flight attendant, motelier and together with David has travelled extensively in New Zealand and overseas, making both well-versed in the needs of travellers.

DIRECTIONS: Dansey Rd is off State Highway 5 on the north west side of Rotorua, 15km from city.

SWISS LODGE ROTORUA

207-209 Kawaha Point Road, Rotorua
Ph (07) 348 5868, Fax (07) 348 5869
Mobile: 021 - 119 1000
e-mail: *reservations@swisslodge.co.nz*
http://www.swisslodge.co.nz

Tariff : N.Z. Dollars

	Double	$155-275
	Single	$125-175
	Child	$25

Bedrooms	Qty
Double	9
Twin	3
Single	

Bed Size	Qty
Super King	
King	6
Queen	3
King Single	6

Bathrooms	Qty
Ensuite	9
Private	1
Guest Share	
Family Share	

**Unique Lake Front Retreat
Luxury Lodge & Holiday Home**

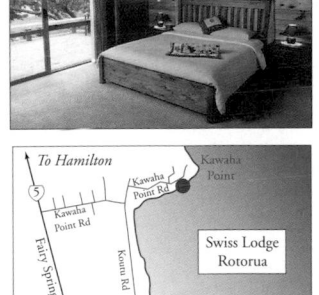

Features & Attractions

- *Direct lake front*
- *Panoramic views*
- *Private beach & jetty*
- *Lakeside spa & sauna*
- *Complimentary green fees*
- *Fishing & hotpool trips*
- *Floatplane flights*
- *Personal guided tours*

"Unique lake front retreat"

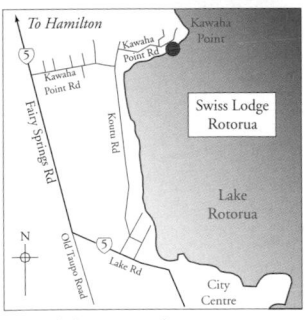

Swiss Lodge is situated on Kawaha Point, a leafy peninsula on Lake Rotorua, the largest of over a dozen lakes in New Zealand's scenic lake district.

It nestles in a peaceful garden setting, offering panoramic views over the lake, just 5 km from the city centre, but away from the sulphur fumes. Guests have a choice of either an ensuite bedroom or a self-contained penhouse and entire holiday house.

Every bedroom is less than a minute's walk from the lake edge. Our own beach and jetty provide a convenient starting point for fishing trips or floatplane flights. Personal guided tours can also be arranged. Relax in our lakeside spa or Finnish sauna or you may prefer to make use of the complimentary green fee for a round of golf at the nearby golf course.

Whether you are a couple, a family or larger group you will find **Swiss Lodge** the ultimate holiday destination.

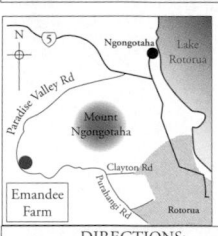

FARM & HOME HOSTS

KIWIHOST

EMANDEE FARM

566 Paradise Valley Road,
RD 2, Rotorua
Ph (07) 348 7530, Fax (07) 348 7501

Features & Attractions

• *Merino sheep, beef cattle*   • *Trout stream*
• *Handy to attractions & City*   • *Join in farm activities*
• *Peaceful, rural, private*   • *Courtesy pick-up*

**Farmstay Bed & Breakfast
Self-contained Accomodation**

Double	$80
Single	$50
Child	Half price

Emandee Farm is 25 acres in beautiful Paradise Valley, 12 km from Rotorua city. A warm welcome awaits and you will experience the farm life with seasonal activities including feeding hay, bottle-feeding orphan lambs, checking and moving stock, and walks over the rolling hills. Our separate facilities for guests comprise of two bedrooms, bathroom, kitchenette, dining and lounge area, television and a laundry. We have 3 (outside) dogs, (2 are David's hunting dogs), and a cat. A generous breakfast is served with style and we can assist you with local knowledge. Our interests include farm and family, sailing and fishing, hunting, touring on our motorbike, walking and tramping. **Emandee Farm** - for wonderful memories.

Bedrooms	Qty
Double	1
Twin	1
Single	
Bed Size	**Qty**
King	
Queen/Double	1
Single	2
Bathrooms	**Qty**
Ensuite	
Private	1
Guest Share	
Family Share	

DIRECTIONS:
From SH 5 north, right into Paradise Valley Rd, after 8 km #566 on left. From city take Sunset or Clayton Rd west, right into Paradise Valley Rd, 1 km past Paradise Valley Springs # 566 on right.

VISA

MasterCard

LYNMORE B&B HOMESTAY

2 Hilton Road, Lynmore, Rotorua
Ph (07) 345 6303, Fax (07) 345 6353
e-mail: kibble@xtra.co.nz

FARM & HOME HOSTS

Features & Attractions

• *Central - 4 km to city*   • *Leonie parle francais*
• *Beauty, comfort, space*   • *Spacious guest lounge*
• *Yummy breakfast (full)*   • *Knowledgeable hosts*

**Bed & Breakfast
Homestay**

Double	$90
Single	$70
Child	

Bedrooms	Qty
Double	2
Twin	
Single	
Bed Size	**Qty**
King	
Queen/Double	2
Single	
Bathrooms	**Qty**
Ensuite	1
Private	1
Guest Share	
Family Share	

Welcome! Discover real character and warmth in lovely Lynmore; easily found, just five minutes drive from the city centre and attractions. Enjoy the beautiful garden with its native collection and birdlife; stroll in the magnificent forest nearby; yet be centrally placed to visit the great variety of thermal, cultural and adventure activities Rotorua offers. Your hosts, Leonie, ex-teacher, and Paul, scientist, delight in being New Zealanders - use their enthusiasm and in-depth knowledge of this remarkable area of lake, forest, volcano, where every feature has its story. And meet Paul's guide dog, Toby, a character in himself. Sleep comfortably in well-appointed rooms: quality linen, electric blankets, robes, fruit, flowers. Relax in the guest lounge, patio, verandah, or garden - there is a choice of sunny and attractive spaces both indoors and out.... Great coffee, a generous and delicious breakfast: fresh fruit and juice, home delights, a choice of cooked course - this couple enjoys food! Smoke-free inside; laundry included.

DIRECTIONS: Route 30 east 2.5 km (towards airport). Turn right at roundabout onto Tarawera/Blue Lake Rd., 3rd street left Lynmore Avenue, 2nd right Hilton Rd, opposite corner store. No 2 is on left.

LAKEHILL COUNTRY RETREAT

1149 Whirinaki Valley Road, RD 1, Ngakuru,
South Rotorua
Ph (07) 333 2829 Fax (07) 333 2029
Mobile 025-507 995
e-mail: *johnshaw@voyager.co.nz*

Tariff : N.Z. Dollars	
Double	$125-150
Single	$90
Child	neg.

Bedrooms	Qty
Double	1
Twin	1
Single	

Bed Size	Qty
Super King	
King	
Queen	1
Single	3

Bathrooms	Qty
Ensuite	1
Private	1
Guest Share	
Family Share	

**Farmstay
Luxury Accommodation**

DIRECTIONS:
From Rotorua, take SH 5 south to SH 30.
Turn right and travel 13 km. Turn left
onto Whirinaki Valley Road, travel
11.5 km to **Lakehill Country Retreat**,
south of Ngakuru Village.

Features & Attractions

- *Warm country hospitality*
- *Hearty breakfasts*
- *Special dinners*
- *Guided farm walks*

- *Pet dog and cat to pamper*
- *Lakehill golf challenge!!*
- *Birdwatching on lake*
- *Local thermal attractions*

"A touch of home - a touch of heaven"

Susan and John offer you a high quality and comfortable stay on our farm in the picturesque Ngakuru Valley.
We are ideally situated, a short distance south of Rotorua and close to Lake Taupo. Our aim is to ensure that you enjoy our home and hospitality and yet still have the freedom to come and go as you please. The homestead interior features New Zealand native timbers, creating a warm and inviting atmosphere. Both bedrooms are light and airy with their own private bathroom facilities. A delicious three-course evening meal is available by prior arrangement.
The spacious landscaped grounds at Lakehill include a 4 hole par three golf course, grass tennis court and swimming pool.
We enjoy showing visitors around the farm with its tame beef cattle and sheep and chestnut orchard, usually accompanied by Max, our black Labrador dog. The very scenic Lake Ohakuri is a mere five minutes stroll from the homestead. It provides good birdwatching sites and is, where John keeps his classic mahogany clinker cabin boat.

"MINARAPA"

620 Oruanui Road, RD 1, P.O. Box 1310, Taupo
Ph (07) 378 1931
Mobile 025-272 2367
e-mail: minarapa@voyager.co.nz
http://www.minarapa.co.nz

Tariff : N.Z. Dollars	
Double	$90-115
Single	$70-85
Child	$30

Bedrooms	Qty
Double	2
Twin	2
Single	

Bed Size	Qty
Super King	
King/Twin	1
Queen	2
Single	2

Bathrooms	Qty
Ensuite	2
Private	1
Guest Share	
Family Share	

 Countrystay Bed & Breakfast

Features & Attractions

- *Tree-lined drive*
- *Park-like grounds*
- *Tennis and billiards*
- *Peaceful and private*
- *Tourist attractions nearby*
- *Dinner by arrangement*
- *German spoken*
- *Lifestyle farming*

Wend your way along a tree-lined drive to enter the peace and tranquility of our 11-acre country retreat, 12 minutes from Taupo, only 45 minutes to Rotorua and within easy reach of thermal areas and other major tourist attractions and activities.

DIRECTIONS:
Please phone for easy directions.

Minarapa has a games room with full-sized billiard table, or you may prefer to relax before the feature fireplace in the lounge. The spacious guest rooms, two with well-appointed ensuite , balcony and TV, have comfortable beds, tea/coffee facilities and individual character. They overlook park-like grounds, where you may relax among mature trees and colourful gardens, play tennis or cross the pond and stream to visit our friendly farm animals.

In addition to continental or cooked breakfast, a three-course evening dinner with wine is available. We enjoy travel, gardening, golf and bridge. Barbara spricht fliessend Deutsch.

"BRACKENHURST"

801 Oruanui Road, RD 1, Taupo
Ph (07) 377 6451, Fax (07) 377 6451

Features & Attractions

- *Close to Taupo attractions*
- *Pitch and putt practice*
- *Dinner by arrangement*
- *Extensive gardens*
- *Lifestyle farming*
- *Peaceful and tranquil*

Farmstay Bed & Breakfast

Double	$100
Single	$60
Child	$30

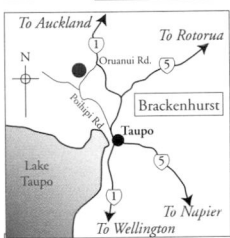

DIRECTIONS: Turn off SH 1 approx. 9km north of Wairakei- "Challenge" fertilizer-bins on Oruanui Rd. corner - 1/2 km on right. Please phone first.

Brackenhurst, set among flower gardens on a hillside overlooking picturesque farmland, offers a warm welcome, wonderful food, peace and tranquility. Enjoy the sounds of tuis and bellbirds. Practise your pitch and putt on the hillside green. A private guest wing in the house or a separate annex offer the ultimate in away from home comfort – fresh flowers and special touches. Breakfast to suit, healthy, indulgent or a little of both. Let us spoil you with fine food, freshly brewed coffee and selection of teas. Guests are welcome to relax by the fire, on the verandah or wander over the farm, viewing the animals. We have a house cat and small poodle. Come and enjoy **Brackenhurst** and share in our warm hospitality. Located close to the many 'wonders' of the Taupo area.

Bedrooms	Qty
Double	2
Twin	
Single	1
Bed Size	**Qty**
King	
Queen/Double	2
Single	2
Bathrooms	**Qty**
Ensuite	1
Private	1
Guest Share	
Family Share	

Bedrooms	Qty
Double	2
Twin	1
Single	1
Bed Size	**Qty**
Queen	1
Double	1
Single	3
Bathrooms	**Qty**
Ensuite	
Private	2
Guest Share	
Family Share	

SOUTH CLARAGH AND BIRD COTTAGE

Ph (07) 372 8848, Fax (07) 372 8047
Mobile 025-620 7325
e-mail: *lhill@reap.org.nz*
http://www.mysite.xtra.co.nz/~aCountryHomestay/

Features & Attractions

- *Tranquil mature gardens*
- *Fine country cooking*
- *Close to Pureora Forest Park*
- *Comfortable relaxed atmosphere*
- *Fresh home grown produce*
- *Friendly donkeys & black sheep*

Countrystay and Self-contained Cottage

Double	$75-100
Single	$20-65
Child	$10-25

Turn into our leafy driveway and relax.... Both Bird Cottage and our comfortable farmhouse are set in rambling gardens. In summer, picnic under the walnut tree, snooze in a hammock or join us for a drink on the wisteria-shaded terrace. In autumn wake to misty, russet mornings, crack walnuts by the fire. In winter, curl up with a book, share good conversation over a glass of wine in the farm kitchen while dinner is cooked for you. In spring, enjoy the awakening garden. Accommodation: 1. The farmhouse - spacious guestroom with bathroom. Also small room available. Farmhouse tariff includes delicious breakfasts. 2. Bird Cottage - through stands of treeferns and redwoods, has french doors to verandahs from both bedroom and livingroom. Self-contained and cosy, Bird Cottage is perfect for two, but will sleep 4/5. Linen and firewood provided. No meals included in Cottage tariff, available by arrangement. "We felt we were staying with friends." For more guest comments, see our website.

DIRECTIONS: Easy to find from which ever direction you come. Contact us by phone/e-mail/fax or check our website for map.

Te Awanui Country Homestay
1506 Poihipi Road, Taupo
Ph (07) 377 6040, Fax (07) 377 6023
e-mail: *te-awanui@bnbnz.com*

Features & Attractions

- *Comfortable beds*
- *Quiet and relaxing*
- *Home-grown food*
- *Wonderful walks and views*
- *Dinner by arrangement*
- *12 min. from Taupo*

	Double	$100
	Single	$60
	Child	$25

Bedrooms	Qty
Double	1
Twin	1
Single	

Bed Size	Qty
King	
Queen	1
Single	2

Bathrooms	Qty
Ensuite	
Private	1
Guest Share	
Family Share	

C | Country Homestay | **H**

Come and enjoy a country stay at **Te Awanui** which is only 12 minutes from Taupo. It is set in a large country garden with magnificent views of the hills and farmland on which we graze sheep, cattle and horses. Our home is spacious with quality accommodation, Sky TV, games room and all home comforts for your use. A fresh home-grown three-course meal with quality wine is available, or just bed and breakfast. Children under 5 years free. Also available are wonderful farm walks.
My husband and I both play golf and fish Lake Taupo. We have travelled the world extensively and have excellent knowledge of all our local activities and would love to help. We really look forward to hearing from you.

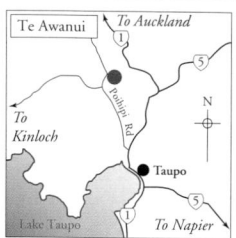

DIRECTIONS:
Very simply find Poihipi Road, north-west of Taupo. Our No 1506. From Taupo 12 minutes.

Kinloch - Taupo YOUR HOSTS: **Elizabeth and Paul Whitelock** Ph: (07) 378 2862

Twynham at Kinloch
84 Marina Terrace, Kinloch, PO Box 326,
Lake Taupo
Ph (07) 378 2862, Fax (07) 378 2868
Mobile (025) 285 6001
e-mail: *twynham.bnb@xtra.co.nz*

VISA **MasterCard**

Features & Attractions

- *Five minutes stroll to Lake*
- *Short 15 min. drive to Taupo*
- *Coffee, cake and relaxation*
- *Compl. kayak/fishing tackle*
- *Hearty breakfasts & dinners*
- *E-mail and fax facilities*

	Double	$125
	Single	$95
	Child	

Bedrooms	Qty
Double	1
Twin	1
Single	

Bed Size	Qty
King	
Queen	1
Single	2

Bathrooms	Qty
Ensuite	1
Private	1
Guest Share	
Family Share	

B | Country Village Accommodation | **H**

Nestled within large private gardens in the picturesque lakeside village of Kinloch - **Twynham** is a haven for fresh air, good coffee and relaxation and unequaled as a base for exploring the delights of the Taupo region, plus the more strenuous delights of golf (adjacent), fishing (5 min.), water sports, snow skiing, bush and mountain walks. Hearty breakfasts, wholesome dinners and warm welcomes assure guests of an enjoyable stay. Guest accommodation is a private wing with bedrooms, bathrooms and elegant lounge. Laundry available. Elizabeth has a wide knowledge of the volcanic and geothermal history of the region. Paul is a New Zealand Kennel Club Judge and golf, music, dog sports and travel are family interests. We are owned by two friendly dogs. Pets are welcome.

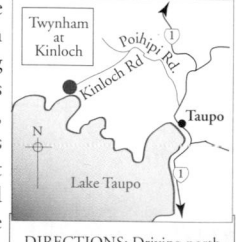

DIRECTIONS: Driving north out of Taupo on SH1 take the TeKuiti/Kinloch turn-off on left (Poihipi Road). Follow Kinloch signs to village.

KINLOCH LODGE

R & G Morrissey
3 Yasmin Lane, Kinloch, Taupo
Ph/Fax (07) 378 6332. Mobile 025-242 0499
e-mail: *kinloch.lodge@hostlink.co.nz*

Tariff : N.Z. Dollars	
Double	$120-145
Single	$85
Child	$15-25

Bedrooms	Qty
Double	2
Twin	1
Single	

Bed Size	Qty
King	1
Queen	1
Super/King/Twin	1
Single	2

Bathrooms	Qty
Ensuite	3
Private	
Guest Share	
Family Share	

**Quality Homestay
Bed & Breakfast**

DIRECTIONS:
Take the Te Kuiti/Kinloch turn-off north
of Taupo on SH 1 (Poihipi Rd.), Turn
left into Whangamata Rd. and follow the
signs to Kinloch. On entering Kinloch,
take the first turning left after the
roundabout (Kenrigg Rd.), then
next left to Yasmin Lane.

Features & Attractions

- 15 minutes from Taupo
- 10 min. walk to lake edge
- Fishing charters available
- 10 hole golf course
- Horse riding
- Bush walks around lake
- E-mail facilities
- Local restaurant

"MAGIC."

Nestled on the Western shores of Lake Taupo, **Kinloch Lodge** offers quality accommodation in a relaxed atmosphere in the picturesque village of **Kinloch**. Fifteen minutes drive from Taupo, **Kinloch Lodge** is an ideal base to explore Rotorua 1 hour, the Central Plateau, Napier, and Waitomo Caves all within 1½ hours drive. A renown **trout fishing** region, **Kinloch Lodge** backs onto the public golf course. A 10 minute walk to the lake's edge, marina, restaurant, bush walks and horse riding.

Purpose built, **Kinloch Lodge** provides guests with ensuite bathrooms to all bedrooms. Privacy of the guest lounge, which opens onto the terrace overlooking the garden and public golf course. Tea, coffee and home-baking provided. Sky TV, e-mail and personal washing facilities are also available. Continental and cooked breakfast included. Evening meals available on request, $45 pp. BYO. Lemon Meringue Pie a speciality. We enjoy hosting in a relaxed family atmosphere and love spoiling. We are Directors of the HOSTLINK NZ network of quality homestays throughout New Zealand and are happy to assist you with your itinerary to ensure your journey throughout New Zealand is a memorable one.

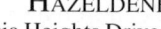

HAZELDENE

119 Acacia Heights Drive, Acacia Bay,
Ph (07) 377 0560, Fax (07) 377 0560
Mobile 025-609 2647
e-mail: *hazeldene@bnbnz.com*

Features & Attractions
- *Quiet and relaxing*   - *Warm, friendly hospitality*
- *Ample parking*   - *Generous breakfast*
- *Stunning views*   - *Fishing & golf nearby*

Hazeldene

$		
Double	$140-170
Single	$110-140
Child	$50

**Bed & Breakfast
Boutique Accommodation**

Bedrooms	Qty
Double	2
Twin	1
Single	
Bed Size	**Qty**
Queen	1
Double	1
Single	2
Bathrooms	**Qty**
Ensuite	3
Private	
Guest Share	
Family Share	

We have lived in England all our lives, but have now retired to New Zealand. We ran a very successful Homestay in Devon, which we are looking to provide here. We very much enjoy meeting people and offering "home from home" accommodation. Judy and Tony, along with Bruno and Sally, our collie dogs, welcome you to **Hazeldene**, a newly built home, opening October 2001. We have outstanding views of Lake Taupo and Mt Tauhara, this is set in 2 acres of land. All our bedrooms have been very tastefully furnished and fitted out with all the luxuries in life, such as TVs, electric blankets, hair dryers, coffee and tea making facilities. Hazeldene is approximately 7 km from Taupo town centre, but also within easy reach of the famous Huka Falls, golf courses, restaurants and geothermal activity.

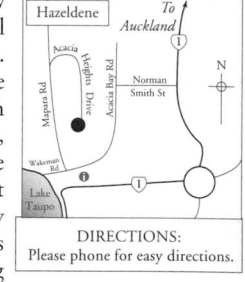

DIRECTIONS:
Please phone for easy directions.

PARIROA HOMESTAY

77A Wakeman Road, Acacia Bay, Taupo
Ph (07) 378 3861, Fax (07) 378 3866
Mobile 025-530 370
e-mail: *pariroa@xtra.co.nz*
www.mysite.xtra.co.nz/~Pariroa

Features & Attractions
- *Magnificent views, very quiet*   - *Close to lake*
- *Interesting walks, good beaches*   - *5 km from Taupo*
- *Restaurant nearby*   - *Breakfast of choice*

**Homestay
by the Lake**

$		
Double	$75
Single	$50
Child	$30

Views Views Views

Our home is Scandanavian style with a natural wooden interior, situated in a very quiet area of Acacia Bay and surrounded by native ferns and plants. We have magnificent, uninterrupted views of Lake Taupo, Mount Tauhara and the ranges, from the guest bedrooms, living room and sun deck. We are retired farmers, who have travelled extensively and enjoy meeting people. Eric, in his younger years, lived in several European countries and was a tea planter in Java before coming to New Zealand. We live 5 kilometres from Taupo and minutes from the beach. If you enjoy fishing, tramping, mountaineering, playing golf or relaxing in hot thermal pools, it is all in this area.

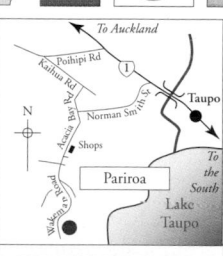

DIRECTIONS: Follow signs to Acacia Bay. Turn down between 95 & 99 Wakeman Rd. We are the last house on this short road.

Bedrooms	Qty
Double	1
Twin	1
Single	
Bed Size	**Qty**
Queen	1
Queen Single	1
Single	1
Bathrooms	**Qty**
Ensuite	
Private	
Guest Share	1
Family Share	

KOORINGA

32 Ewing Grove, Acacia Bay, Taupo
Ph (07) 378 8025, Fax (07) 378 6085
Mobile 025-272 6343
e-mail: *kooringa@xtra.co.nz*
http://www.kooringa.co.nz

Tariff : N.Z. Dollars	
Double	$110
Single	$60
Child	

Bedrooms	Qty
Double	2
Twin	
Single	
Bed Size	**Qty**
Super King	
Double	1
Queen	1
Single	1
Bathrooms	**Qty**
Ensuite	1
Private	
Guest Share	
Family Share	

      Homestay Bed & Breakfast

Features & Attractions

- *All activities easily arranged*
- *Close to all major attractions*
- *Wake to Tui & Bellbird song*
- *Watch the fantastic sunrise*
- *Magnificent views*
- *Generous breakfasts*
- *Quiet and relaxing*
- *2 min. to lake edge*

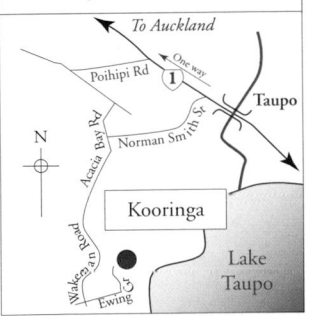

DIRECTIONS: Follow the signs to Acacia Bay. Drive to the end of Wakeman Road, turn left into Ewing Grove, **Kooringa** is at the end of the grove.

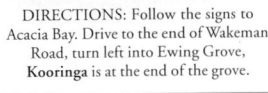

Kooringa is situated in sheltered Acacia Bay (2min. walk to the lake), surrounded by native bush and gardens with magnificent views of Lake Taupo and Mount Tauhara. The guest suite is tastefully furnished with the two bedrooms, comfortable lounge with Sky TV, tea & coffee making facilities and private deck area. We are a retired professional couple, have travelled extensively with our two sons, lived overseas and now enjoy a relaxed life-style in this beautiful area.

We are within easy distance of fascinating geothermal activity, famous Huka Falls, bush walks, golf courses, restaurants and numerous other attractions. Our interests include gardening, sport, travel and hospitality. A generous breakfast with plenty of variety is served in the conservatory overlooking the lake. We assure you of a warm welcome and comfortable stay.

Please phone, fax or e-mail for bookings.

111

ALBION LODGE

358 Lane Terrace
Ph (07) 378 7788, Fax (07) 378 2966
Mobile 021-116 8496
e-mail: *info@albionlodge.co.nz*
http://www.albionlodge.co.nz

Tariff : N.Z. Dollars	
Double	$210-390
Single	$150-220
Child	$150-220

Bedrooms	Qty
Double	4
Twin	
Single	
Bed Size	**Qty**
Super King	3
King	
Queen	1
Single	
Bathrooms	**Qty**
Ensuite	2-3
Private	1
Guest Share	
Family Share	

 Luxury Fishing Lodge

Features & Attractions

- *Each bedroom individually interior designed*
- *Evening meals arranged around fishing*
- *In house NZPFGA fishing guide*
- *Premium New Zealand wine list*
- *Four golf courses within 15 min.*
- *Partner activities guide*
- *Close to all major attractions*
- *Secure storage for skis*

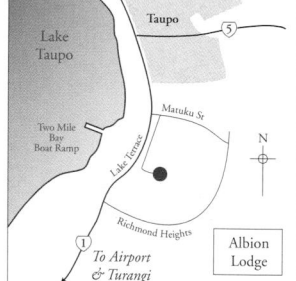

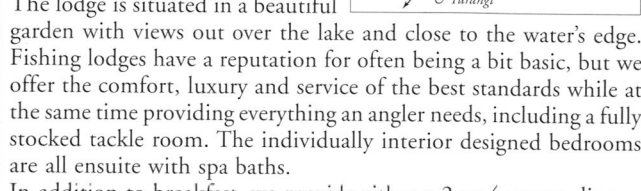

Albion Lodge is primarily a fishing lodge, but we welcome everybody interested in enjoying a unique experience.

The lodge is situated in a beautiful garden with views out over the lake and close to the water's edge. Fishing lodges have a reputation for often being a bit basic, but we offer the comfort, luxury and service of the best standards while at the same time providing everything an angler needs, including a fully stocked tackle room. The individually interior designed bedrooms are all ensuite with spa baths.

In addition to breakfast, we provide either a 2 or 4 course dinner, with some of the best and most difficult to obtain premium New Zealand wines.

Dinner is served to suit your schedule, be it at 5.00 in the afternoon, so you are free to catch the evening rise or see a concert, or as late as you need so you can eat after arriving late or after a long day out on the back country streams. We have a resident NZPFGA member fly fishing guide and can call upon other expert guides if needed.

PAEROA LAKESIDE HOMESTAY

21 Te Kopua Street, Acacia Bay, Taupo
Ph (07) 378 8449, Fax (07) 378 8446
Mobile 025-818 829
e-mail: *bibby@reap.org.nz*
http://www.taupohomestay.com

Tariff : N.Z. Dollars	
Double	$175-225
Single	$150-225
Child	POA

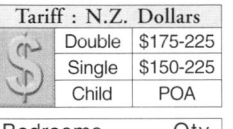

Bedrooms	Qty
Double	3
Twin	
Single	
Bed Size	**Qty**
Super King	2
King	
Queen	1
Single	
Bathrooms	**Qty**
Ensuite	3
Private	
Guest Share	
Family Share	

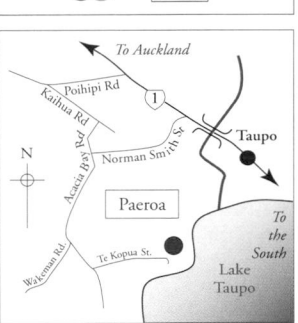

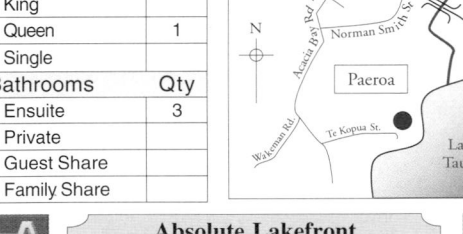

**Absolute Lakefront
Luxury Accommodation**

Features & Attractions

- *Comfortable beds*
- *Private beach & jetty*
- *Generous breakfasts*
- *Quiet and relaxing*
- *Uninterrupted panoramic views*
- *Boat fishing, sightseeing trips*
- *Close to all major attractions*
- *Hot pool and golf nearby*

Paeroa Lakeside Homestay set on the lake edge with private beach, native bush and gardens, in sheltered Acacia Bay, with panoramic views of Lake Taupo and beyond. A warm, welcoming environment waits – comfort, private facilities, spacious lounge areas and outdoor living. Guest areas and beds are warm, comfortable and tastefully decorated. TV and tea and coffee facilities in rooms, e-mail and laundry service available.

We are both 5th generation New Zealanders. Retired sheep farmers, we enjoy living in our peaceful, private home beside the beach next to a bushwalk, just minutes from the town centre. 3 golf courses, thermal areas, restaurants, boating, fishing and all major attractions and within easy driving distance from mountains, National Park, extended thermal areas and wineries. Amongst our interests are travel, golf, gardening, fishing, hospitality, having travelled and fished extensively overseas. Guided fishing and sightseeing experiences available from John's new 30 foot cruiser. The catch can be smoked or may be cooked for breakfast. A welcome tea or coffee on arrival.

We assure you of a memorable stay. Please e-mail, fax or phone for bookings.

MAGNIFIQUE

52 Woodward Street, Nukuhau, Taupo
Ph (07) 378 4915. Mobile 021 - 388 498
e-mail: *raeden@clear.net.nz*

Features & Attractions

- *Magnificent sweeping views* • *Short walk to town*
  and stunning sunsets • *Golf, fishing, skiing*
- *Dinner by arrangement* • *Guest laundry*

Double	$90-110	
Single	$60	
Child		

Bed & Breakfast Homestay

Bedrooms	Qty
Double	2
Twin	1
Single	

Bed Size	Qty
King	
Double	2
Single	2

Bathrooms	Qty
Ensuite	
Private	2
Guest Share	
Family Share	

Welcome to **Magnifique** with stunning views of beautiful Lake Taupo, framed by the snow clad Central Plateau and mountain ranges. Only 7 min. walk to Taupo's superb shops and restaurants. The accommodation includes a choice of an upstairs double bedroom with private bathroom or downstairs self-contained double unit with living and kitchen facilities, TV and guest bathroom. We can direct you to the great variety of wonderful things to experience and see in and around Taupo. Rex is always looking for an excuse to take the boat on the lake. Our focus in life is "people", having many friends within and far beyond NZ with capacity for many more. Enjoy a relaxed stay in our spacious warm home. Please phone/e-mail for booking.

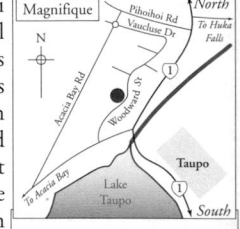

DIRECTIONS: From north (SH 1) turn off to Acacia Bay, then 1st left twice. From south (SH 1) - just over bridge, take 1st left, then 1st right.

CATLEY'S HOMESTAY

55 Grace Crescent, Taupo
Central North Island
Ph (07) 378 1403, Fax (07) 378 1402
e-mail: *taupo@actrix.gen.nz*

Features & Attractions

- *Quiet, peaceful area* • *Spacious home*
- *Close to lake* • *Stunning views*
- *Colourful garden* • *Great fishing*

Homestay Bed & Breakfast

Double	$100	
Single	$70	
Child	$30	

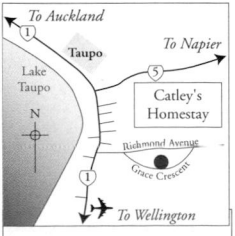

DIRECTIONS:
Approx. 5km south of town centre turn into Richmond Ave. Grace Crescent is first right.

If you want a quiet Homestay with panoramic views of lake and mountains, generous breakfasts and warm hospitality, this is the place for you.

Upstairs guest rooms open onto a sheltered sundeck with extensive views of the lake and snow capped volcanoes. We also have a comfortable self-contained unit with its own garden entrance, bathroom and lounge with TV, microwave and tea making facilities.

All Taupo's famous attractions are nearby, including Huka Falls and thermal pools. With prior notice we can offer an evening meal. Laundry facilities are available.

We know you will enjoy your stay in this lovely area. To avoid disappointment, booking is recommended.

Bedrooms	Qty
Double	2
Twin	1
Single	

Bed Size	Qty
Queen	1
Double	1
Single	2

Bathrooms	Qty
Ensuite	
Private	1
Guest Share	
Family Share	1

AMBLESIDE

5 Te Hepera Street, Taupo
Ph/Fax (07) 378 1888, Mobile 025-836 888
e-mail: *scandic@xtra.co.nz*
www.ambleside.co.nz

Tariff : N.Z. Dollars	
Double	$110-120
Single	$110
Child	$30

Bedrooms	Qty
Double	2
Twin	
Single	

Bed Size	Qty
Super King	
King	
Queen	2
Single	

Bathrooms	Qty
Ensuite	1
Private	1
Guest Share	
Family Share	

   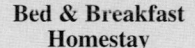
Bed & Breakfast Homestay

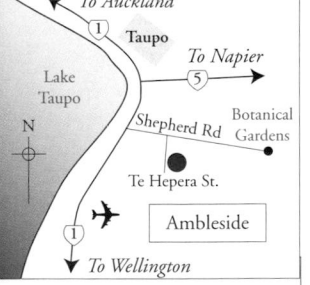

To Auckland
Taupo
To Napier
Lake Taupo
N
Shepherd Rd
Botanical Gardens
Te Hepera St.
Ambleside
To Wellington

DIRECTIONS:
Travelling south on SH1 take 2nd left turn
after Napier SH 5 turnoff, onto Shepherd Rd,
then 1st right into Te Hepera St.

Features & Attractions

- *Quality accommodation in private and tranquil setting*
- *Panoramic lake, mountain & town views*
- *Delicious cuisine & warm hospitality*
- *Private thermal pool*
- *Fishing, sightseeing on lake*
- *Close to local attractions*
- *Ample off-street parking*

Magnificent views; Private Thermal Pool; Delicious Cuisine; "Five Star Friendliness" – just some of the pleasant surprises that await you when you stay at **Ambleside.**

Built for the sun and views, our home is situated in a quiet cul-de-sac, a stroll away from the lake and restaurants. Upstairs is exclusive to you. The two queen bedrooms offer stunning views. Both have cable T.V., refrigerators (complimentary refreshments) and tea/coffe facilities. One bedroom has a well equipped guest lounge, and these open onto a sunny balcony. Capture one of life's better experiences when you relax in our hot mineral pool, set in the fern garden. You are welcome to use our e-mail and Internet facilities at no extra expense.

As one guest put it "It's all about human warmth and wit". Enjoy sharing travel stories and life's adventures with us whilst you enjoy a gourmet breakfast. Take the opportunity to use our knowledge to plan your day, and experience the magic of Taupo.

FAIRVIEWS

8 Fairview Terrace, Taupo
Ph (07) 377 0773
e-mail: *fairviews@reap.org.nz*
http://www.reap.org.nz/~fairviews

Tariff : N.Z. Dollars	
Double	$100-130
Single	$85-100
Child	

Bedrooms	Qty
Double	1
Twin	
Single	1
Bed Size	Qty
Super King	
King	
Queen	1
Single	2
Bathrooms	Qty
Ensuite	1
Private	1
Guest Share	
Family Share	

**Homestay
Boutique Accommodation**

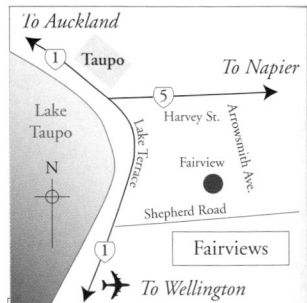

DIRECTIONS:
From State Highway 1, turn onto State Highway 5. Take 1st turn right then 2nd turn right. **Fairviews** is on the left.

Features & Attractions

- *Tranquil surroundings*
- *Generous breakfasts*
- *Tea & Coffee making facilities*
- *Private entrance/ patio*
- *Lake views*
- *Courtesy pick-up at airport*
- *E-mail facilities*
- *Off-street parking*

Welcome to Taupo. Make yourself at home at **Fairviews** – a large, modern home, with views of Lake Taupo, situated in a quiet, tranquil neighbourhood. Relax in and enjoy the beautiful gardens **Fairviews** has to offer. Be as private as you wish or take the opportunity to socialise indoors or around the barbeque table. I have a wide knowledge of the area and have travelled extensively throughout New Zealand. I am able to assist you with on-going travel arrangements. My interests include theatre, antiques and collectables, gardening, tramping, travel and keep-fit. **Fairviews** is situated 4.5 km from town, five minutes to the Lake, Botanical Gardens and the Taupo Hot Springs. e-mail facilities are available at a small charge and my laundry is at your disposal. Escape the hustle and bustle of city life and relax at **Fairviews** during your stay in this beautiful town.

LOCHINVER

33 Tamatea Road, Taupo
Ph (07) 377 0241, Mobile-025-278 1422
e-mail: *gabrielle.thom@xtra.co.nz*
http://www.homestead.com/Lochinver/lochinverpa.html

Tariff : N.Z. Dollars	
Double	$95
Single	$75
Child	

Bedrooms	Qty
Double	1
Twin	
Single	
Bed Size	**Qty**
Super King	
King	
Queen	1
Single	
Bathrooms	**Qty**
Ensuite	
Private	1
Guest Share	
Family Share	

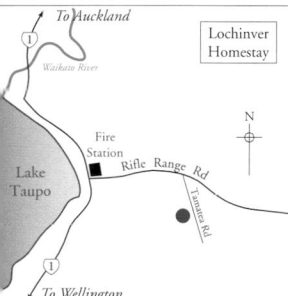

Lochinver Homestay

To Auckland
Waikato River
Fire Station
Rifle Range Rd
Tamatea Rd
Lake Taupo
To Wellington

DIRECTIONS:
Heading south continue along Lake Tce.
past main shopping area. At fire station turn
left onto Rifle Range Rd. Tamatea Rd.
is the 9th street on your right.

**Bed & Breakfast
Homestay**

Features & Attractions

- *Off-street parking*
- *Private guest lounge*
- *Priv. bathroom/sep. shower*
- *Home-baking & preserves*
- *Pleasant garden setting*
- *Restaurants/attractions close*

We aim to provide warm hospitality and a restful stop for friends and visitors. Being our only guests you are the centre of our attention! Or you may choose to enjoy the privacy of your own sun-filled lounge with television, VCR, and well-stocked bookshelf. There is also a refrigerator, tea/coffee making facilities, complimentary homebaked cookies and fruit. Cooked or continental breakfast is provided, with home-made preserves a 'specialty of the house'.

In fine weather you may prefer to enjoy coffee on the deck overlooking the tree-fringed private garden. Our home is well situated for visiting the area's many attractions. Golf courses and restaurants are also within easy driving distance.

The garden and house reflect Gae's interest in old roses, and floral art. Ray is ex RNZNVR, and now enjoying active semi retirement. We are well-travelled and are delighted to meet people from all walks of life. Our aim is to be welcoming hosts but at the same time respect our guests' privacy.

PATAKA HOUSE

8 Pataka Road, Taupo
Ph: (07) 378 5481, Fax:(07) 378 5461
Mobile (025) 547 3881

 http://www.travelwise.co.nz

Features & Attractions

- *Quality hospitality*
- *Large colourful garden*
- *Quality restaurants nearby*
- *Private garden room/ensuite*
- *Spacious home in quiet area*
- *Central to Taupo's attractions*

 (BB logo)

Homestay and Self-contained Cottage

 (H and $ logos)

	Double	$100-110
	Single	$60
	Child	$30

DIRECTIONS:
We are 100 metres off the Lake Taupo lakefront drive. Please phone or fax for bookings or directions.

Raewyn and Neil extend a warm welcome from **Pataka House** and enjoy meeting new people and making new friends. You will find us very easily, just 100 metres from Lake Taupo, and very close to restaurants and shops. Our home is off a quiet road, up a tree-lined driveway and most privately situated. You are provided with a beautiful environment where you are welcome to wander about the garden. **Pataka House** is spacious and has a private guest wing of three attractively furnished double bedrooms. We also offer a cosy honeymoon garden suite with a tastefully decorated ensuite. We are proud of our homestay business which offers all guests - hospitality, use of lounge, laundry facilities, swimming pool, barbecue and roomy carpark. We also prepare a hearty breakfast whether it be continental or cooked and use homemade preserves and home-baked bread. We aim to be welcoming in sharing our home and hospitality with you.

Bedrooms	Qty
Double	2
Twin	2
Single	
Bed Size	**Qty**
King	
Queen	2
Single	4
Bathrooms	**Qty**
Ensuite	1
Private	1
Guest Share	1
Family Share	

YEOMAN'S LAKEVIEW HOMESTAY

23 Rokino Road, Taupo
Ph (07) 377 0283, Fax (07) 377 4683

Features & Attractions

- *Beautiful views*
- *Warm, friendly hospitality*
- *Dinners a speciality*
- *Spacious, comfortable home*
- *Close to local attractions*
- *Vegetarians catered for*

 (H and $ logos)

	Double	$100
	Single	$50
	Child	$25

Homestay Bed & Breakfast Lake & Mountain Views

(BB logo)

DIRECTIONS: Turn into Huia St. from lake front, take fourth turn on right into Rokino Road.

Bedrooms	Qty
Double	1
Twin	1
Single	1
Bed Size	**Qty**
King	
Queen	1
Single	3
Bathrooms	**Qty**
Ensuite	1
Private	
Guest Share	1
Family Share	

Our lake and mountain view homestay is handy to all of Taupo's local attractions and golf courses, only 2 minutes drive to shops and restaurants and a short walk to the lake. One hour drive to Rotorua thermal area, 1½ hours to Ruapehu ski fields. A very warm welcome awaits all who are looking for relaxing homestay. Guest bedrooms are comfortable and tastefully furnished. Our spacious lounge and sun-deck are yours to enjoy, especially the beautiful sunsets (and log fires in winter). Washing and ironing facilities are available and ample off-street parking.

Our interests since retiring from farming are travelling both home and abroad, golfing, handwork, traditional New Zealand meals and home hospitality.

"THE PILLARS"

7 Deborah Rise, Bonshaw Park, Taupo
Ph (07) 378 1512, Fax (07) 378 1511
Mobile 025-246 0777
e-mail: *enquiries@pillarshomestay.co.nz*
http://www.pillarshomestay.co.nz

Tariff : N.Z. Dollars	
Double	$250-450
Single	
Child	13 yrs.+

Bedrooms	Qty
Double	4
Twin	
Single	

Bed Size	Qty
Super King/Twin	1
King/Twin	1
Californian King Twin	2

Bathrooms	Qty
Ensuite	4
Private	
Guest Share	
Family Share	

DIRECTIONS: 5.7 km from the lake
edge up SH 5 towards Napier. Turn
into Caroline Drive. Deborah Rise
is the first on your left.

 Luxury Homestay Retreat

Features & Attractions

- *Offers privacy and tranquility*
- *Five acre park-like rural grounds*
- *Lake and mountain views*
- *Tennis court & swimming pool*
- *World famous trout fishing*
- *Golf courses nearby*
- *Ski fields only 1 hour away*
- *Hot pools nearby*

Welcome to Taupo's exclusive Homestay Retreat offering privacy and tranquility amidst five acres of park-like rural grounds with views of lake and mountains. At Lake Taupo, – New Zealand's largest lake, covering 616 square kilometres, – you will be amazed about how much there is to do in both summer and winter. **The Pillars**, built in Mediterranean style, is set in landscaped gardens, featuring pond, gazebo, swimming pool and tennis court (racquets and balls provided). All rooms have underfloor heating, complimentary toiletries and quality furnishings, including TV, radio-clock, fridge with bottled water, selection of teas and coffee, fresh fruit and complimentary bottle of wine. Fresh flowers, home-cooked biscuits, bathrobes and hair dryers will add to the enjoyment of your stay with us. The room and winter rates includes a continental breakfast. With prior notice we will provide a three-course evening meal with aperitifs, nibbles and a night cap for $55 per person. If you wish to visit Taupo's many bars and restaurants, we will provide complimentary transport. Brochure available on request.

119

"RICHLYN"

1 Mark Wynd, Bonshaw Park, Taupo
Ph (07) 378 8023, Fax (07) 378 8023
Mobile 025-908 647
e-mail: *richlyn.james.taupo@extra.co.nz*
http://www.richlyn.co.nz

Features & Attractions

- *Peaceful, secluded, friendly*
- *Firm, comfortable beds*
- *Full cooked breakfast*
- *Eight acres to enjoy*
- *Gardens and views*
- *10min. to Lake Taupo*

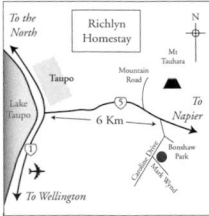

DIRECTIONS: From Taupo up Napier Rd 6km, right into Caroline Drive (Bonshaw Park) 2km to Mark Wynd on left, first drive on left is "RICHLYN".

Country Homestay Boutique Accomm.

Double	$140
Single	$100
Child	neg.

It's hard to praise your own place, but I will try. Our large house is at the end of a long tree lined drive in a peaceful 8 acre park. It gets all day sun and panoramic views of the beautiful Lake Taupo area. We have made our home friendly and comfortable,quiet no smoking rooms, thick curtains, wonderful beds, friendship, privacy, secure car parking and breakfasts to remember - things that we have often looked for when travelling. There is a spa pool hidden in the extensive informal garden that surrounds the house. Our four big guestrooms allow us to cater for up to 4 couples. We offer group, off peak, firefighter and multiple night discounts. Our 2 toy poodles, 2 black cats and lovebird are always happy to welcome guests and provide some entertainment. Our interests are travel, reading, gardening, each other and lots of other things. Bookings are essential, inquiries welcome.

Bedrooms	Qty
Double	3
Twin	1
Single	
Bed Size	**Qty**
Super King	1
Queen	2
Single	2
Bathrooms	**Qty**
Ensuite	1
Private	
Guest Share	1
Family Share	

"AMANZIKULU"

57 Mahuta Road, Five Mile Bay, Taupo
Ph (07) 377 0859. Fax (07) 377 0859
Mobile 025 200 1813
e-mail: *amanzikulu@travelwise.co.nz*

Features & Attractions

- *Just a few steps to lake*
- *Safe swimming*
- *Friendly helpful hosts*
- *Home of well known cricketer*
- *Waitahanui River 2 minutes*
- *1 hour to Rotorua, 4 skifields*

Homestay Bed & Breakfast or Holiday Flat

Double	$85-105
Single	$50-60
Child	neg.

Amanzikulu – (Zulu for "by the water") is a peaceful homestay, just 8 kilometres south of Taupo, and a few steps from the lake edge. Easy access to golf courses, and excellent fishing, skifields, and hot pools. We provide an interesting perspective to your New Zealand holiday, as we are well travelled, know the area, **and quickly turn visitors into friends**.
If you are interested in cricket - John's cricket career included a ten year stint captaining New Zealand, and at present he holds the position of ICC Match Referee. His study is filled with international memorabilia, which will make your visit even more interesting. We offer you warm and comfortable accommodation, two lounges, a shady cool verandah, and delicious meals.
Dinner by arrangement, with times to suit the fisherman! We welcome you to our home.

Bedrooms	Qty
Double	1
Twin	1
Single	
Bed Size	**Qty**
King	
Queen	1
Single	2
Bathrooms	**Qty**
Ensuite	1
Private	1
Guest Share	
Family Share	

DIRECTIONS: Five Mile Bay. 8 km south of Taupo SH 1. Phone for easy directions.

LAKE EDGE LODGE

60 Mahuta Road, Five Mile Bay, RD 2, Taupo
Ph/Fax (07) 378 0563,
Mobile (021) 1122822
e-mail: *jean@lakeedgelodge.co.nz*
www.lakeedgelodge.co.nz

Tariff : N.Z. Dollars	
Double	$130-140
Single	$85
Child	neg.

Bedrooms	Qty
Double	2
Twin	
Single	
Bed Size	**Qty**
Super King	
King	1
Double	2
Single	
Bathrooms	**Qty**
Ensuite	2
Private	
Guest Share	
Family Share	

VISA   MasterCard

Homestay & Self-contained Accommodation

Features & Attractions

- *Absolute lake edge*
- *Two lakefront suites*
- *Panoramic views*
- *Conservatory*
- *Double spa bath*
- *Complimentary email, laundry*
- *Fishing charters a speciality*
- *10 minutes from Taupo*

Lake Edge Lodge is privately nestled in almost half an acre of gardens and lawns, bordering the beautiful shores of Lake Taupo. Two minutes to the pools of the Waitahanui Stream, 30 minutes to the world famous Tongariro River and an hour's drive to the ski fields of Whakapapa. This is just a taste of the myriad of outdoor activities available right on our doorstep. We invite you to enjoy our relaxed and welcoming home away from home. Both our warm and sunny ground floor suites are self contained; with kitchenette, TV, ensuite, heating, lake views and having private access to the beachfront. Our Tui Room can sleep four and has all the ambience and charm of an Edwardian era, whilst our Kowhai Room compliments with modern luxury and caters for two guests. Whether soaking up the panoramic views from the breakfast table, fly fishing at the lake edge, or relaxing by the cosy log fire, we would like to share with you the tranquility of our lakeside living.

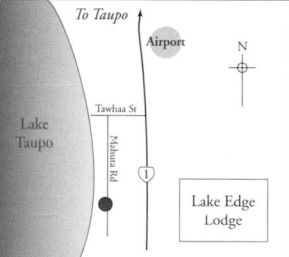

DIRECTIONS:Five Mile Bay is clearly signposted on SH 1, 10 min. south of Taupo.

Gisborne - Eastland

YOUR HOSTS: **Chris and Jenny Meban**   Ph: (06) 862 1822

TE HAU STATION FARMSTAY

332 Te Hau Road, (RD 4, Te Karaka) Whatatutu
Ph (06) 862 1822, Fax (06) 862 1997
Mobile 025-844 574
e-mail: *tehaustn@xtra.co.nz*

Features & Attractions

- *5700 acres*
- *All meals available*
- *Lots of pets*
- *100 year old homestead*
- *Spa and swimming pool*
- *Children welcome*

**Farmstay
Bed & Breakfast**

Double	$95
Single	$60
Child	half price

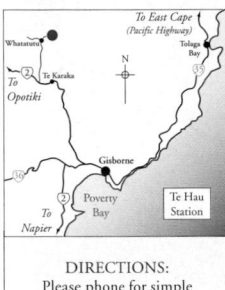

DIRECTIONS:
Please phone for simple
directions.

Our 100 year old Colonial Farmhouse, on a large hill country station, is an easy 40 minute drive from Gisborne, off SH 2 north. Enjoy hands-on farm experiences, learning about life on a sheep and cattle station. Watch the shepherds riding horses and expertly handling stock with their sheep dogs. Walking, clay-bird shooting and hunting are other options or choose to relax and enjoy the many facilities we have to offer. Our two young sons take pleasure in showing guests their many pets. Delicious country meals available.
**Winner of Eastland Tourism 2000 Award for
"Hosted Accommodation".**

Bedrooms	Qty
Double	2
Twin	1
Single	
Bed Size	**Qty**
Queen	1
Double	2
Single	2
Bathrooms	**Qty**
Ensuite	1
Private	
Guest Share	
Family Share	1

Mahia Peninsula

YOUR HOSTS: **Louise Schick**   Ph: (06) 837 5898

REOMOANA

Mahanga Road, RD 8, Nuhaka, Hawkes Bay
Ph (06) 837 5898, Fax (06) 837 5990
e-mail: louiseschick@hotmail.com

Features & Attractions

- *Panoramic ocean view*
- *Morere Hot Springs*
- *Mahia Scenic Reserve*
- *Safe, white sandy beaches*
- *Fishing Charters arranged*
- *Sunset Point Restaurant 6 km*

**Coastal Bed & Breakfast
Self-contained Unit**

Double	$100
Single	$60
Child	$20

DIRECTIONS:
Please phone for easy directions.

Welcome to **Reomoana** – the voice of the sea. Pacific Ocean front farm at beautiful Mahanga Beach on the Mahia Peninsula, the spacious, rustic home with Hungarian and NZ creativity makes this a home of character, with cathedral ceilings and hand-carved furniture. Breath taking views to the Pacific. Come and relax and bring your paints - the area is a painter's paradise. Enjoy the miles of white sandy beaches. Go swimming, surfing, fishing or discover the unique rocky reefs of Mahia. Lake Waikaremoana in the Urewera National Park can be enjoyed for a day trip - or visit Mahia's Scenic Reserve. "Sunset Point Restaurant" is 6 km away or else dinner may be served by prior arrangement.
Reomoana is one hour south of Gisborne or 2¼ hours north of Napier.

Bedrooms	Qty
Double	2
Twin	
Single	
Bed Size	**Qty**
King	
Queen/Double	2
Single	1
Bathrooms	**Qty**
Ensuite	1
Private	1
Guest Share	
Family Share	

93 BY THE SEA

93 Buller Street, New Plymouth
Ph (06) 758 6555, Mobile 025-230 3887
e-mail: *pabron@xtra.co.nz*
http://mysite.xtra.co.nz/~93bythesea

Features & Attractions

- *Central yet peaceful*
- *City, sand, surf, walkways*
- *Exclusive - 1 party only*
- *National Park nearby*
- *Off-street parking*
- *Dinner by prior arrangement*

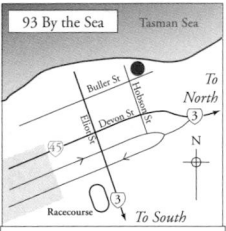

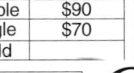

	Double	$90
	Single	$70
	Child	

Boutique Bed & Breakfast

Bedrooms	Qty
Double	1
Twin	1
Single	
Bed Size	**Qty**
King	
Queen/Double	1
King/Twin	1
Bathrooms	**Qty**
Ensuite	
Private	1
Guest Share	
Family Share	

C**onvenient:* An idyllic spot, combining tranquillity of a quiet cul-de-sac with closeness of the sea, riverside parks, restaurants and City Centre. ***Comfortable: Have exclusive use of **private lounge** (TV, fridge, tea/coffee, homemade goodies). **Spa bath**, shower, laundry. Breakfast served in lounge or shared with hosts while enjoying the sights, sounds and feel of gardens and ocean. ***Commendable:*** From the Visitors Book: "Fantastic breakfast, beautiful bed, great shower, lovely hosts, we couldn't have found a better place."

"The sound of waves upon the shore,
The smell of roses by the door,
A spa to ease the muscles sore,
Who could ask for anything more?"
Dale Cameron, Auckland

DIRECTIONS:
Please phone for easy
directions.

BALCONIES BED & BREAKFAST

161 Powderham Street, New Plymouth, Taranaki
Ph (06) 757 8866, Fax (06) 757 8262
Mobile 025-423 789
e-mail: *balconies@paradise.net.nz*

Features & Attractions

- *110 year old character home*
- *Central location*
- *Warm, relaxing atmosphere*
- *Walking distance to park*
- *Attractive garden setting*
- *Close to many attractions*

Central Character Style Home

	Double	$75
	Single	$55
	Child	neg

DIRECTIONS:
500m west of city centre
on Powderham Street

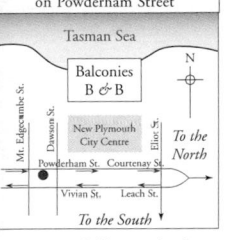

Bedrooms	Qty
Double	1
Twin	2
Single	
Bed Size	**Qty**
King	
Queen	3
Single	2
Bathrooms	**Qty**
Ensuite	
Private	
Guest Share	1
Family Share	

***B**alconies* is nestled amongst mature trees and lovely gardens in the heart of the city, just 5 min. walk to New Plymouth's shopping centre. Our warm, comfortable 110-year old character-style home offers three tastefully decorated guest rooms, large guest bathroom with claw-foot bath, separate toilet facilities and spacious guest lounge with tea and coffee making facilities. Heated guest rooms are downstairs, beds are queen size and have electric blankets. Laundry facilities, courtesy transport and off-street parking available. Within walking distance are the art gallery, library, museum, Heritage Walks, indoor pool complex and beautiful Pukekura and Brooklands Parks. You will be served a generous fully cooked or continental breakfast. Unwind in the peaceful surroundings of Balconies, we will ensure you have a comfortable night's rest.

BIRDHAVEN
26 Pararewa Drive,
New Plymouth, Taranaki
Ph (06) 751 0432, Fax (06) 751 3475
e-mail: *info@birdhaven.co.nz*
http://www.birdhaven.co.nz

Tariff : N.Z. Dollars		
	Double	$77-85
	Single	$54-65
	Child	neg.

Bedrooms	Qty
Double	1
Twin	1
Single	

Bed Size	Qty
Super King	
King	
Queen	1
Single	2

Bathrooms	Qty
Ensuite	
Private	
Guest Share	1
Family Share	

 Homestay Bed & Breakfast

Features & Attractions

- *Beautiful, peaceful country setting*
- *Native bush with abundant bird life*
- *Restful, friendly atmosphere*
- *Delicious complimentary homebaking*
- *Spectacular mountain view*
- *Free airport transfer*
- *Special candlelit dinner*
- *5 min. from city or port*

DIRECTIONS:
From clock tower (opposite Queen St.)
on Devon St. West, travel west 3.4 km
to Spotswood College (LHS). Turn first
left 800m later into Barrett Road.
We are the fifth street on the right.

We have lived in England, South Africa and New Zealand and love to travel. We really enjoy welcoming guests to **Birdhaven** and endeavouring to exceed your expectations. Ensuring your comfort and pleasure is most important to us. This is reflected in the quality furnishings in the inviting guest room and throughout the house, the complimentary refreshments and the special breakfast of fresh seasonal and home-made temptations. Come and share the tranquillity and space of our comfortable, tastefully refurbished home. Relax in the secluded gardens, in the sun room or on one of the patios overlooking the flight paths of numerous birds as they flit amongst the trees. Stroll down to the duck pond and delight in the native bush, marsh and woodlands within our three acre farmlet. We want you to feel at home, relax and enjoy being at **Birdhaven**, sharing our appreciation of beautiful Taranaki and our spectacular view of Mt Egmont. "True hospitality at its very best – absolutely perfect, don't change a thing!", wrote one guest. Our visitors' book also includes: "Wonderful hospitality. The picnic hamper was superb. The attention to detail in all aspects of our stay has been memorable. We will be back." and "Found a gem! Superb meals. Shall be back!"

ANDERSON'S ALPINE LODGE

922 Pembroke Road, Stratford, Taranaki
Ph (06) 765 6620, Fax (06) 765 6100
Mobile 025-412 372
e-mail: *mountainhouse@xtra.co.nz*
http://www.mountainhouse.co.nz

Features & Attractions

- *Native bush and garden*
- *Panoramic alpine views*
- *Egmont National Park*
- *Absolute peace and quiet*
- *Pet sheep, pigs, ducks, etc.*
- *International restaurant nearby*

F **Farmstay Alpine Chalet** **B**A

Double	$95-130
Single	$95-130
Child	

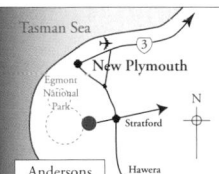

DIRECTIONS: Head west from Stratford 9km up Pembroke Road to Egmont National Park

Our Swiss Chalet rests in five acres of native bush with views of Mount Egmont/Taranaki on our doorstep. The Egmont National Park starts opposite our front gate. We are five kilometres from the Mountain House and its internationally famed restaurant and a further 3km to the Stratford Plateau and skifields. The National Park offers family tramps, round the mountain trek, summit climbs (guides available) and snow skiing. Trout stream, gardens, museums and scenic drives nearby. Private helicopter for summit scenic flights. We have pet sheep, pig, ducks etc. Kiwi Keith and Swiss Berta Anderson owned mountain lodges since 1973 and won many tourist and hospitality awards. Keith is a noted Taranaki artist, specialising in landscapes and mountain scenes.

Bedrooms	Qty
Double	1
Twin	1
Single	1
Bed Size	**Qty**
King	1
Queen/Double	1
King Single	1
Bathrooms	**Qty**
Ensuite	3
Private	
Guest Share	
Family Share	

TE POPO GARDENS

636 Stanley Road, RD 24, Stratford, Taranaki
Ph (06) 762 8775, Fax (06) 762 8775
e-mail: *tepopo@clear.net.nz*
http://www.tepopo.co.nz

Features & Attractions

- *Idyllic rolling country*
- *Famous for its birds*
- *Private guest wing*
- *Dinner a speciality*
- *Music, art, library*
- *Savour Taranaki*

DIRECTIONS:
East from Midhurst on Beaconsfield Road for 6 km.
Left into Stanley Road for 6.3 km to signpost on right.

Double	$120-130
Single	$90-100
Child	

LA **Country Retreat Bed & Breakfast** **C**

Bedrooms	Qty
Double	2
Twin	1
Single	
Bed Size	**Qty**
Queen	2
King Single	1
Single	1
Bathrooms	**Qty**
Ensuite	3
Private	
Guest Share	
Family Share	

We have a special place which we love to share. Everything is in place for you to have a relaxing, memorable stay. Sarsen House is set in Te Popo Gardens (34 acres) – intriguing woodland, park and perennial gardens encircled by deep river gorges and native bush. A magnificent setting. Each of the three spacious guest rooms in the separate wing opens out to the guests' garden. Ensuite bathroom, woodburning fires and superior beds. Three or two course dinner - fine food and wines. Special breakfast served in the sun-filled conservatory. Excellent hosting and service (plus 2 middle-aged dogs!). Self catering with full kitchen facilities available. Ideally situated to explore the mountain, national parks, golf courses, world renowned gardens and Taranaki's attractions.

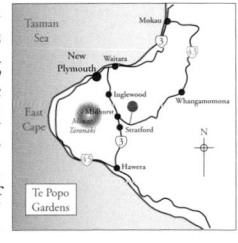

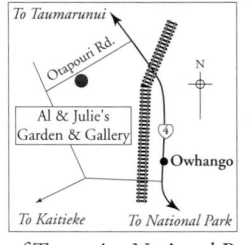

DIRECTIONS: 18km south of Taumarunui, 20km north of Tongariro National Park.

AL & JULIE'S GARDEN & GALLERY

Otapouri Road, RD 1, Rural # 157, Owhango
Ph (07) 895 4669
e-mail: *gardens@taunarunui.com*

Features & Attractions

- Extensive bush & house gardens
- Breakfast essentials included
- Dinner: Asian/European on request
- Close to ski fields
- Hot baths in bush setting
- Wood turning gallery

Countrystay
Self-contained Accom.

Double	$75
Single	$60
Child	$15

Bedrooms	Qty
Double	2
Twin	
Single	

Bed Size	Qty
King	
Queen	2
Single	1

Bathrooms	Qty
Ensuite	
Private	
Guest Share	1
Family Share	

To Taumarunui
Otapouri Rd.
N
Al & Julie's Garden & Gallery
Owhango
To Kaitieke   To National Park

We welcome you to our rural 10 acre property, landscaped into gardens, bush walks and water gardens. Our home is set amongst rolling hills with pathways to explore at your leisure. Visit Allan's workshop, he is a professional wood turner, watch him at work and visit the gallery. Our self-contained unit, adjoining our home, is a fully restored jail from the 1860's and features fittings of solid New Zealand timbers. The unit has stunning views over farmland to Tongariro State Forest and beyond the volcanoes of Tongariro National Park. We provide generous breakfast essentials. Evening meals are available by arrangement, and as Allan is Malaysian Chinese, Asian foods are a speciality. However, we are equally happy to provide hearty NZ fare. We look forward to meeting you and sharing local knowledge to make your stay here memorable.

MOUNTAIN HEIGHTS LODGE

State Highway 4 (PO Box 43) National Park
Ph (07) 892 2833, Fax(07) 892 2833
e-mail: *mountainheights@xtra.co.nz*
http://www.mountainheights.co.nz

Features & Attractions

- 15 minutes to ski fields
- Hot spa
- Tongariro Crossing
- Dinner by arrangement
- Delicious breakfasts
- Spacious, SC accomm.

Double	$90-140
Single	$60
Child	neg.

Bed & Breakfast
Self-contained Accomm.

Bedrooms	Qty
Double	4
Twin	2
Single	

Bed Size	Qty
Queen	2
Double	2
Single	4

Bathrooms	Qty
Ensuite	4
Private	
Guest Share	1
Family Share	

Mountain Heights is situated on the edge of Tongariro National Park, a World Heritage Area. An ideal place from which to explore the mountains and volcanoes of the Central Plateau. Activities abound for all abilities, including the world renowned **Tongariro Crossing**, classed as the best one-day walk in New Zealand. Excellent mountain bike rides, horse trekking, canoeing the Wanganui River and scenic flights across the volcanoes.

For the less strenuous, enjoy the comfort of our centrally heated lodge. Soak in the hot spa or relax in front of the log fire with a good book or a game of chess. After a good night's sleep enjoy a delicious breakfast with fresh bread and home-baking.

To Auckland & Hamilton
Taupo
Lake Taupo
Taumarunui
Tokanui
Turangi
National Park
N
Mountain Heights Lodge
Raetihi
Ohakune
Taihape
To Wellington

SPIRAL GARDENS

Raurimu Road (RD 1, Owhango) Raurimu
Ph (07) 892 2997 Fax (07) 892 2997
Mobile 025 753 482

Tariff : N.Z. Dollars	
Double	$95
Single	$40
Child	neg.

Bedrooms	Qty
Double	2
Triple	3
Single	
Bed Size	**Qty**
Super King	
Queen	2
Double	4
Single	6
Bathrooms	**Qty**
Ensuite	3
Private	1
Guest Share	
Family Share	

Homestay - Bed & Breakfast & Self-contained Cabin

Features & Attractions

- Location, Location, Location
- Skiing, golf, tramping
- Discover hidden treasures
- Dinner by arrangement
- Central to activities/attractions
- Fishing, hunting, biking
- Families welcome
- Vegetarians catered for

Our new home overlooks the Piopiotea Stream and a magnificent stand of native bush. We are 5 minutes North of National Park Village, gateway to the Tongariro and Wanganui National Parks. The Whakapapa ski area is a 25 minute drive. Transport to the world renowned 'Tongariro Crossing' day walk is available at National Park Village. We can organise any of the adventure activities on offer in the central plateau area, horsetreks, river rafting, guided hunting and fishing tours. Our luxury suites feature a queen bed, a double bed settee, casual chairs and table, dresser, writing bureau and refrigerator. The bunk room sleeps six and features a double bunk with single above, twin bunks and a single bed, ideal for the larger family. Duvets and central heating throughout. Coffee and tea making facilities are on hand in our timber and granite kitchen and we encourage you to use the lounge and decks in casual relaxation. The cottage is small and cosy with a pot belly fire, private deck and carport and is self catering unless by arrangement.

127

ESKVIEW HEIGHTS

261 Hill Road, Napier, P.O.Box 83, Bayview, Hawkes Bay
Ph (06) 836 7190, Fax (06) 836 7390
Mobile 025-939 004
e-mail: *eskviewheights@hotmail.com*

Tariff : N.Z. Dollars		
	Double	$90
	Single	$50
	Child	$15

Bedrooms	Qty
Double	2
Twin	
Single	

Bed Size	Qty
Super King	
King	
Queen	3
Single	2

Bathrooms	Qty
Ensuite	
Private	1
Guest Share	
Family Share	

**Semi rural
Self-contained Accommodation**

Features & Attractions

- *Panoramic views of Napier*
- *Close to Eskdale River*
- *Spacious living area, log fire
  and full kitchen facilities*
- *Private deck with barbecue*
- *Relax in pool or spa*
- *Private squash court*
- *Wineries nearby*

Eskview Heights is located just north of Napier. We offer self-contained semi-rural accommodation with panoramic views of the Esk Valley and Napier.

Features include spacious living area with full kitchen, log fire and private deck with barbecue. The separate bedroom has a queen-size bed, two single bunk beds and a double bed settee. An extra cabin with a double bed is also available.

Guests will enjoy relaxing by the pool or in the spa, or may feel like releasing some tension on the private squash court or in home gym. There is a trampoline, table tennis, petanque and croquet set for use.

Linden Estate, Esk Valley Estate and Crab Farm Wineries are all very close and Napier is only 12 minutes away. The combined attractions of the Hawke's Bay area are all within a half hour drive.

Long term rates are available.

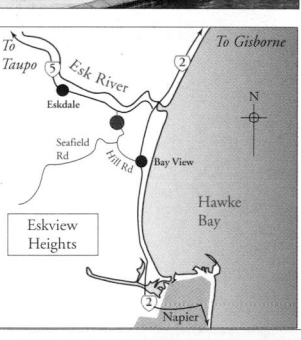

DIRECTIONS: <u>From Napier</u> - drive north on S H 2. At Bayview turn left towards Eskdale. Hill Rd. is 4th road on left after BP Service Station. Go through intersection and wind to top of Hill Rd.
<u>From Taupo</u> - After Eskdale Church take 1st road right, then to top of Hill Rd. <u>From Gisborne</u> - right at Napier/Taupo turn-off. Take 2nd left and go to top of Hill Rd.

"279" CHURCH ROAD

279 Church Road, Taradale, Napier
Ph(06) 844 7814, Fax (06) 844 7814
Mobile 025-265 6760
e-mail: *sandy.279@homestaynapier.co.nz*
http://www.homestaynapier.co.nz

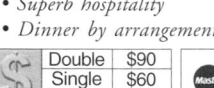

Features & Attractions

- *Quality accommodation*
- *Superb hospitality*
- *Dinner by arrangement*
- *Adjacent to wineries & restaurants*
- *Golf courses & Art Deco nearby*
- *Internet, fax, laundry available*

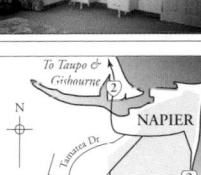

	Double	$90
	Single	$60
	Child	

**Quality Homestay
Bed & Breakfast**

Bedrooms	Qty
Double	1
Twin	1
Single	1
Bed Size	**Qty**
King	
Double	1
Single	3
Bathrooms	**Qty**
Ensuite	
Private	
Guest Share	1
Family Share	

"279", an elegant spacious home set in 3/4 acre of gardens and trees, offers New Zealand and Overseas visitors a peaceful haven to unwind from travelling or exploring the regions Wineries, Architecture etc.

Bedrooms are located upstairs, while living areas, including lounge and games room, are downstairs. Breakfast, Continental or Full, is served at a time to suit you and nearby restaurants offer a variety of cuisine for evening dining. As your host, I delight in offering relaxed and friendly hospitality, and strive to make your stay a memorable experience - My Visitors Book is a testament to this. I look forward to welcoming you to "279" and helping to make your stay in Hawkes Bay the highlight of your travels.

DIRECTIONS:
From Greenmeadows shops take Avenue Road to Church Road. Turn left.

KERRY LODGE

7 Forward Street, Greenmeadows, Napier
Ph (06) 844 9630, Fax (06) 844 1450
Mobile 025-932 874
e-mail: *kerrylodge@xtra.co.nz*
http://www.berrylodge.co.nz

Features & Attractions

- *Tranquil spacious gardens*
- *Restful friendly atmosphere*
- *Close to wineries & restaurants*
- *Handy to Taradale shops*
- *Relax in spa or pool*
- *Laundry available*

	Double	$90-85
	Single	$60
	Child	half price

**Homestay
Bed & Breakfast**

Bedrooms	Qty
Double	2
Twin	1
Single	
Bed Size	**Qty**
Super King	1
Queen	1
Single	2
Bathrooms	**Qty**
Ensuite	1
Private	
Guest Share	1
Family Share	

DIRECTIONS:From Napier, travel along Kennedy Road and Gloucester Street until Greenmeadows. Turn right into Avenue Road, and then left into Forward Street.

Set in spacious tranquil gardens, we invite our guests to share the warmth and comfort of our home.

Our large rooms offer heating, refreshment facilities, colour television and electric blankets. A mobility ensuite and wheelchair access is available for guests convenience. A laundry is also available for guests to use.

Your day with us begins with a scrumptious breakfast and a chat to help plan your day's activities in our twin cities. After your busy day you are welcome to relax in our swimming pool or hot spa and enjoy refreshments on the patio. Our dogs, Tess and Hogan and cat, Tabitha, also wait to welcome you.

COBDEN VILLA

11 Cobden Road, Bluff Hill, Napier
Ph (06) 835 9065, Fax (06) 833 6979
Mobile 025-286 1789
e-mail: *stay@cobdenvilla.com*
http://www.cobdenvilla.com

Tariff : N.Z. Dollars	
Double	$185-365
Single	$180
Child	

Bedrooms	Qty
Double	3
Twin	1
Single	
Bed Size	**Qty**
Super King	
King	1
Queen	2
King Single	2
Bathrooms	**Qty**
Ensuite	3
Private	1
Guest Share	
Family Share	

Bed & Breakfast Boutique Accommodation

Features & Attractions

- *Stunning sea and harbour views*
- *Kiwi hospitality with American accents*
- *Beautiful surrounding gardens*
- *10 min. drive to wineries & golf*
- *Delicious full breakfast*
- *10 minutes walk to city centre and strand*
- *Art Deco furnishing throughout*
- *Internet, email and fax facilities*

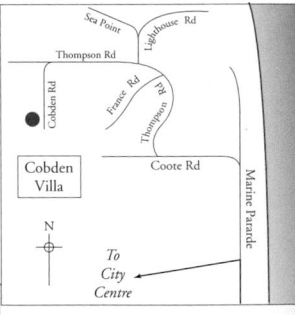

DIRECTIONS:
Marine Parade to Coote Rd (at Centennial Gardens). Right turn onto Thompson Rd. Follow up around and remain left. Left turn onto Cobden Rd (#11).

Our picturesque 1870 Villa has been completely restored and fully furnished in the Art Deco style. For this task we brought our enthusiastic interest, together with artistic talent, from America – to live in Napier, "The Art Deco City". Situated on Bluff Hill ... you may start your day enjoying breakfast in the spacious conservatory, while watching the ocean sunrise. Then relax after days end with a glass of local wine and watch the harbour sunset from the surrounding veranda or elegant dining room. We offer stylish bedrooms with ensuite or private bath, custom-comfort beds, fine quality linens and European down duvets. We also offer a "romantic" king bedroom with an ensuite that includes a deluxe jet spa tub with a separate double steam shower and adjoining private garden verandah. All rooms have central heating and air conditioning with accessible porches for outdoor smoking. Our interests include applical art, decorative antiques, conversational entertaining and sporty activities. German is well understood.

"TWINPEAK"

100 Puketapu Road, Taradale, Napier
Ph (06) 844 9319, Fax (06) 844 9219
Mobile 025-840 450
e-mail: *soe.twinpeak@xtra.co.nz*

Tariff : N.Z. Dollars		
	Double	$80
	Single	$60
	Child	neg.

Bedrooms	Qty
Double	1
Twin	1
Single	1
Bed Size	**Qty**
Super King	
King	
Double	2
Single	1
Bathrooms	**Qty**
Ensuite	1
Private	
Guest Share	
Family Share	1

    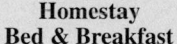
**Homestay
Bed & Breakfast**

DIRECTIONS:
Please telephone for easy directions.

**ADVANCE BOOKING
RECOMMENDED.**

Features & Attractions

- *Spacious and private*
- *Nestled in extensive gardens overlooking Taradale and Napier*
- *Close to wineries and shops*
- *Midway between Napier and Hastings*
- *PC/printer – no charge*

Twinpeak is situated in a tranquil setting away from the hustle and bustle of urban life, yet only minutes away from all the action. Wine trails, art deco walks, trout fishing, craft shops, sports grounds and the choice of four excellent shopping options. Taradale is five minutes away. Napier to the north – 9km. Hastings south – 10 km and Havelock North to the east – 12km.

Twinpeak, nestled in the hills overlooking the Bay, ensures a warm welcome from your host, Soe Schofield.

If weary after your journey or if arriving late, or if you want to be pampered, a meal can be pre-arranged at a reasonable additional cost. Two course $12.00 each, three course $15.00 each. Extra special silver service special occasion $25.00.

For the executive a PC and printer as needed – at no extra charge.

JERVOIS ROAD BED & BREAKFAST

51 Jervois Road, Taradale, Napier
Ph (06) 844 9446, Fax (06) 844 9446
Mobile 025-415 740
e-mail: *croft@paradise.net.nz*
http://www.geocities.com/ashcroft_homestay

Tariff : N.Z. Dollars	
Double	$80
Single	$55
Child	neg.

Bedrooms	Qty
Double	3
Twin	
Single	

Bed Size	Qty
Super King	
King	
Queen	2
Double	1

Bathrooms	Qty
Ensuite	2
Private	
Guest Share	
Family Share	1

Homestay
Bed & Breakfast

Features & Attractions

- *Semi rural*
- *Halfway Napier - Hasting*
- *Restaurants, golf courses nearby*
- *Minutes from wineries & shops*
- *Friendly atmosphere*
- *Large swimming pool*
- *10 minutes from beach*
- *Peaceful garden setting*

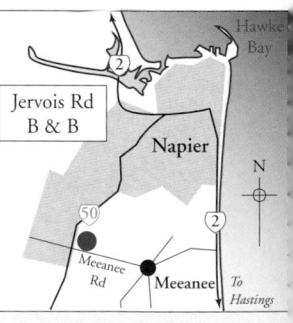

DIRECTIONS:
From motorway turn into Meeanee Road,
then first left into Jervois Road.

Our home is semi-rural, situated halfway between Napier and Hastings.

We have a large sunny bedroom - living area, suitable for a family, with a queen and two single beds and ensuite. It opens out onto a decking and garden.

Our double room has a bathroom and toilet next door.

Our new private room has its own ensuite and overlooks our pool.

All rooms have tea and coffee making facilities.

Relax by the pool or under the trees in summer or visit wineries, orchards and other attractions of Hawkes Bay. Nearby are parks, golf courses and restaurants.

We enjoy people and like to make our home a "home away from home".

Having worked in garden centres, we specialise in a variety of tropical plants.

GREENWOOD HOMESTAY

62 Avondale Road, Taradale, Napier
Ph (06) 845 1246, Fax (06) 845 1247
Mobile 025-795 403
e-mail: *greenwood@clear.net.nz*
http://www.home.clear.net.nz/pages/greenwood

Features & Attractions

- *All rooms have ensuite*
- *Spacious deck*
- *Separate guest lounge*
- *Relaxed garden surroundings*
- *Evening meals by arrangement*
- *Eggs Benedict for breakfast!*

Double	$90-95
Single	$60-65
Child	

Very Comfortable Homestay

Bedrooms	Qty
Double	2
Twin	1
Single	
Bed Size	**Qty**
King	
Queen	2
Single	2
Bathrooms	**Qty**
Ensuite	3
Private	
Guest Share	
Family Share	

We offer quality suburban accommodation close to the twin cities of Napier and Hastings. The Hawke's Bay region has many tourist attractions, natural features and fine wineries and restaurants, all of which are within easy driving distance. Beautiful scenery enhances the region's reputation as one of New Zealand's most abundant food-producing areas. The layout of our home allows you to relax in privacy or join us to share our many interests, including education, art, history, golf, aviation, family, theatre, reading, conversation etc. We have a spacious garden with trees to filter the afternoon sun, and we love to make tourists welcome and to help them make the most of their stay in the area.

Anne and Mike from England can have the last say: "...you were not bettered, for friendliness, facilities, food, indeed anything. So rest assured, you've got it right."

BRAMBLE HEDGE

527 State Highway 2, RD 2, Hastings
Ph (06) 870 1070. Fax (06) 870 1075
Mobile 021 - 509 441
e-mail: *bramblehedge@xtra.co.nz*

Features & Attractions

- *Between Hastings & Napier*
- *Close to Gannet sanctuary*
- *Attractive garden setting*
- *Palm tree nursery & shop*
- *Restaurant nearby*
- *Off-street parking*

Boutique Bed & Breakfast

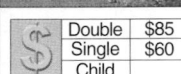

Double	$85
Single	$60
Child	

A warm welcome awaits you at **Bramble Hedge**, set on 2 acres of landscaped grounds. This John-Scott-designed house is full of character and well appointed with a delightful ambience. We have an outdoor spa, set in private gardens for summertime use and two lounges, both with wood fires for the colder months. The property is not suitable for children. Our interests include growing palm trees and cycads, gardening, travelling and following motor sports. Some guest book comments: "Laid back and relaxing, great spa, good food. Thanks"– Palmerston North. "Superb, love the interior décor." – Wellington. "Thankyou for your friendly welcome and for letting us share your lovely home." – England. "We like the garden and this people here." – Sweden. "Thankyou for being so kind and caring, we've loved our stay here. You're the real spirit of NZ." – England.

Bedrooms	Qty
Double	1
Twin	1
Single	
Bed Size	**Qty**
King	
Queen	1
Single	2
Bathrooms	**Qty**
Ensuite	
Private	1
Guest Share	1
Family Share	

DIRECTIONS: From north - 8 km south of Napier on SH 2, then 3 km south of Clive.
We are the 6th property on left from Wool Scour building. From south - 5 km north of Hastings.
Watch for the red Bramble Hedge sign on the right.

OPTIONS

92 Simla Avenue, Havelock North
Hawkes Bay
Ph (06) 877 0257, Mobile 025 278 5095
e-mail: *gr.duff@xtra.co.nz*

Tariff : N.Z. Dollars		
	Double	$120
	Single	$85
	Child	neg.

Bedrooms	Qty
Double	1
Twin	
Single	
Bed Size	Qty
Super King	
King	1
Queen	
King Single	1
Bathrooms	Qty
Ensuite	1
Private	
Guest Share	
Family Share	

Bed & Breakfast
Homestay

Features & Attractions

- *Within 30min. of wineries*
- *Gannets and Art Deco*
- *Close to Te Mata Peak*
- *Petanque court*
- *Elevated position - lovely views*
- *Heated swimming pool & spa*
- *Located in private cul de sac*
- *Four private patios*

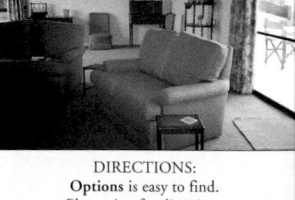

DIRECTIONS:
Options is easy to find.
Please ring for directions

Options is halfway between the centre of Havelock North village and **Te Mata Peak.**
Te Mata Peak at 399m. is the best place to start sightseeing in Hawkes Bay. From there it is only 30 minutes to **Gannet tours**, 10 minutes to the **Te Mata** wineries and 30minutes to the Art Deco buildings of Napier.
Options, and there are many, offers a large bedroom with ensuite, 4 private patios that give the choice of sun or shade all day long, lounge with fire and a small petanque court, together with the heated swimming pool and spa.
Options allows you to cook for yourself on the barbecue, using Hawkes Bay's famed produce and wine, share a family meal at small additional cost, or try one of the 20 recommended restaurants within a 20 minute drive.
Options for cooked or continental breakfast are included in the tariff.

WAIWHENUA FARMSTAY
808 River Road, RD 9, Hastings
Ph (06) 874 2435, Fax (06) 874 2465
Mobile 025-759 369
e-mail: *kirsty.hill@xtra.co.nz*

Features & Attractions
- *Extensive farming & Orchard operation*
- *Families & children welcome*
- *Historic 120 year old homestead*
- *Trout fishing*
- *Informative farm tours*
- *Fresh farm-style meals*

$		
Double	$80
Single	$50
Child	$40

F

Unique
Farm & Orchard Stay

BB

Bedrooms	Qty
Double	2
Twin	2
Single	
Bed Size	**Qty**
Cot	1
Double	2
Single	3
Bathrooms	**Qty**
Ensuite	
Private	1
Guest Share	
Family Share	1

The perfect place to experience a genuine farmstay and friendly rural hospitality at our 120 year old historic homestead, farm and orchard. Come and join us on our extensive 440 ha sheep, beef and deer farm and organic apple and pear orchard. Enjoy guided tours and farm activities on the day, fish in our trout-filled river, or just relax with a book on our cool verandahs or in our garden. Our home and family offer guests a friendly environment, catering for individuals or families interested in the outdoor life. (Two night stay recommended.) Enjoy specialty farm-cooked meals of homegrown beef, lamb or venison, complimented with fresh organic garden vegetables and fruit. Enrich your stay by including other outdoor activities at our backdoor; hunting, fishing, bush and farm walks, garden tours, jet boating and extensive mountain hikes, plus many attractions in the greater sunny Hawkes Bay area. To avoid disappointment, please book ahead.

DIRECTIONS: Turn off SH 50 between Napier and Hastings into Taihape Road at Omahu/Fernhill. Travel 35 km to River Road RHS. Travel along River Road for 8 km. **Waiwhenua** #808. Drive up hill 100 m from mail box RHS.

MYNTHURST FARMSTAY
912 Lindsay Road, RD 3,
Waipukurau, Hawkes Bay
Ph: (06) 857 8093, Fax:(06) 857 8093
Mobile (025) 232 2458
e-mail: *mynthurst@xtra.co.nz*

Features & Attractions
- *Excellent working farm*
- *Trout fishing*
- *Children welcome*
- *Swimming pool - trampoline*
- *Dinner by arrangement*
- *Farm tours complimentary*

H

Genuine Farmstay
Excellent Accomodation

F

$		
Double	$150
Single	$85
Child	$25

Mynthurst is a genuine working sheep and cattle farm covering 1350 acres. Guests from New Zealand and around the world have been welcomed and entertained for over 16 years. The homestead is large, warm and comfortable, in idyllic surroundings, with unspoilt views of the Ruahine Ranges. Feel free to observe the farm activities. Farm tour complimentary. Relax beside the pool, trampoline, tennis. Trout fishing available in local streams. 3 golf courses nearby. Visit local vineyards. Enjoy the many attractions of Hawkes Bay. Dinner available on request, we use only the finest locally grown produce. Children of all ages welcome. If you are looking for a short break in the heart of beautiful Hawkes Bay, you'll find Mynthurst the perfect retreat. Booking avoids disappointment.

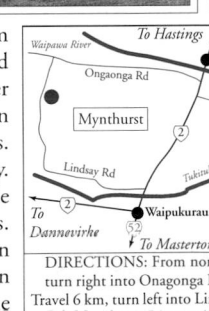

DIRECTIONS: From north, turn right into Onagonga Rd. Travel 6 km, turn left into Lindsay Rd. **Mynthurst** 3 km on left. From south left into Lindsay Rd. **Mynthurst** 9 km on right.

🚭

Bedrooms	Qty
Double	2
Twin	1
Single	1
Bed Size	**Qty**
Super King/Twin	1
Double + Cot	1/1
Single	3
Bathrooms	**Qty**
Ensuite	1
Private	1
Guest Share	
Family Share	

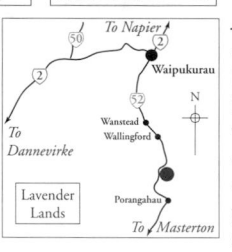

LAVENDER LANDS
3505 Porangahau Road, Wallingford
Hawkes Bay
Ph (06) 855 5525, Fax (06) 855 5526
e-mail: *patcon@bigfoot.com*

Features & Attractions

- Serene and tranquil setting
- Magnificent, safe beaches nearby
- Comfortable, elegant old homestead
- Dinner by arrangement
- Golf links
- Laundry available

**Farmstay
Bed & Breakfast**

$		
Double	$80
Single	$65
Child	$25

Bedrooms	Qty
Double	1
Twin	1
Single	
Bed Size	**Qty**
King	
Queen	1
Single	2
Bathrooms	**Qty**
Ensuite	
Private	1
Guest Share	
Family Share	

A captivating turn of the century grand old homestead set amongst landscaped gardens, mature trees and rolling countryside, 25min. from Waipukurau and 10min. from Porangahau's golden beach and golf links (Neal enjoys any excuse for a game of golf and will be glad to join you). Relax on the verandah under the wisteria, enjoy the views of rolling hills, or explore the countryside and magnificent beaches dotting the coastline. Bedrooms open to the lawn where in the warmer months you can enjoy food gathered from the farm and garden, or when cold seated beside a roaring fire. Come and share in our bounty. We are retired lecturers, Ruth is English and Neal a Kiwi, and have travelled extensively. Having lived and worked for 20 years in Asia we are able to converse fluently in Indonesian.

DIRECTIONS: Coming from north cross straight over Waipukurau's main street into Porangahau Road. After 35 km find us on the left at #3505. From south turn right at end of Waipukurau's main street - then as above.

THE HERMYTAGE
158 Arthur Road, RD 11
Norsewood, Southern Hawkes Bay
Ph (06) 374 0735 Fax (06) 374 0735
Mobile 025-847 418
e-mail: *hermy@ihug.co.nz*

Features & Attractions

- Quiet, peaceful area
- Scandinavian settlement
- Historic village museum
- Dinner by arrangement
- Tea and coffee facilities
- Laundry available

**Farmstay
Bed & Breakfast**

$		
Double	$80
Single	$65
Child	

Bedrooms	Qty
Double	1
Twin	
Single	
Bed Size	**Qty**
King	
Queen	1
Single	1
Bathrooms	**Qty**
Ensuite	1
Private	
Guest Share	
Family Share	

Guests will be warmly welcomed to our spacious home, where you can relax and enjoy the peace of the country, or be included in the farm activities.
We live on a dairy heifer grazing block and have a town-supply dairy farm.Our district is steeped in Scandinavian history with a very interesting museum. We have a golf course just around the corner, and you can do a day tramp in the Ruahine Ranges.
The men run a hay contracting business and you are welcome to watch the harvesting if you wish.
Waken from a refreshing night's sleep to the aroma of home-made bread and a nourishing breakfast. Then Wayne will take you for a tour of the dairy farm and points of interest in the district.
We enjoy people, love entertaining and a good game of cards, especially 500.

DIRECTIONS
From Upper Norsewood go over the overhead bridge over the highway. Turn left - 100m - then right into Arthur Road. We are 1.5km on the right.

DESTINATIONS MOTOR LODGE

197 High Street, Dannevirke, Southern Hawkes Bay
Ph (06) 374 8055, Fax (06) 374 8655
e-mail: *destinations.motel@xtra.co.nz*

Tariff : N.Z. Dollars	
Double	$98-118
Single	$89-104
Child	P.O.A.

Bedrooms	Qty
Double	10
Twin	2
Single	
Bed Size	**Qty**
Super King	
King	2
Queen	8
Single	4
Bathrooms	**Qty**
Ensuite	12
Private	
Guest Share	
Family Share	

Qualmark
Your Sign of Quality

**Bed & Breakfast
Quality Motor Lodge**

Features & Attractions

- *Very central "stop-over" enroute to Hawkes Bay, Wellington, Interislander*
- *Easy to find on State Highway 2*
- *Farm or country garden tours arranged*
- *Great rural visits*
- *Superb rural restaurants nearby*
- *Spa bath units*
- *Guest laundry*

We offer you warm country hospitality in our beautifully appointed Qualmark ★★★★+ rated complex. You have the choice of studio units with ensuite bathroom and kitchenette or one and two bedroom apartment-style units with spa bath in the ensuite and fully equipped kitchen. All rooms feature microwave oven, fridge, hair dryer, radio-alarm, telephone, iron and ironing board.

A continental or cooked breakfast will be delivered to your room with the morning paper.

There are superb restaurants within walking distance (some will deliver evening meals to you) or if you prefer, you can buy local produce and cook for yourself. Dannevirke was originally a Scandinavian settlement and is now a prosperous service and marketing centre for the surrounding dairy, beef and sheep farms and manufacturing plants. If you would like to visit a local farm or country garden and have morning or afternoon tea with a farming family, we can arrange that for you. We are easy to find – just north of the shops on the main highway. Our Travelwise guests are extra special - **do let us know, if you are travelling with Travelwise!**

PLAISTED PARK HOMESTAY

11 Feltham Street,
Hunterville,
Rangitikei
Ph (06) 322 8215, Fax (06) 322 8215

Tariff : N.Z. Dollars	
Double	$75-120
Single	$45-60
Child	

Bedrooms	Qty
Double	1
Twin	2
Single	
Bed Size	**Qty**
Super King	
King	
Queen	1
Single	4
Bathrooms	**Qty**
Ensuite	2
Private	1
Guest Share	
Family Share	

 Homestay Bed & Breakfast

Features & Attractions

- *Tranquil setting*
- *5 acres of park*
- *Lovely bush walks*
- *Garden tours*
- *Golf - unique course*
- *Excellent fishing*
- *Antique shops & cafés*
- *Dinner by arrangement*

Map showing To Auckland, Hunterville, Plaisted Park Homestay, Feltham St., To Wellington, N.

Plaisted Park offers you tranquility, privacy and our house is just two minutes from State Highway One and five minutes walk from Hunterville township. Our warm and spacious home is secluded in five acres of park with many native trees and bush walks including sixty-year-old rhododendrons, a giant redwood tree and a variety of native birds. The house, built for the local solicitor in 1927, is ideal for entertaining friends and guests. Our bedrooms are comfortable with garden views, there is a family room and a spacious lounge. Local attractions are fishing, jet boating, rafting, and garden walks, 'Rathmoy' and 'The Ridges' are but two of the beautiful gardens to visit locally. The Rangitira Golf Course is a must for golfers – it is unique with six holes on three levels, returning from the eighteenth by cable car.

A three-course dinner is available by arrangement – $25 per person, and there are two local cafés.

ROTHESAY

10 Bruce Street, Hunterville
Ph (06) 322 8122
e-mail: *d-r.mcnie@xtra.co.nz*

Features & Attractions
- *Golf courses*
- *Bungy jumping*
- *Trout fishing*
- *Jet boating, river rafting*
- *Skiing*
- *Antique & Craft shops*

	Double	$90-100
Historic Bed & Breakfast	Single	$60
	Child	neg.

R othesay, previously the Hunterville post office, was built in 1903. A heritage building listed with Historic Places Trust Category 1. This lovely old building, close to SH 1, has been tastefully renovated and converted to superior guest accommodation on the first floor with large comfortable bedrooms and separate guest lounge. Our garden with stream is a perfect place to relax in after a day of travel. Your hosts Robyn and Duncan welcome you and invite you to experience the ambience of a bygone era. The atmosphere at **Rothesay** is friendly, relaxed and informal. A hearty breakfast is included and dinner is provided by arrangement. Hunterville is centrally located in the lower North Island region of the Rangitikei and is an ideal place for exploration. The surrounding area offers stunning scenery, many attractive gardens to visit, as well as numerous other activities.

Bedrooms	Qty
Double	3
Twin	1
Single	
Bed Size	**Qty**
Queen	3
Double	1
Single	1
Bathrooms	**Qty**
Ensuite	2
Private	
Guest Share	1
Family Share	

OPERIKI

River Road 3302, RD 6
Wanganui
Ph (06) 342 8159

Features & Attractions
- *Working farm*
- *Hill country walks*
- *Dinner Bed and Breakfast*
- *Overlook Whanganui River*
- *Macadamia orchard*
- *Canoeing, jet boat rides*

	Double	$70
	Single	$35
	Child	Half price

Farmstay Dinner, Bed & Breakfast

Bedrooms	Qty
Double	1
Twin	1
Single	
Bed Size	**Qty**
King	
Queen/Double	1
Single	2
Bathrooms	**Qty**
Ensuite	
Private	
Guest Share	
Family Share	1

DIRECTIONS: Turn off SH 4 into Whanganui River Road. **Operiki** is 33 km from turn off. Approximately 1 hour drive from Wanganui (45 km).

W e have a working sheep and cattle farm, with a few deer and a macadamia orchard - overlooking the Whanganui River en route to the Bridge to Nowhere.
Enjoy a country walk and picnic or other farm activities - according to season.
Links to other river attractions can be arranged: Canoeing, jet boat rides, horse riding, mountain bike riding.
Explore the Whanganui River history from Operiki.
Dinner is available by arrangement, $20 per person, 1/2 price for children, lunch included where necessary.

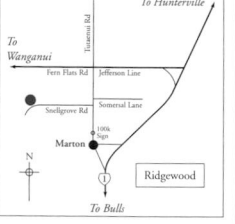

RIDGEWOOD

Rural # 5990, Snellgrove Road, RD 2, Marton
Ph (06) 327 8887, Fax (06) 327 8767
Mobile 025-467 057
e-mail: *gayg@rangitikei.co.nz*
http://www.rangitikei.co.nz/ridgewood.htm

  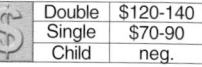

Features & Attractions

- *100 year old historic homestead*
- *Private guest wing*
- *Dinner by arrangement*
- *Email and fax facilities*
- *Gardens and bush walks*
- *Golfing, fishing, rafting*

Farmstay Bed & Breakfast

Double	$120-140
Single	$70-90
Child	neg.

Want to escape to the tranquility of a peaceful retreat? **Ridgewood** is a delightfully restored historic homestead, where you will enjoy warm hospitality and gracious living in tasteful "old world" charm. Idyllically nestled in acres of private native bush with mature rhododendrons and camellias fringing the large garden and tennis court, **Ridgewood** commands one of the best vistas in the Rangitikei. Experience activities of a sheep and cattle farm, play a game of tennis or just amble and watch the Cape Baron Geese, hand-reared pheasants, peacock and varieties of pure-bred land and water fowl free range the farm. Children always welcome. Two hours drive from Wellington. Bookings recommended. Come visit and enjoy the ambience of **Ridgewood Farm**.

Bedrooms	Qty
Double	2
Twin	2
Single	
Bed Size	**Qty**
Double	2
Single	4
Porta-cot	1
Bathrooms	**Qty**
Ensuite	
Private	1
Guest Share	1
Family Share	

From Marton Township Shell Service Station, travel north on Tutaenui Rd till you reach the 100k sign. Snellgrove Rd (no exit road) is the 2nd on your left 3.8 km on. **Ridgewood** is 1st carriageway on your right ¹/₂ km up Snellgrove Rd.

THE PHOENIX

102/104 West Street, Feilding
Ph (06) 323 9463, Fax (03) 323 9463
Mobile 025 679 4221
e-mail: *eyule@clear.net.nz*
http://www.phoenixhomestay.com

Features & Attractions

- *Cont. or cooked breakfast*
- *Full kitchen facilities*
- *Pets welcome*
- *Dinner/lunch by arrangement*
- *Courtesy transfer avail.*
- *Fully equipped laundry*

Double	$150
Single	$120
Child	

Self-contained Homestay

Bedrooms	Qty
Double	2
Twin	
Single	
Bed Size	**Qty**
King	
Queen	2
Single	
Bathrooms	**Qty**
Ensuite	2
Private	
Guest Share	
Family Share	

Originally built in the 1940's, but recently redesigned by Brian Elliott of Designgroup Elliott Architects to a modern Homestay/Bed & Breakfast facility.

The Phoenix comprises two individually designed bedrooms complete with ensuites. There is a large lounge, fully equippped kitchen and laundry, with decking at the front of the facility and private decking at the rear.

The Phoenix is located alongside the home of hosts Elaine and Nook Yule, which was the original Feilding Manse built 100 years ago. Feilding, located in the Manawatu region, offers a unique look at rural New Zealand.

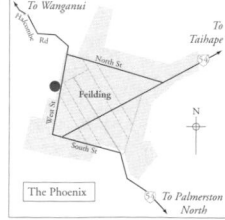

Ro Nali

11 Mountain View Road,
Palmerston North
Ph/Fax (06) 357 6551, Mobile 025-477 456

Features & Attractions

- *Quiet, comfortable home*
- *Panoramic views*
- *Warm hospitality*
- *Close to city and restaurants*
- *Walking tracks & golf courses*
- *Contin. & cooked breakfast*

Double	$75	
Single	$45	
Child		

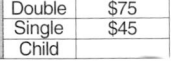

**Homestay
Bed & Breakfast**

Bedrooms	Qty
Double	1
Twin	
Single	
Bed Size	**Qty**
King	
Queen/Double	1
Single	
Bathrooms	**Qty**
Ensuite	
Private	1
Guest Share	
Family Share	

Relax and enjoy rooms with a view in our spacious, comfortable home overlooking Palmerston North city and mountains. Close proximity to Massey University, International Pacific College, the beautiful esplanade gardens and the Lido swimming complex, golf courses and many interesting walking tracks. Feel free to wander around our garden too and listen to the tuis and bellbirds in season. We are ex farmers and enjoy meeting tourists. Our interests are gardening, walking, travel, and Ron plays golf.

Our home is smoke free inside, and we have off-street parking for your vehicle. Please phone for reservations if this sounds right for you.

Typical New Zealand café scene.

LARKHALL
42 The Strand, Palmerston North
Ph (06) 353 3749, Fax (06) 353 3748
Mobile 025-416 890

Tariff : N.Z. Dollars		
	Double	$130
	Single	$100
	Child	

Bedrooms	Qty
Double	1
Twin	1
Single	
Bed Size	**Qty**
Super King	
King	1
Queen	
King Single	2
Bathrooms	**Qty**
Ensuite	2
Private	
Guest Share	
Family Share	

 Luxury Accommodation Homestay Bed & Breakfast

Features & Attractions

- *First class accommodation*
- *Quiet, peaceful location*
- *Great rural visits*
- *Indoor heated pool*
- *Private luxury facilities*
- *Outstanding views*
- *Close to City and University*
- *Within City boundary*

A stunning, newly created up-market home with picturesque views of Palmerston North City and the Manawatu Region. Your hosts, John and Lyndall, have a wealth of local knowledge and international experience. They can assist and direct you to a wide selection of sights and activities. Palmerston North, apart from local attractions, is on the central pathway leading to Wellington (New Zealand capital and Harbour City), Kapiti Coast and West Coast beaches, Lake Taupo (trout-fishing and unique scenery), Mount Ruapehu (skiing in winter months) and the Hawkes Bay (Art Deco and world-class vineyards of New Zealand). An added attraction is that Palmerston North is a centre of major agricultural, educational (Massey University and International Pacific College), business and sporting (Adidas Rugby Academy and museum) activities and interests. Palmerston North Airport offers domestic and international services.

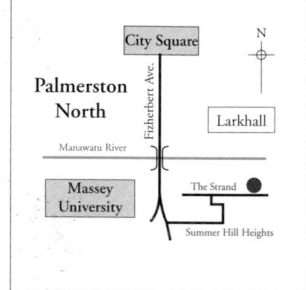

John and Lyndall invite you to enjoy the scenery and native dell as you take in the views from the patio. A warm welcome awaits you.

142

THE PALM & OAKS

183 Grey Street, Palmerston North
Ph (06) 359 0755, Fax(06) 359 0756
Mobile 025-232 7863
e-mail: *enquiries@thepalm-oaks.co.nz*
http://www.thepalm-oaks.co.nz

Tariff : N.Z. Dollars	
Double	$125-250
Single	
Child	

Bedrooms	Qty
Double	4
Twin	
Single	
Bed Size	**Qty**
Super King	
King	
Queen	3
Single	2
Bathrooms	**Qty**
Ensuite	2/3
Private	
Guest Share	1
Family Share	

**Luxury
Self-contained Villa**

Features & Attractions

- *Innovative architecture*
- *Exclusive use of villa*
- *Golf - 4 courses nearby*
- *Herbs/health/honey*
- *Quality restaurants nearby*
- *Central, 5 min. walk to CBD*
- *Spa pool, tennis court on site*
- *Palmerston North Airport/Massey 10 min*

The Palm & Oaks is a luxurious self contained villa, nestled between an established orchard and tennis court. The villa has an Italian/Deco style, an elegance of simple lines and striking contrasts in design and décor, set in illuminated Mediterranian walled gardens enhanced with relaxing water features that grace the outdoors. The villa is self catering with luxurious full house facilities and state of the art kauri/rimu kitchen. The four bedrooms are sunny with quality beds and cotton linen and ensuite access.

Provisions for breakfast at your leisure include fresh eggs, continental selection and homemade conserves on day of arrival.

The villa is within easy walking distance to shops, quality restaurants, Regent theatre, public and private hospitals. **The Palm & Oaks** is ideal for special occasions, corporate meetings, corporate/international visitors, for short/medium stays.

Retreat, relax and replenish and treat yourself to inner city life in style at **The Palm & Oaks**.

FANTAILS ACCOMMODATION

40 MacArthur Street, Levin,
Kapiti /Horowhenua
Ph (06) 368 9011, Fax (06) 368 9279
e-mail: *fantails@xtra.co.nz*
www.fantails.co.nz

Tariff : N.Z. Dollars	
Double	$100-120
Single	$60-80
Child	neg.

Bedrooms	Qty
Double	3
Twin	1
Single	
Bed Size	**Qty**
King	1
Queen	1
Double	1
Single	5
Bathrooms	**Qty**
Ensuite	3
Private	1
Guest Share	
Family Share	

DIRECTIONS: Please
Phone for easy directions

 Bed & Breakfast Homestay & Self-contained Cottages

Features & Attractions

* Quiet, peaceful surrounding
* Cafés, antique shops
* River rafting, horse riding
* Gardens, vintage cars, museums
* Tramping, bird attractions
* Golf courses, mountain biking

Organic food a speciality.

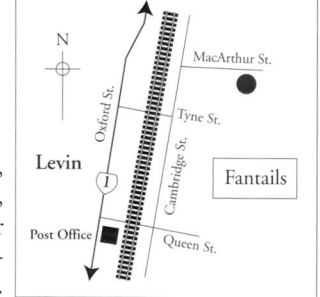

The Fantails, a hidden oasis of native bush, mature trees, native birds and other species, all set in two acres of park-like gardens. Heather and Peter have lovingly restored their English-style home, to provide guests with every comfort. Aga cooking and central heating for those winter days. Organic food also cooked by this method. Breakfasts with such a lovely view of fantails, pigeons and other birdlife. All bedrooms in the house have a lovely view to the garden. Evening meals are provided if required. If you feel like a longer break, we can provide extra eats for that period. Courtesy transport and tours can be arranged to other bird attractions and many more activities. Levin is a great place to stop when travelling to the South Island or heading north from the Ferry Terminal, only 1 hour away. Excellent climate.

We also have self-contained cottages (two – four people). Ideal for honeymoons or anniversaries and just getting away to relax. A mini lavendar field and much more when you come and stay at the friendly **Fantails**. Browse through our Gifts and Souvenirs shop.

SERENDIPITY

1236R State Highway 1, Manakau, Otaki/Levin
Ph (06) 362 6031, Fax (06) 362 6331
Mobile 021-326 303
e-mail: *bookings@serendipitynz.co.nz*
http://www.serendipitynz.co.nz

NEW ZEALAND
FARM & HOME
HOSTS

Tariff : N.Z. Dollars		
	Double	$100-130
	Single	$80-110
	Child	

Bedrooms	Qty
Double	3
Twin	
Single	
Bed Size	**Qty**
Super King	1
King	
Queen	2
Single	1
Bathrooms	**Qty**
Ensuite	2
Private	
Guest Share	1
Family Share	

      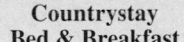 Countrystay Bed & Breakfast

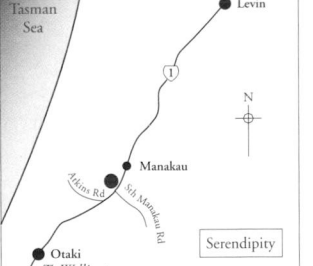

Features & Attractions

- *1 hour from Wellington*
- *Superb uncrowded beaches*
- *Campervans welcome*
- *Mini farm*
- *Air-conditioned bedrooms*
- *Vintage cars, museums*
- *Visits to organic farms may be arranged*

Chris and Barbara invite you to unwind and relax at **Serendipity.** Our home has an extensive garden with both  mature and new plantings for you to enjoy. Native trees have been especially planted to encourage our native birds to visit. Enjoy a generous breakfast that includes homemade preserves and free-range eggs. We can also offer, by arrangement, an evening meal, featuring New Zealand produce and wines. We are able to provide tasty picnic lunches for day trips, as you explore our lovely area, or packed lunch boxes for your onward travel. Quiet air-conditioned rooms, furnished with your comfort in mind.

Manakau is ideally situated: one hour from the Inter Island Ferry, close to the attractions of the Kapiti Coast and Horowhenua – glorious beaches, great picnic spots, river adventures, tramping or guided walks, museums, antique shops, cafés, restaurants, gardens and golf courses.

We have travelled extensively and enjoy meeting people from all around the world.

"NAUMAI" OTAKI GRACIOUS LADY

112 Waerenga Road, Otaki, Kapiti Coast
Ph (06) 364 8440

e-mail: *naumai-kapiti@xtra.co.nz*
http://www.travelwise.co.nz

Features & Attractions

- *Warm hospitality*
- *Quiet peaceful garden*
- *Inter-Island Ferry 1 hour*
- *Off-street parking*
- *Historic Otaki*
- *Wheelchair friendly*

Double	$80
Single	$55
Child	

Historical Boutique Accomodation

Bedrooms	Qty
Double	1
Twin	2
Single	
Bed Size	Qty
King	
Queen/Double	1
Single	4
Bathrooms	Qty
Ensuite	
Private	
Guest Share	1
Family Share	

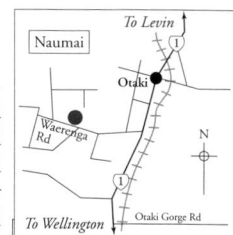

DIRECTIONS:
Turn off SH 1. At New World Supermaket into Waerenga Road, travel 500 m to B&B sign.

Enjoy a stay in our restored 1911 Edwardian Villa. **"Naumai"** is an historic home built in rimu, matai and kauri timbers, with original high ceilings, wide doors and stained glass windows. **"Naumai"** is set in an old world garden with magnolias, kowhai holly ewe and three lovely walnut trees. It has an orchard of citrus, crab apple and plum trees. Otaki is rich in native Maori history and culture with the Te Wananga O Raukawa, the Maori University: Pukekaraka Maori mission, with the historical St Mary Catholic Church. We can arrange for you to visit Kapiti Island and experience its rare endangered native bird life. "Naumai" is a good base to visit Wellington and Te Papa, the National Museum or travel on the inter-island ferries to the South Island.

HURUNUI HOMESTEAD

15 Hurunui Street
Waikanae
Ph (04) 902 8571, Fax (04) 902 8572
e-mail: *hurunui@lineham.co.nz*
www.hurunui.lineham.co.nz

Features & Attractions

- *Romantic Secluded Gardens*
- *Swimming Pool & Private Spa*
- *Tennis Court & Petanque*
- *50minutes from Wellington*
- *Native Birds & Forest Walk*
- *Private Idyllic Paradise*

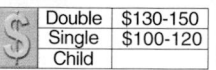

Double	$130-150
Single	$100-120
Child	

Exquisite Bed & Breakfast Superior Accommodation

Bedrooms	Qty
Double	2
Twin	
Single	1
Bed Size	Qty
King	
Queen/Double	3
Single	
Bathrooms	Qty
Ensuite	1
Private	1
Guest Share	
Family Share	

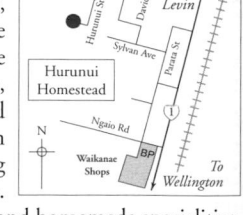

From welcome refreshments on arrival to the exquisite surroundings, on-site facilities and unexpected extras, you will feel especially welcome, pampered and relaxed. Wake to birdsong from your beautifully decorated room in the upstairs guest wing of our large home. Enjoy quality linens, bathrobes, handmade patchwork quilts, fresh flowers and fine china. Formal and casual lounges available (log fires in winter), plus upstairs gallery sitting room with breathtaking pool and garden vistas, and tea and coffee making facilities. Indulgent breakfasts, elegantly served, include seasonal fruits and homemade specialities. 2 acres of gardens and native trees. See and hear NZ native birds in their natural habitat. Erica is an art quilter and guests may visit her studio. Unsuitable children under 10yrs. Smoke-free. Off street parking available. Beach and golf courses nearby. Enjoy!

COUNTRY PATCH

18 Kea Street, Waikanae
Ph (04) 293 5165, Fax (04) 293 5164
Mobile 025- 578 421
e-mail: *countrypatch@actrix.co.nz*
http://www.countrypatch.co.nz

FARM & HOME HOSTS

Tariff : N.Z. Dollars		
	Double	$90-160
	Single	$70-130
	Child	

Bedrooms	Qty
Double	3
Twin	3
Single	
Bed Size	**Qty**
Super King Twin	2
King	
Queen	1
Single	
Bathrooms	**Qty**
Ensuite	3
Private	
Guest Share	
Family Share	

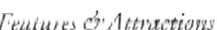
**Self-contained
Bed & Breakfast**

Features & Attractions

- *Delightful country style*
- *Magnificent views*
- *Cosy and comfortable*
- *Hearty meals available*

- *2 minutes drive from SH 1*
- *7 min. to Wellington commuter train*
- *Cottage has large verandah and wheelchair access*

It's the little extras.....that keep guests staying an extra night. Our visitor's book glows with appreciative accolades. 2 delightful self-contained accommodation sites....**Country Patch** studio with its own entrance and deck, has a queen bed with ensuite and twin beds on the mezzanine floor of the kitchen-lounge. **Country Patch** cottage has an open fire and large verandah with magic views. It is wheelchair accessible and the two bedrooms (ech with ensuite) have superking beds that can unzip to make twins. Set on 2¹/₂ acres in the Waikanae foothills with breathtaking views over the Kapiti Coast and historic Kapiti Island, the property is handy to Wellington and the Manawatu. Bush walks can be enjoyed from over the back fence. Hosts Brian (homemaker) and Sue (GP) with their children Kate and Simon, and labrador Holly, display an infectious hospitality. Try breakfast of fresh eggs from the house chooks! Superb restaurants are close by, or arrange a hearty meal with Grandma and Grandpa next door.
 A treat you can't beat!

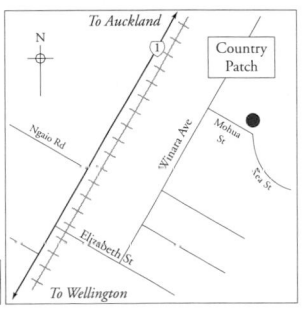

To Auckland
Country Patch
N
Ngaio Rd
Winara Ave
Mahoe St
Kea St
Elizabeth St
To Wellington

Raumati Beach - Kapiti Coast YOUR HOSTS: Brent and Sylvia Henderson   Ph: (04) 902 1388

KAPITI BEACH BED & BREAKFAST
15 Matatua Road, Raumati Beach, Kapiti Coast
Ph (04) 902 1388 Fax (04) 902 1388
Mobile 025-628 6005
e-mail: *brenth@clear.net.nz*
 http://www.kapiti-beach.co.nz

Features & Attractions

- *Beautiful sea views*
- *45 min. Wellington City*
- *Private swimming pool*
- *Discount for self-catering*
- *Short stroll cafés, restaurants*
- *Centrally located*

 Self-contained Bed & Breakfast

Double	$135
Single	$120
Child	$10

Bedrooms	Qty
Double	2
Twin	
Single	
Bed Size	**Qty**
King	
Queen	2
Single	
Bathrooms	**Qty**
Ensuite	
Private	1
Guest Share	
Family Share	

A magical beachside retreat. Literally 20 footsteps to the beach, the cottage opens onto a beautiful view which can be enjoyed from the comfort and serenity of your room. It's a very short stroll to local amenities; restaurants, park, local heated swimming pool, etc. Two rooms with two double beds make it ideal for a getaway, family stay or two couples. Bright and sunny in summer, cosy and warm in winter. Fully equipped kitchenette if self-catering preferred. Relax on private deck or dive into private pool. Laundry, internet, child minding, sea kayaks, mountain bikes also available. Close proximity to local Kapiti attractions: Kapiti Island, Lindale, Southwards Car Museum, golf courses, etc.

DIRECTIONS: North from Wellington, turn left to Raumati Beach on SH 1, 4 km before Paraparaumu. At end of Raumati Rd turn right into Matatua Rd. 1st house on left, beachside.

Waikanae - Wellington   YOUR HOSTS: Eppie and Paul Murton   Ph: (04) 293 1936

RIVERSTONE GARDEN
111 Ngatiawa Road, Waikanae, Kapiti Coast
Ph (04) 293 1936. Fax (04) 293 1936
e-mail: *riverstone@paradise.net.nz*

Features & Attractions

- *Rural self-contained*
- *Local dining out*
- *River and bird song*
- *Bush and local walks*
- *Shops, beach, Lindale*
- *Golf & car museum*

 Rural Homestay Bed & Breakfast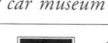

The cottage has self-contained accommodation with bedrooms, bathroom, lounge and kitchenette. Courtyard and barbecue area with views of river and bush. Continental or full breakfast. Paul is an engineer and writer, and Eppie sketches and paints. Laundry facilities. Local café, pottery and birdpark with river walks and you can swim in the river.

There are more restaurants in Waikanae village, six minutes drive, and in Paraparaumu, ten minutes towards Wellington. Craftshops and boutiques at Lindale and general shopping at Paraparaumu. Beaches and swimming pools in both centres. The capital city Wellington is 45 minutes away and has the airport, interisland ferries, modern shops, art galleries and museums.

Double	$90
Single	$60
Child	$45

Bedrooms	Qty
Double	1
Twin	
Single	1
Bed Size	**Qty**
King	
Queen	1
Single	1
Bathrooms	**Qty**
Ensuite	
Private	1
Guest Share	
Family Share	

DIRECTIONS: Turn off SH 1 across railway lines onto Akatarawa Rd. At 5km turn left before small church into Ngatiawa Rd. 1 km to **Riverstone** on left.

BURNARD GARDENS

236 Reikorangi Road, RD, Waikanae
Ph (04) 293 3371, Ph (04) 293 3378
Mobile 025-222 5675
e-mail: *mary@burnardgardens.co.nz*
www.burnardgardens.co.nz

Tariff : N.Z. Dollars	
Double	$100-120
Single	$80-100
Child	$10

Bedrooms	Qty
Double	
Triple	1
Single	
Bed Size	**Qty**
Super King/twin	
King	
Queen	1
Single	1
Bathrooms	**Qty**
Ensuite	
Private	1
Spa Bath	
Guest Share	

**Countrystay Self-contained
Bed & Breakfast**

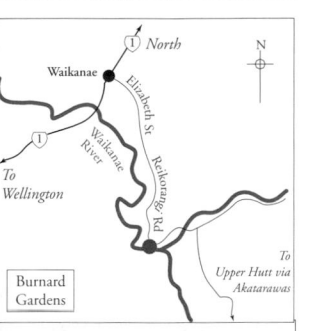

Features & Attractions

- Beautiful well-known garden
- Private, safe swimming hole
- Restaurants & shops nearby
- Spacious self-contained accom.
- Quiet, peaceful surroundings
- Tennis court
- Dutch, French
  and German understood

The house and attached self-contained guest accommodation, built in 1986, is located in the picturesque Reikorangi Valley on twenty acres, ten of which have been developed into a landscaped English-style garden with herbaceous borders, a rose garden, spring garden, woodland garden and a vegetable garden, all set against a natural native bush backdrop and bounded by the Waikanae River. The garden, which is a popular venue for weddings, special functions and group garden visits, is open from mid-September to the end of March. The accommodation unit is available throughout the year. It is very spacious and occupies the attic area of a 3-car garage directly behind the house. There is a kitchenette with dining facilities and a lounge area (with TV, radio and telephone) as well as a double and a single bed in the same room. A private bathroom with shub/shower is downstairs.

We are semi-retired. Robert is a lawyer and Mary a garden writer and landscape designer. We have travelled extensively in NZ and overseas and lived in the USA, England, Holland and Switzerland. (Mary understands and speaks conversational Dutch, German and French).

DIRECTIONS: Travelling north from Wellington on SH1 turn right at Waikanae traffic lights and drive towards Reikorangi for 3km.

149

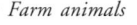
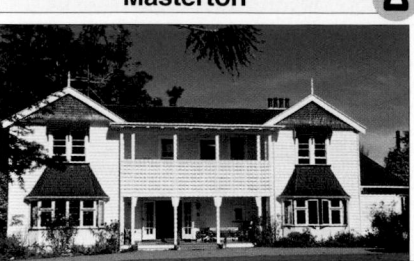

LLANDAFF COUNTRY RESIDENCE

155 Upper Plain Road, RD 8 Masterton
Ph (06) 378 6628. Fax (06) 378 6612
e-mail: *llandaff@xtra.co.nz*

Features & Attractions

- *Historic 1880 homestead*
- *Rural elegance*
- *Farm animals*
- *Close to wineries*
- *Near wildlife reserve*
- *Less than 5 min. to town*

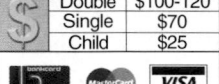

Double	$100-120
Single	$70
Child	$25

Boutique Bed & Breakfast

Llandaff Country Residence is a large historic 1880 homestead, now operating as a boutique Bed & Breakfast. Elegantly restored, the homestead boasts beautiful original New Zealand timbers throughout, wood paneled rooms, polished floors, spacious bedrooms, old pull-handle toilets, a "coffin" bath, open fireplaces and a cosy wood-burning kitchen stove.

Explore the historic hayloft and stables, washhouse, dunny, produce shed, gardener's shed, pavilion and dove cote. Soak up the peaceful country atmosphere, relax in the majestic garden beneath 120 year old trees, or wander the farm and feed the animals. Bike riding, cricket, croquet and petanque are available to guests. Enjoy a country cooked breakfast, dinner is provided on request. **LLandaff Country Residence** is less than 5 minutes to town and restaurants, yet is located 1 km off the road in quiet countryside.

Bedrooms	Qty
Double	2
Twin	1
Single	
Bed Size	**Qty**
King	
Queen	2
King Single	2
Bathrooms	**Qty**
Ensuite	
Private	
Guest Share	2
Family Share	

SOUTHEY MANOR

182 West Street
Greytown
Ph (06) 304 9367, Fax (06) 304 9789
Mobile 025-424 035

Features & Attractions

- *Spacious, relaxed atmosphere*
- *Walk to village shops*
- *Swimming pool & barbecue*
- *Cafes, restaurants nearby*
- *Only ten minutes to golf course and vineyard*

Double	$80-90
Single	$45-80
Child	

Bed & Breakfast

Bedrooms	Qty
Double	2
Twin	1
Single	
Bed Size	**Qty**
King	
Queen	2
Single	2
Bathrooms	**Qty**
Ensuite	1
Private	
Guest Share	1
Family Share	

Our home offers a spacious relaxed atmosphere. We enjoy guests' company, but respect their desire for privacy if they need to just relax.

We are situated within walking distance from Greytown's cafés, restaurants and village shops. Ten minutes drive to Martinborough's vineyard and golf course. Facilities include a queen bedroom with ensuite, twin bedroom and queen bedroom with shared bathroom, lounge andsatellite TV.

Outdoor areas with pool and barbecue. Tariff includes continental breakfast at your leisure.

We look forward to your company.

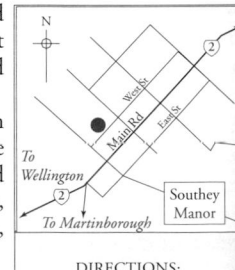

DIRECTIONS:
Please phone for easy directions.

CARRBRIDGE HOUSE
31 Andrew Street, Masterton
Ph(06) 370 2999, Fax (06) 370 2950
e-mail: *hols@xtra.co.nz*

Tariff : N.Z. Dollars	
Double	$100-120
Single	$90
Child	

Bedrooms	Qty
Double	2
Twin	
Single	
Bed Size	**Qty**
Super King	
King	
Queen	2
Single	
Bathrooms	**Qty**
Ensuite	2
Private	
Guest Share	
Family Share	

Country - Homestay

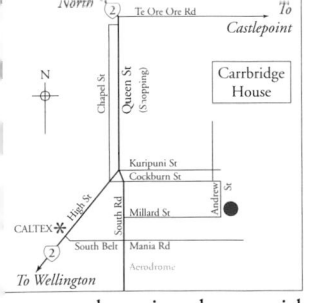

Features & Attractions

- *Park-like grounds*
- *Rural setting*
- *Generous breakfast*
- *Bicycles, croquet, petanque*
- *Wineries, gardens, crafts*
- *Golf courses, hot air ballooning*
- *Mt Bruce Wildlife Centre*
- *Smoking is allowed on verandahs*

Carrbridge House offers you a relaxing stay in our comfortable home, situated on 4 acres of rural Masterton. On your arrival you will be welcomed into our warm and spacious home with afternoon tea. Our guest bedrooms both have ensuites, one having TV and its own private lounge attached. Settle into the well appointed rooms with cut flowers, complimentary port, bath robes and hairdryers, or just relax on the large verandahs which each room opens onto. Start the day with a generous country breakfast which includes fresh fruit, home-made fare, including muffins, muesli and a cooked option. All this can be enjoyed in the dining room or on the verandah. For your additional relaxation we offer petanque, croquet and bicycles. An ideal base to go visiting the many scenic attractions, vineyards and restaurants. We have travelled widely ourselves and made friends in many places. We look forward to making your visit a memorable one.

TERRACOTTA LODGE
6 Rutland Road, Carterton
Ph (06) 379 5583, Fax (06) 379 5593
Mobile 025-732 962
e-mail: *ronaldvkeene@xtra.co.nz*
http://www.wairarapa.co.nz/terracottalodge

Tariff : N.Z. Dollars	
Double	$160
Single	$120
Child	

Bedrooms	Qty
Double	2
Twin	1
Single	
Bed Size	**Qty**
Super King	
King	
Queen	2
Single	2
Bathrooms	**Qty**
Ensuite	3
Private	
Guest Share	
Family Share	

  Luxury Homestay

Features & Attractions

- *Scenic country setting*
- *Home with historic connections*
- *Dine with your hosts*
- *Tours and activities arranged*

- *Extensive gardens*
- *Craft studio*
- *Hot spa pool*
- *Petanque court*

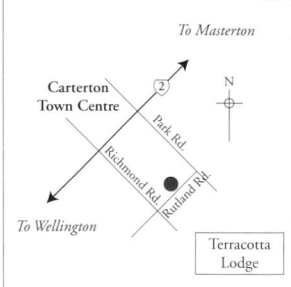

Nestled in five acres with large established gardens and developing orchard, **Terracotta Lodge** is an idyllic home away from home with all the amenities of a luxury lodge. While away your time with a book from the library, play petanque, take a relaxing hot spa, visit the doll and gift studio or just wander the garden and take in the warm Wairarapa sunshine. You will enjoy the individual attention given by your hosts, Kaye and Ron Keene, and the delicious breakfasts included in the room rates. Bush walks in the nearby Tararua Park, hot air ballooning, river or sea fishing, golf at one of the four local golf courses, craft and wine trails are some of the many leisure activities close by.

Your hosts will help you plan relaxing days before your return to the Lodge for dinner by arrangement. Both Ron and Kaye are excellent chefs and innovative four-course dinners, at $60 per person including wine, using the fresh produce of the Wairarapa, are an additional delight to conclude a day of enjoyment of the Wairarapa.

THE AMBERS

78 Kuratawhiti Street, Greytown, Wairarapa
Ph (06) 304 8588. Fax (06) 304 8590
Mobile 025-994 394
e-mail: *ambershomestay@xtra.co.nz*
http://www.ambershomestay.co.nz

Tariff : N.Z. Dollars	
Double	$90-110
Single	$65
Child	$20

Bedrooms	Qty
Double	3
Twin	
Single	
Bed Size	**Qty**
Super King	
King	1
Queen	2
Single	
Bathrooms	**Qty**
Ensuite	1
Private	1
Guest Share	1
Family Share	

**Boutique Accommodation
Bed & Breakfast**

DIRECTIONS:
North through Greytown
to old post office, turn left,
past cricket grounds to
78 Kuratawhiti Street
'The Ambers'.

Features & Attractions

- *Glorious garden setting*
- *Close to wineries*
- *Beautiful breakfast*

- *Cafés and antique shops*
- *Quiet, peaceful surrounds*
- *Cosy open fire*

The Ambers is nestled in two acres of garden with many old trees. Our guest wing is separate enough to provide you with privacy without feeling isolated from us.

We offer guests secluded verandahs, a spa pool and a guest lounge with open fire.

The **Cherub Room** has a queen bed and private bathroom. The **Vintage Room** has a king bed with ensuite bathroom. If two couples wish to share a bathroom, we have our **Oak Aged Room** with double bed.

Breakfast includes homemade muffins and fresh fruit in season. We are within walking distance of Greytown's Main Street with unique wooden Victorian architecture, cafés and 10 minutes drive to Martinborough's vineyards.

WHISPERING PINES

207 Colletts Road, RD 1, Mangaroa, Upper Hutt
Ph (04) 526 7785, Fax (04) 526 7785
Mobile: 025 233 0999
e-mail: *whisperingpines@xtra.co.nz*

Tariff : N.Z. Dollars		
Double	$100
Single	$60
Child	neg.

Bedrooms	Qty
Double	1
Twin	1
Single	1
Bed Size	**Qty**
Super King	
Queen/Double	1
King/Single	3
Single	1
Bathrooms	**Qty**
Ensuite	1
Private	
Guest Share	1
Family Share	

**Farmstay
Bed & Breakfast**

Features & Attractions

- *Spacious and comfortable*
- *Enchanting views*
- *Dinner by arrangement*
- *Comfortable, firm beds*
- *Out of town stopover (ferry/airport)*
- *Peaceful location*
- *Home-grown produce in season*
- *67 acres (27 hectares) of farmland*

Our spacious Swiss Chalet style home has a Douglas Fir theme and is set at the end of Colletts Road on 67 acres of elevated farmland. A quiet location with enchanting views, overlooking the north end of the Mangaroa Valley.

We breed pedigree Hereford cattle and also keep coloured sheep, goats, poultry, bees, a collie dog and one cat. It is an ideal out-of-town stopover, when you travel to or from the Wellington Ferry or just want to get away for a change.

Our travels have taken us to many countries. Now semi-retired, we particularly enjoy meeting people from around the world. The farm, garden and handcrafts along with our local Church keep us active.

You may wish to join us for a three-course evening meal, which usually consists of produce from our farm, garden and orchard, all grown without artificial fertilizer.

Please contact us for reservations at earliest convenience. We are 6 km from SH 2.

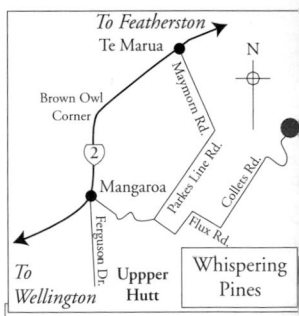

DIRECTIONS:
Please phone for bookings and easy directions. We are only 6km from State Highway 2.

ARAWA HOMESTEAD

280 Paekakariki Hill Road, Pauatahanui, Wellington
Ph (04) 237 9022, Fax (04) 237 6614
Mobile 021 425 872
e-mail: *contactus@arawahomestead.co.nz*
http://www.arawahomestead.co.nz

Tariff : N.Z. Dollars	
Double	$300
Single	$150
Child	neg.

Bedrooms	Qty
Double	1
Twin	1
Single	1
Bed Size	**Qty**
Super King	1
King	
Queen	
Single	3
Bathrooms	**Qty**
Ensuite	1
Private	1
Guest Share	
Family Share	

   **Luxury Countrystay**

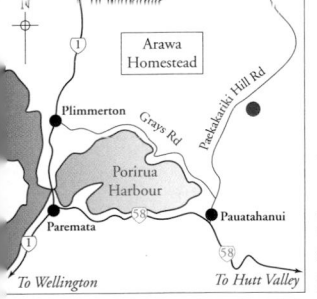

Features & Attractions

- *Luxury and romance*
- *Tranquillity*
- *Log fires, crisp linen*
- *Fresh flowers*
- *Home cooking*
- *Woodland garden*
- *Single party bookings*
- *20-30min. Wellington & ferry*

Built in the early 1850s for a large pioneering family, **Arawa Homestead** is steeped in history. It is still the hub of a 24-hectare (60 acre) farm. The architecture, typical of early colonial New Zealand, has been faithfully restored, featuring leadlights and New Zealand native timbers, complemented by many fine antiques. Nestled in a large woodland garden, surrounded by hills with views of the Pauatahanui countryside, **Arawa Homestead** offers a peaceful, relaxing stay for guests. It's a picture-perfect wedding venue too. The guest wing comprises a spacious super-king ensuite bedroom, a twin and single bedroom with private spa bathroom. Every aspect of your comfort has been carefully considered. Single party bookings are favoured. Wander across the lawns. Enjoy a quiet lunch in the dell beside the reflecting pond, in the fragrant shade of the wisteria-draped patio or in the cool comfort of the gazebo. Relax in the library beside a log fire. Greet the animals on a farm stroll or take a leisurely bush walk and unpack a picnic hamper in the bush reserve where native birds abound. Julie provides New Zealand country cooking using fresh produce for all meals by arrangement. Unwind and enjoy the magic which is **Arawa**.

155

BRAEBYRE

Flightys Road, Pauatahanui, Wellington
Postal: Flightys Road, RD 1, Porirua
Ph (04) 235 9311, Fax (04) 235 9345
e-mail: *braebyre@paradise.net.nz*

Tariff : N.Z. Dollars		
	Double	$100-160
	Single	$90-150
	Child	

Bedrooms	Qty
Double	4
Twin	1
Single	
Bed Size	**Qty**
Super King	1
King	1
Queen	2
Single	2
Bathrooms	**Qty**
Ensuite	3
Private	
Guest Share	1
Family Share	

**Countrystay
Luxury Garden Suites**

VISA MasterCard

Features & Attractions

- *2 studio suites*
- *Large landscaped gardens*
- *Close to Picton Ferry*
- *Dinner by arrangement*
- *Mohair goats and jerseys*
- *Golf courses nearby*
- *Hostlink member*
- *Accommodation for disabled*

A re you looking for something special and restful away from city noise yet easily accessible and just 20 minutes away on major highways? Stay close but not in the city, at **Braebyre**, one of Wellington's fine country homes, nestled in a beautiful rural environment on a small mohair goat farm with four acres of landscaped gardens. You will love the peace and tranquillity and the opportunity to experience seasonal activities with a tour of the garden and the goats. Jenny and Randall (Rotarian) have been hosting fo many years and enjoy the experience. Two new spacious studio suites in the garden are self-contained with wheelchair access. The private guest wing in the house includes a lounge, table tennis and ar indoor spa pool. Evening dinner featuring homegrown produce is available on request. Home baking and preserves are a speciality.

We are a vital link in the active HOSTLINK network of quality homestays throughout New Zealand and are happy to assist with forward bookings.

DIRECTIONS:
Blue Bed & Breakfast sign on State
Highway 58. 2km east of Pauatahanui

PENRYN COVE

32 Penryn Drive, Paremata, Wellington
Ph (04) 233 8265, Fax (04) 233 8265
Mobile 025-815 525
e-mail: *JWClark@xtra.co.nz*

Tariff : N.Z. Dollars	
Double	$110-120
Single	$70
Child	neg.

Bedrooms	Qty
Double	2
Twin	
Single	

Bed Size	Qty
Super King	
King	
Queen	2
Single	

Bathrooms	Qty
Ensuite	
Private	1
Guest Share	1
Family Share	

    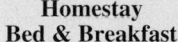

**Homestay
Bed & Breakfast**

Features & Attractions

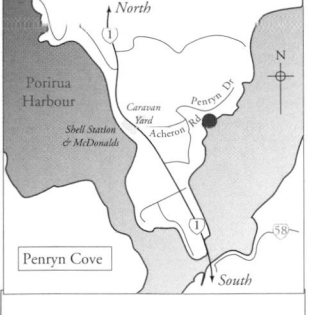

DIRECTIONS:
Two minutes from SH 1. Please
phone for easy directions.

- *Peaceful and tranquil location*
- *Adjoins native bush reserve*
- *Bird sanctuary*
- *Dinner by arrangement*
- *NZ breakfasts and home baking*
- *Close to café and restaurants*
- *2 min. SH 1, 20 min. Wellington*
- *Private and spacious guest area*

We extend a warm welcome to our guests. Enjoy the tranquil, peaceful setting of Penryn Grove, surrounded by native bush reserve, set on the edge of a peninsula, overlooking the picturesque Pauatahanui inlet and bird sanctuary. Private and easy access onto inlet walkway will provide you with some relaxing recreation, or simply relax and enjoy the garden, peace, sun and views on the decks or in our private courtyard and pergola. We have travelled extensively and enjoy meeting and sharing our home with fellow travellers. – Your home away from home.
Easy walking distance café, restaurants, shops, rail and historic Plimmerton village and beach. Private, spacious guest area with magical views, private deck.

157

AQUAVILLA
16 Steyne Avenue, Plimmerton
Ph (04) 233 1146
Mobile 025-231 0141
e-mail: *aquavilla@paradise.net.nz*

Features & Attractions
- *Architecturally designed*
- *Village shops and cafés*
- *Historic seaside village*
- *Close to SH 1 and rail*
- *Next door to beach*
- *20 minutes to ferry*

$		
Double	$120	
Single	$100	
Child	neg.	

Bedrooms	Qty
Double	1
Twin	
Single	
Bed Size	**Qty**
Queen	1
Double Settee	1
Single	1
Bathrooms	**Qty**
Ensuite	
Private	1
Guest Share	
Family Share	

SC — Self-contained
Bed & Breakfast Accom.
BB MasterCard VISA

Plimmerton is a small picturesque seaside village only 20 minutes north of Wellington City. Aquavilla is in the centre of the village with great cafés and shops. You can walk to everything and have the choice of eating in or out. We are only 50 m from one of Wellington's best beaches with sunsets you will never forget. This superior, self-contained unit has a bedroom, kitchenette, lounge, bathroom and its own courtyard. We have travelled extensively overseas and throughout New Zealand. We love art, photography, water sports, travel and the outdoors. Carolyn is an artist photographer, her breakfasts are something you will remember. We love it here and you will too. Ours is a smoke free home.

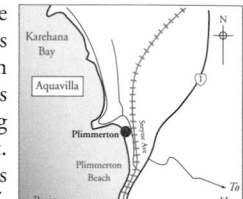

DEVENPORT ESTATE
1 Korokoro Road, Korokoro, Petone, Wellington
Ph (04) 586 6868. Fax (04) 586 6869
VISA
Mobile 025-274 0394
MasterCard
e-mail: *devenport_estate@hotmail.com*
http://homepages.paradise.net.nz/devenpor

Features & Attractions
- *Edwardian-style charm*
- *Unrivalled sea views*
- *Close to Picton Ferry*
- *Free Internet / NZ tollcall*
- *Bohemian restaurants*
- *Continental breakfast*

$		
Double	$100	
Single	$80	
Child		

Bedrooms	Qty
Double	1
Twin	1
Single	
Bed Size	**Qty**
King	
Queen	1
Single	2
Bathrooms	**Qty**
Ensuite	
Private	
Guest Share	1
Family Share	

BA — Vineyard Estate
Private Bed & Breakfast
BB

Stay at the closest vineyard to the capital, only 15 minutes north of Wellington. An Edwardian-style homestead, overlooking Wellington Harbour, built at the turn of the century (2000!) based on the MacDonald family home in Scotland. 400 Pinot Gris grapevines cling to the Korokoro hills around the homestead – inspired by vineyards in the Moselle Valley during a holiday in Germany.

Devenport was built for views and comfort. We offer: guest living room with wood burner and guest bedroom with chairs, TV, writing desk and own hand basin. Two guest toilets. Free Internet access, NZ toll calls after 7pm, laundry service, Petone railway station pickup - see Devenport's website for more details. Ample off-street parking on our 1.2 acre section. Smoking outdoors. Child-stays by appointment. Enjoy the gardens, play petanque or sink back into a deckchair and admire Somes Island. Alasdair, Christopher, Marlene and two cocker spaniels welcome you to a comfortable stay in Wellington on our vineyard estate.

SHALIMARES

9 Shalimar Crescent, Khandallah, Wellington
Ph (04) 479 1776, Fax (04) 479 1786
Mobile 021-895 996
e-mail: *sales@shalimares.co.nz*
http://www.shalimares.co.nz

FARM & HOME HOSTS

Tariff : N.Z. Dollars	
Double	$240-295
Single	$240-295
Child	

Bedrooms	Qty
Double	2
Twin	2
Single	

Bed Size	Qty
Super King	2
King	
Queen	
Single	4

Bathrooms	Qty
Ensuite	1
Private	1
Guest Share	
Family Share	

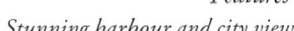
Luxury Bed & Breakfast
Stunning Harbour & City Views

Features & Attractions

- *Stunning harbour and city views*
- *Quiet and tranquil setting*
- *Spacious bedrooms with balconies*
- *Spa bath*
- *3 km to Inter Island Ferry*
- *10 minutes to Te Papa*
- *5 km to central city*
- *Minutes to cafés & restaurants*

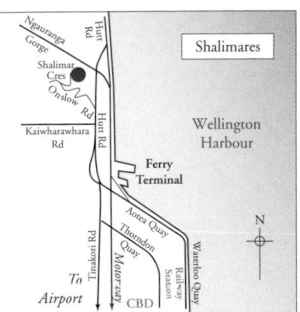

Shalimares is a large modern Mediterranean home. Spacious bedrooms welcome you with balconies for you to enjoy the spectacular harbour and city views. Located in the exclusive Wellington suburb of Khandallah, 3 kilometres to the Inter Island Ferry Terminal, 5 kilometres to the central city attractions and 20 minutes to the Airport.

Many golf courses are within 15-20 minutes drive. Our luxury guest wing has two spacious bedrooms and private lounge with Sky TV, complimentary drinks in fridge, tea and coffee making facilities, fresh fruit and home-made cookies. Jerningham Suite has a dressing room and ensuite with spa bath, bidet, double vanity and shower. The Halswell Room has a private bathroom with shower. Bedrooms have lounge chairs, desks, phones, TV and extra jackpoints for modem connections. Taxis can be arranged for pickup from airport or ferry terminals. Parking available. Laundry and drycleaning service. Caterers can be arranged for special occasions, but prior notice must be given. Our interests are golf, horse racing and watching sports on TV.

HOMESTAY WELLINGTON

56 Fox Street, Ngaio, Wellington
Ph (04) 479 5325, Fax (04) 479 4325
e-mail: *jennifer.timmings@clear.net.nz*
http://www.travelwise.co.nz

Tariff : N.Z. Dollars	
Double	$95-120
Single	$75-100
Child	neg.

Bedrooms	Qty
Double	3
Twin	1
Single	2
Bed Size	**Qty**
Super King	
Queen	1
Double	2
Single	4
Bathrooms	**Qty**
Ensuite	3
Private	1
Guest Share	
Family Share	

**Homestay
Self-contained Accommodation**

Features & Attractions

- *Family home atmosphere*
- *Safe, quiet surroundings*
- *Off-street parking*
- *Extensive views*
- *2 min. walk to local train station*
- *Ferry 5min., city 10min.by car*
- *Booking assistance - tours/ferry*
- *Music salon*

Welcome to Wellington! Capital City of New Zealand, spectacular scenery, beautiful harbour, dramatic skies, the seat of government, home of "Te Papa" National Museum, Westpac Sports Stadium, theatres, art galleries, churches, exciting restaurants and cafés, botanic gardens – it's all happening in Wellington and we love it! Share your Wellington experience with us and enjoy personalised hospitality. We have an unconventional open-plan family home in the suburb of Ngaio. Guests have their own area with french doors opening onto a deck and private garden. Tea/coffee facilities in room. Two single rooms adjacent to ensuite room allow a family to be together yet separate. The two fully furnished apartments are separate from the house, giving guests their own space and independence. Each unit has one double bedroom, bath, shower, laundry, equipped kitchen, couch in lounge converts to additional double bed, cable TV, phone, linen. Our interests are people, music, arts, outdoors. Jennifer is a pianist and Brian formerly an accountant. Breakfast is continental. Evening meals optional, $25 pp. Dinner with live harp music $35pp. Discounts offered for longer stays. Disabled persons may enquire.

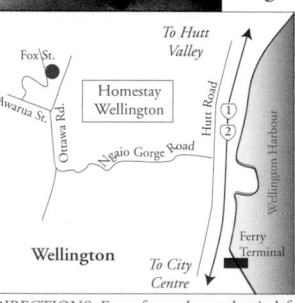

DIRECTIONS: From ferry take north exit, left at first traffic lights – Ngaio Gorge Rd., at roundabout take Ottawa Rd. fork, at shops turn left Awarua St. – Fox St. is second on right. Use driveway at No.56.

Bedrooms	Qty
Double	2
Twin/Triple	1
Single	1
Bed Size	**Qty**
Queen/Double	3
King Single	
Single	2
Bathrooms	**Qty**
Ensuite	2
Private	
Guest Share	1
Family Share	

BOOKLOVERS B & B

123 Pirie Street, Mt. Victoria, Wellington
Ph/Fax (04) 384 2714, Mobile 021-262 3120
e-mail: *booklovers@xtra.co.nz*
http://www.bbnb.co.nz

Features & Attractions

- *Close to downtown*
- *Cafés, theatres, Te Papa*
- *Bus stop and bush walks*
- *Books and magazines*
- *Breakfasts to suit*
- *Big, sunny deck*

Double	$140	
Single	$100	
Child	negotiable	

A Booklovers Bed & Breakfast

For people who love books. Every room has books and magazines, and a table to write on. There's a good New Zealand collection, and a shelf of books you can start here ... and take with you. Your host is a freelance writer, author of best-selling "Convent Girls" and award-winning historical biography "Ettie" (Rout). The 1895 double bay villa, conveniently situated between the airport and downtown, has bus stops outside the gate for trips to downtown, the railway station or stadium. Courtenay Place with its restaurants, cafés and theatres, and the national museum, Te Papa, are comfortably walkable. The city's "green belt" is next door for those who want to ramble through bush (to beach and baths at Oriental Bay).

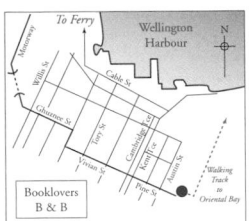

Photos -Evening Post

DREAMCATCHER - ARTS & ACCOMMODATION

56 Pirie Street, Mount Victoria
Ph(04) 801 9363
Mobile 021-210 6762

Features & Attractions

- *Wellington historic suburb*
- *5 minutes stroll to attractions*
- *Spacious, warm VIP suite*
- *Self-contained second story*
- *Helpful hosts*
- *Generous breakfasts*

Arts & Accommodation

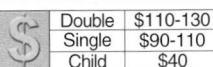

Double	$110-130	
Single	$90-110	
Child	$40	

DreamCatcher is a renovated and restored spacious Victorian house in central, picturesque, historic Mount Victoria, only 5 minutes stroll from Wellington's day/night vibrant attractions. Quality accommodations available – 1. The "VIP suite" - a private living room, double bedroom and ensuite. 2. The "Upstairs" – a self-contained second story includes 2 bedrooms, guest-share bathroom, deck, verandah, living/kitchen area, sun and city views. Art and craft objects everywhere add to the warm ambience. Taly, John, their teenage daughter and two cats, keen travellers themselves, welcome the city visitor to enjoy the relaxed comfort of home and the fresh generous breakfasts served in the main kitchen or back garden. They are able to assist with Wellington holiday experiences.

Bedrooms	Qty
Double	3
Twin	
Single	
Bed Size	**Qty**
Queen	1
Double	2
Single	2
Bathrooms	**Qty**
Ensuite	1
Private	
Guest Share	1
Family Share	

DIRECTIONS: Look for KFC on the corner of Kent Terrace and Vivian Street.
Pirie Street is the road going up Mount Victoria.

MATAI HOUSE

41 Matai Road, Hataitai, Wellington
Ph (04) 934 6985. Fax (04) 934 6987
e-mail: *matai@paradise.net.nz*
http://www.travelwise.co.nz

Tariff : N.Z. Dollars	
Double	$170
Single	$150
Child	

Bedrooms	Qty
Double	2
Twin	
Single	
Bed Size	**Qty**
Super King	
King	2
Queen	
Single	
Bathrooms	**Qty**
Ensuite	2
Private	
Guest Share	
Family Share	

Superior Bed & Breakfast
Beautiful Water Views

Features & Attractions

- *Quiet residential area*
- *Extensive sea views*
- *City 4 min., airport 5 min.*
- *Suites adjoin guest lounge*
- *Delicious full breakfast*
- *Espresso coffee*
- *20 channel cable TV*
- *Ferry 10 min. drive*

Matai House takes its name from its surroundings. Matai, translated from Maori, means "gaze out to sea".

Built in 1913, this fine two storey villa is conveniently located in the eastern inner suburb of Hataitai, between the airport and city. A quiet residential area with great sea views and a small garden of New Zealand native plants. City bus is just a 300 m walk. Off-street car park available.

DIRECTIONS:
On State Highway 1 follow airport signs until exiting Mt. Victoria tunnel, (2nd tunnel) drive ahead into Hataitai, left and then right into Waitoa Rd. Drive up Waitoa Rd. and 2nd left into Matai Rd. From airport Highway 1 turn right at lights into Evans Bay Parade, 2nd left into Rata Rd., left and left again into Matai Rd.

The purpose-built guest suites are refurbished in harmony with the era of the home and have folding doors onto decking overlooking the garden and sea views and access a lounge with private entrance. Each room is tastefully decorated, heavenly king-size beds, with a thick pillow-top mattress, crisp linen, goose down covers and plump pillows. Ensuites feature hair dryer, toiletries, bathrobes and heated towel rail. Tea and coffee making facilities, fridge, laundry and ironing facilities. Fresh flowers. Breakfast includes espresso coffee, homemade muesli, fruit and cooked options at a time to suit. Enjoy an open fire in evenings.
Telephone, fax and e-mail facilities available.

TOP O' T'ILL

2 Waitoa Road, Hataitai, Wellington
Ph (04) 386 2718, Fax (04) 386 2719
Mobile 025-495 410
e-mail: *top.o.hill@xtra.co.nz*

Tariff : N.Z. Dollars	
Double	$85-120
Single	$55-110
Child	neg

Bedrooms	Qty
Double	2
Twin	1
Single	1

Bed Size	Qty
King	
Queen	2
Double	
Single	3

Bathrooms	Qty
Ensuite	2
Private	1
Guest Share	1
Family Share	

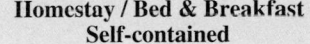

Homestay / Bed & Breakfast
Self-contained

Features & Attractions

- *Friendly and helpful hosts*
- *Attractive warm rooms*
- *Popular suburb near city*
- *Spa pool*
- *Continental/cooked breakfast*
- *Excellent local restaurants*
- *Self-contained, serviced studio*
- *Studio – long-term rates available*

DIRECTIONS: Please phone, write or fax.

Hataitai ('breath of the ocean') is situated in the eastern suburbs of Wellington, midway between Airport and City. A homely atmosphere is provided for guests in our comfortable 1919 two storey home, which has been in our family over 60 years. From the bedrooms there are views of Evans Bay, Hataitai Village and Mount Victoria. The lovely new studio (Áit Siocháin - Peaceful Place), has a fully appointed kitchenette, ensuite, cable TV, phone line, private entrance and patio. We enjoy the beauty of our vibrant harbour city, including its cultural life and range of superb restaurants. Distance to the CBD, airport, ferry, Te Papa National Museum and sports venues, is 5-10 minutes by bus or car.

We have travelled widely overseas and in New Zealand, and share interests in music, the arts, historic places and meeting people. We will be glad to help you make the most of your visit to Wellington. Our home is smokefree inside and not suitable for young children.

FRANCESCA'S HOMESTAY
10 Monro Street, Seatoun,
Wellington
Ph (04) 388 6719, Fax (04) 388 6719

Tariff : N.Z. Dollars	
Double	$80
Single	$50
Child	$25

Bedrooms	Qty
Double	1
Twin	1
Single	
Bed Size	**Qty**
Super King	
King	
Queen	1
Single	2
Bathrooms	**Qty**
Ensuite	
Private	
Guest Share	1
Family Share	

 Homestay Bed & Breakfast

Features & Attractions

- *Quiet seaside village*
- *Personalised service*
- *Cooked breakfast included*
- *Home away from home*
- *Handy to Wellington Airport*
- *Excellent bus service*
- *Good restaurants nearby*
- *Laundry facilities available*

Handy to Wellington Airport (only 3 km away) our modern home is located in a quiet seaside village. A unique 'Fairy Shop' is a must to visit. Enjoy a NZ-style dinner or dine at the local Village Inn or at one of the many nearby restaurants. A warm welcome awaits those who want a home away from home. I have varied interest but mainly in sport, craft and travel. I play golf regularly at the Links close by. Laundry facilities are

available to those who have been travelling.

Seeing Wellington by bus: From our home walk one minute to the bus stop, then travel around Wellington 'The City of a Thousand Views' on a **Day Tripper Ticket** Discover New Zealand history by visiting 'Te Papa' Wellington's unique new museum.

DIRECTIONS:
Entering Wellington from the north or off the Interisland Ferry follow signs to the airport, then using the left lane follow the signs to Seatoun. Monro Street. is the 2nd on the left after the shops. From the airport take the 1st turn right then as above.

FRINTON BY THE SEA

55 Rona Street, Eastbourne, Wellington
Ph (04) 562 7540, Fax (04) 562 7860
Mobile 025-417 365
e-mail: *frinton@voyager.co.nz*
http://www.frintonbythesea.co.nz

Tariff : N.Z. Dollars		
	Double	$90-115
	Single	$70-95
	Child	n/a

Bedrooms	Qty
Double	2
Twin	
Single	1
Bed Size	**Qty**
King	
Queen	2
Double	1
Single	
Bathrooms	**Qty**
Ensuite	1
Private	1
Guest Share	
Family Share	1

    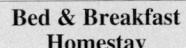

Bed & Breakfast Homestay

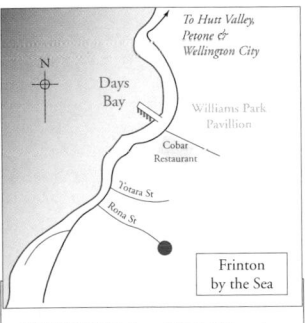

To Hutt Valley, Petone & Wellington City
Days Bay
Williams Park Pavillion
Cobar Restaurant
Totara St
Rona St
Frinton by the Sea

DIRECTIONS: From SH 2, follow signs to Petone, Seaview and Eastbourne. Then continue around Bay Road as shown.

Features & Attractions

- *Family atmosphere*
- *Peaceful surroundings*
- *Comfortable, cosy rooms*
- *Generous breakfasts*
- *5 minutes stroll to beach*
- *Near excellent restaurants*
- *Local ferry to Wellington*
- *Lovely bush walks nearby*

Our warm and comfortable home is nestled into native bush overlooking our glorious Wellington harbour. All rooms are bright and cosy and have direct access to decks/balconies, where you can relax and enjoy the bush, bird life and harbour scenes with ever-changing shipping and sky patterns. Eastbourne is a seaside village, 24 km harbour side drive or 20 minutes ferry ride from Wellington. It boasts excellent restaurants, gift shops and galleries. Wellington, stepping stone to the South Island, is a thriving, bustling city with a magnificent café/arts/theatre scene and home to the national museum Te Papa. You are welcome to join Wendy, Doug, Rosy our dog and two lazy cats in our family sitting room, read, listen to music, each bedroom has a TV. Refreshments are always available, the choices are yours to enjoy. Our interests are many and varied with arts, theatre, music, good food and wine being closely followed by the enjoyment in sharing our lifestyle and interests with you. We look forward to welcoming you to our home.

A rather "Unique Stay"?

South Island

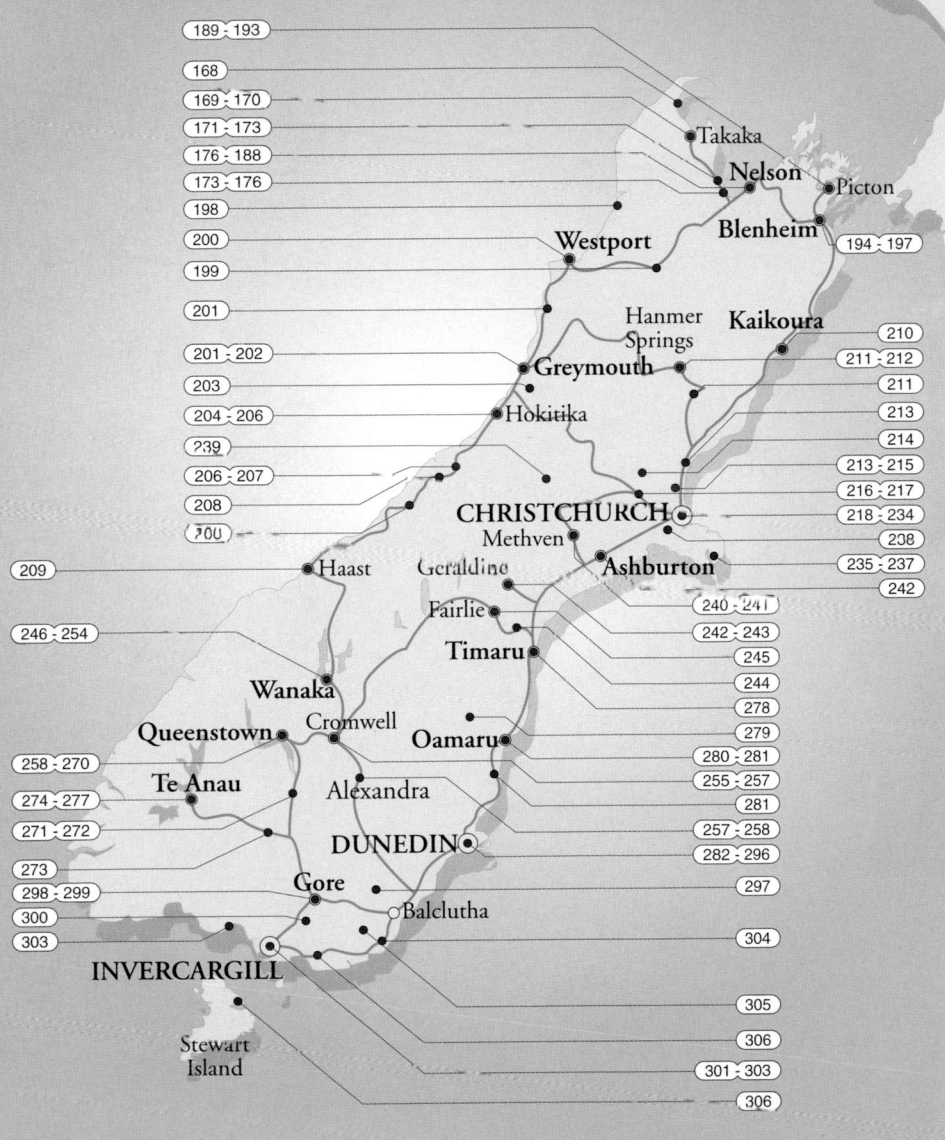

189 - 193
168
169 - 170
171 - 173
176 - 188
173 - 176
198
200
199
201
201 - 202
203
204 - 206
239
206 - 207
208
200
209
246 - 254
258 - 270
274 - 277
271 - 272
273
298 - 299
300
303

Takaka
Nelson
Picton
Blenheim
Westport
194 - 197
Hanmer Springs
Kaikoura
210
Greymouth
211 - 212
211
Hokitika
213
214
213 - 215
216 - 217
CHRISTCHURCH
218 - 234
Methven
208
Geraldine
Ashburton
235 - 237
Haast
242
Fairlie
240 - 241
Timaru
242 - 243
245
244
278
Wanaka
279
Cromwell
280 - 281
Queenstown
Oamaru
255 - 257
Te Anau
281
Alexandra
257 - 258
DUNEDIN
282 - 296
Gore
297
Balclutha
304
INVERCARGILL
305
306
Stewart Island
301 - 303
306

TWIN WATERS LODGE

Totara Avenue, PO Box 33,
Collingwood
Ph/Fax (03) 524 8014, Mobile (025) 956 766
e-mail: *twinwaters@xtra.co.nz*

Tariff : N.Z. Dollars	
Double	$120-150
Single	$105-120
Child	

Bedrooms	Qty
Double	2
Twin	1
Single	

Bed Size	Qty
Super King/Twin	1
King	
Queen/Double	2
Single	

Bathrooms	Qty
Ensuite	3
Private	
Guest Share	
Family Share	

 **Boutique Accommodation
Bed & Breakfast**

VISA
MasterCard

Features & Attractions

- Bookings and pick-up point for Farewell Spit Tours
- 50 metres to Sand Beach
- Peaceful setting
- Abundant birdlife
- Comfortable beds
- Guest lounge w. woodburner
- Meals prepared by Chef

Nestled harmoniously beside a tidal estuary, **Twin Waters Lodge** features curved timber ceilings, floor to ceiling windows and multi level decks. The ensuite rooms open onto private decks, and the cosy guest lounge has pleasant views of the estuary and forested hills. **Twin Waters Lodge** is a great base to explore the Golden Bay region. Wander along the wild West Coast beaches, take a tour of Farewell Spit, a bird sanctuary of world renown, visit Kahurangi and Abel Tasman National Parks, try your hand at gold panning, horse trekking or sea kayaking. Indulge your passion for walking, swimming, tennis or golf, or join Clemens and Laurel for a game of petanque. Visit local artists and find out what it is about Golden Bay that inspires them. Waking to the sound of tuis, breakfasting in the sun, or savouring a delicious dinner, there's sure to be a special moment to remember your stay. Laurel and Clemens have been in the hospitality industry for many years, and take pride in creating a relaxing atmosphere for you. They also have a passion for travelling and love meeting fellow travellers and sharing their experiences.
"Chef's Dinner" by prior arrangement $25-$40 pp.

DIRECTIONS: 9km north of Collingwood towards Farewell Spit.

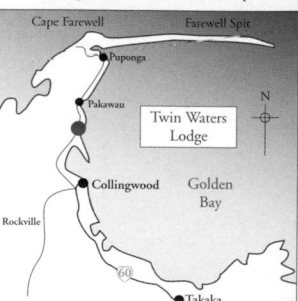

OBAN

Charlett Point Road, Rangihaeata, RD 2, Takaka
Ph (03) 525 9904, Fax (03) 525 9910
e-mail: *oban@voyager.co.nz*

Features & Attractions

- *Quality accommodation*
- *Centrally located*
- *Laundry facilities avail.*
- *Your party are our only guests*
- *Restful coastal setting*
- *Local courtesy pick up*

Boutique Accommodation Bed & Breakfast

Double	$90
Single	$60
Child	neg.

We are centrally located – 10 minutes north of Takaka Township. You are welcomed with complimentary café style refreshments as soon as you arrive in the Bay. **Oban** was built in the 1920's. Our restored home features twin and double guest rooms with private facilities. There is a separate guest lounge. You may also share our family facilities.

Oban is adjacent to Charlett Point Beach. You can swim at high tide, meander along the beach or explore the rock pools at low tide. The walk around Rangihaeata Heads features "pancake" rock formations, fossils and wildlife.

Early retirement has allowed us to travel and enjoy our interests which include patch work and quilting, bridge, gardening, fishing and making country wines. We accept only one booking at a time. A full cooked breakfast is provided. You are welcome to share the evening meal which features local produce. The cost is $35 per person and includes complimentary country wines.

Bedrooms	Qty
Double	1
Twin	2
Single	
Bed Size	**Qty**
King	
Queen/Double	1
Single	4
Bathrooms	**Qty**
Ensuite	
Private	1
Guest Share	
Family Share	

GLENDALE

Golden Bay Homestays, Dodson Road,
Takaka, Golden Bay
Postal: *RD 1, Takaka 7172*
Ph (03) 525 9593

Features & Attractions

- *Warm hospitality*
- *Excellent cuisine*
- *Peaceful countryside*
- *Gateway to Farewell Spit*
- *Two National Parks nearby*
- *Beautiful beaches abound*

Homestay Bed & Breakfast

Double	$90
Single	$60
Child	half price

A warm welcome awaits you at **Glendale**, our rural homestay, just 3 min. drive from Takaka township in beautiful Golden Bay. Situated on 6 hectares of peaceful countryside, including a large garden and small kiwifruit orchard, we offer rest and relaxation, warm hospitality, excellent cuisine and a base from which to explore the many attractions of the area. We are close to both the Abel Tasman and Kahurangi National Parks, beautiful beaches for swimming and fishing, safari tours to famous Farewell Spit, tramping, horse trekking or farm visits. We provide tastefully furnished double or twin rooms with private facilities, including own lounge area and welcome family groups. By arrangement we can provide a delicious evening meal and cater for any dietary requirement. We are Kiwihosts and look forward to meeting you.

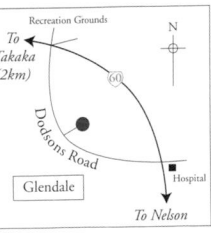

Bedrooms	Qty
Double	1
Twin	2
Single	1
Bed Size	**Qty**
King	
Queen	1
Single	5
Bathrooms	**Qty**
Ensuite	
Private	1
Guest Share	1
Family Share	

BEAUTIFUL PATONS ROCK
SEA & BEACHVIEW HOMESTAY
Patons Rock, RD 2, Takaka, Golden Bay
Ph (03) 525 7230, Fax (03) 525 7231
kaliswj@voyager.co.nz

Tariff : N.Z. Dollars	
Double	$75-80
Single	$50
Child	neg.

Bedrooms	Qty
Double	1
Twin	2
Single	

Bed Size	Qty
Super King	
King	1
Queen	
Single	5/6

Bathrooms	Qty
Ensuite	
Private	2
Guest Share	
Family Share	

 Homestay Bed & Breakfast & Self-contained Accommodation

Features & Attractions

- *View over whole of Golden Bay*
- *Private lounge/kitchen/balcony*
- *Separate shower and bathroom*
- *Safe, clean beach 2min.*
- *Good log burner*
- *Very comfortable & cosy*

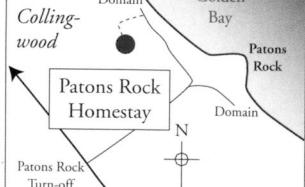

DIRECTIONS: From Takaka Post Shop drive 10km towards Collingwood, take Patons Rock turn-off. At end of Road take private track "Byders Terrace" We are last house on left.

Our separate upper floor gives a beautiful view over the Bay from Farewell Spit to Separation Point. We are only two minutes from a safe, clean, good walking beach. You will enjoy our big lounge with log burner and TV. Bathroom, toilet and shower are separate. A balcony on three sides gives ample room to sit and enjoy the views. Patons Rock area has about 100 houses and no shops.
In Takaka or Collingwood you find facilities like restaurants, pubs and shops , only 12km away. Golden Bay has plenty to offer with its variable scenery and good walkways. We can pick you up from the Tasman or Heaphy Track or in Takaka or drop you off at Collingwood for a Farewell Spit Safari. Kayak, windsurfer and BBQ available.

Self-contained option:
Our downstairs self-contained flat comprises of an open-plan kitchen/ living area and has one bedroom with queen-size bed and one bedroom with 3 single beds. Divan in lounge. Tariffs per night: $45 for double and $35 for single, extra person $10. Breakfast is available ($5 p.p.)

TWIN VIEWS BED & BREAKFAST
Tokongawa Drive, Split Apple Rock, RD 2, Motueka
Ph (03) 527 8475, Fax (03) 527 8479
Mobile 025 318 937
e-mail: *twinviews@xtra.co.nz*

Tariff : N.Z. Dollars	
Double	$125
Single	$90
Child	

Bedrooms	Qty
Double	2
Twin	
Single	

Bed Size	Qty
Super King	
King-Twin	1
Queen	1
Single	

Bathrooms	Qty
Ensuite	2
Private	
Guest Share	
Family Share	

**Panoramic Sea Views
Bed & Breakfast**

Features & Attractions

- *Magnificent sea views*
- *Native bush setting*
- *Close to two beaches*
- *Both guest rooms with ensuite*
- *Abel Tasman track 5 min.drive*
- *Great hospitality*
- *Your own private terrace*
- *New architecturally designed home*

Wake to the sound of waves breaking on the beach below, in this new purpose built, architecturally designed home with panoramic sea views overlooking Tasman Bay.

Each room has magnificent sea views, ensuite, fridge, tea/coffee making facilities, TV, hairdryer, heated towel rail and comfortable seating.

Breakfast can be served in either, the guest lounge or on your own private terrace.

Take a stroll down to Split Apple Rock Beach, Tower Bay and to the bush walks or just sit and watch the kayaks and boats go by.

We are 5 minutes drive from the start of Abel Tasman Track. Several excellent restaurants are within a short driving distance.

Photo of the view is taken from the guests' terrace.

DIRECTIONS:
Proceed past Kaiteriteri Beach towards Marahau for 4 kilometres. Turn right onto Tokongawa Drive. Twin Views Bed & Breakfast is right at the top.

"DOONE COTTAGE"

Motueka Valley, RD 1, Motueka, Nelson Region
Ph (03) 526 8740, Fax (03) 526 8740
e-mail: *doone-cottage@xtra.co.nz*

Tariff : N.Z. Dollars		
	Double	$130-175
	Single	$110-155
	Child	

Bedrooms	Qty
Double	2
Twin	1
Single	

Bed Size	Qty
Super King	
King	1
Queen	1
King Single	1

Bathrooms	Qty
Ensuite	3
Private	
Guest Share	
Family Share	

DIRECTIONS: From Motueka: Turn off SH 60 at Clocktower (Caltex Service Station) onto Motueka Valley H'way. **Doone Cottage** 28km. From South: Turn off SH6 at Motupiko (Kohatu Hotel). **Doone Cottage** 26km

 Country Homestay

Features & Attractions

- *100 year old homestead*
- *Dinner by arrangement*
- *Trout fishing*
- *Three National Parks*
- *Cottage gardens*
- *Weaving & wool craft studio*
- *Art, craft and wine trails*
- *Mountain scenery*

Homely hospitality, peace and tranquility, fishing, beautiful garden, native birds, house pets, sheep, chickens, ducks and donkeys, all abound at **Doone Cottage**, which we have enjoyed sharing with guests for many years. A lovely country home, comfortably furnished cottage style, set in a secluded 4 acre setting of native trees and flower gardens overlooking the Motueka Valley and the Mt Arthur range in Kahaurangi National Park. Guest rooms - 2 inhouse plus **Garden Chalet**, all full ensuite. Countrystyle meals, homemade breads, preserves, homegrown produce, free range eggs etc. Activities within 45 minutes include: access to 3 National Parks, (Abel Tasman, Kahaurangi, and Nelson Lakes); Beaches (kayaking, boat trips), Mountains (horse trekking, walking), Golf Courses. The Motueka River is at the gate with several other trout streams closeby, offering excellent brown trout fishing. (Licences & guiding available) This is one of NZ's main fruit producing regions where the sun shines over 2,400 hours annually.

Hosts will gladly assist with bookings for activities/ongoing accommodation. We are members of the **Hostlink Network**.

CENTRE RIDGE FARMSTAY

Blackbird Valley 176.
RD 2 Upper Moutere, Nelson
Ph (03) 543 2882, Fax (03) 543 2882

Features & Attractions

- *Spacious family home*
- *Farm dinners arranged*
- *Laundry available*
- *Amzing sheep dogs working*
- *See shearing demonstration*
- *Abel Tasman National Park*

Double	$80
Single	$55
Child	half price

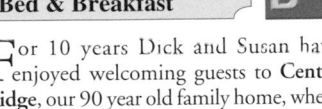
Farmstay Bed & Breakfast

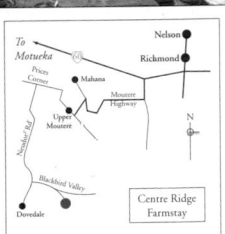

Bedrooms	Qty
Double	2
or Twin	2
Single	
Bed Size	**Qty**
Super King	1
Queen	1
Single	1
Bathrooms	**Qty**
Ensuite	1
Private	1
Guest Share	
Family Share	

For 10 years Dick and Susan have enjoyed welcoming guests to **Centre Ridge**, our 90 year old family home, where you can enjoy our sunny deck, our garden and the valley views. Surrounded by a 400 acre sheep farm, we also grow 8 different coloured calla lillies for export. Feel free to go walking on our farm or a ride can be arranged. Upper Moutere is halfway between Nelson and the Abel Tasman National Park in an area of wineries and close to lovely beaches. Stay a night or more, enjoy an evening meal with us (by arrangement), $20pp with local wine. Sample farm food, home-made bread and jams with a cooked or continental breakfast. Our king/twin room has a double spa in the bathroom.

DIRECTIONS: 1.5 km south of Richmond turn right. After 6 km turn left (Moutere Highway). After 17 km turn left at Prices Corner. Travel 4.4 km to Blackbird Valley, turn left. Find us after 1.76 km.

MAHANA COUNTRY HOMESTAY

338 Old Coach Road, Upper Moutere
Ph/Fax (03) 543 2626, Mobile 025-483 903
e-mail: *jtucker@xtra.co.nz*

Features & Attractions

- *Quiet, peaceful garden*
- *Wonderful views*
- *Warm hospitality*
- *Abel Tasman National Park*
- *Beaches and sea kayaking*
- *Crafts and wine trails*

Double	$85
Single	$50
Child	half price

Countrystay Bed & Breakfast

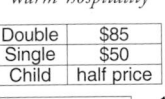

Bedrooms	Qty
Double	1
Twin	1
Single	1
Bed Size	**Qty**
King	
Queen/Double	2
King/Single	3
Bathrooms	**Qty**
Ensuite	
Private	1
Guest Share	1
Family Share	

A warm welcome awaits you at our comfortable home surrounded by lovely gardens and apple orchard. Enjoy our outdoors with the bird life and breathtaking view over Tasman Bay and Nelson in a quiet, relaxed atmosphere. Our spacious guest rooms are comfortable, heated and supplied with electric blankets. (Twin share includes private bathroom facilities.) We welcome you to share our family area. In the morning enjoy an appetizing continental or cooked breakfast, including a selection of home-made jams and other delicious food in our sunny dining room. A delectable three-course traditional New Zealand dinner and wine shared with hosts is available by prior arrangement ($20pp). We are halfway between Richmond and Motueka – the gateway to the Abel Tasman National Park, Kaiteriteri and Golden Bay. A great place to stay, with everything you need close by, 10 30 minutes to beaches, golf course, pottery, wine trails and many other outdoor activities like sea kayaking. We look forward to meeting you soon.

DIRECTIONS: On SH 60 to Motueka, 16km from Richmond turn Dominion Rd. 2km, turn right, 3rd house on right.

KIMERET PLACE

Bronte Rd East, Nr Mapua
RD 1 Upper Moutere, Nelson
Ph (03) 540 2727, Fax (03) 540 2726
e-mail: *stay@kimeretplace.co.nz*
http://www.kimeretplace.co.nz

Tariff : N.Z. Dollars	
Double	$110-140
Single	$85-95
Suites	$170-250

Bedrooms	Qty
Double	2
Twin/King	3
Single	
Bed Size	**Qty**
Super King	
King/Twin	3
Queen	2
Single	
Bathrooms	**Qty**
Ensuite	4
Private	1
Guest Share	
Family Share	

**Boutique
Bed & Breakfast**

Features & Attractions

- *Stunning views*
- *Swimming pool & Spa*
- *Self-contained cottage*
- *Craft & wine trails*
- *Space, Peace, Privacy*
- *Eligant rooms & Suites*
- *Award winning Restaurants*
- *National Parks & Beaches*

At **Kimeret Place** the emphasis is on comfort and relaxation. Enjoy the peace of our secluded 4 acres overlooking the Waimea inlet. Soak up the sun and the stunning views from our heated pool and terrace or escape to the hammock and the shade of mature trees. Then, in the evening, after a fabulous meal at a local restaurant, soak in the spa under the star-filled Southern sky. What better way to recharge the batteries? Situated in the heart of Nelson's wine and craft area, **Kimeret Place** is an ideal base to explore the diversity of the region, from the gentle beauty of the Able Tasman NP to the dramatic mountains of Kahurangi NP. We have accommodation to suit all tastes and budgets, stylish rooms, a self-contained cottage (ideal for families or small goups) and our new Luxury suites each with spa bath, sitting area and balcony. All guests benefit from complimentary tea and coffee, TV, toiletries, hairdryers, Internet, laundry.

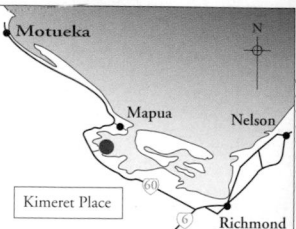

DIRECTIONS: From Richmond on SH 60 turn right after 12 km into Bronte Rd East. We are 750 m on right. From Mapua: - 4 km on left.

ESTUARY BED & BREAKFAST

6a Moreland Place, Mapua Village
Ph (03) 540 2458, Fax (03) 540 2458
e-mail: *estuarybnb@paradise.net.nz*
http://homepages.paradise.net.nz/estuarybnb

Features & Attractions

- *Centrally located*
- *Quiet waterfront site*
- *Beautiful beach walks*
- *Continent./cooked breakfast*
- *Wir sprechen deutsch*
- *Excellent restaurants nearby*

Beach walk

	Double	$85
	Single	$55
	Child	half price

Homestay Bed & Breakfast

Bedrooms	Qty
Double	1
Twin	1
Single	
Bed Size	**Qty**
King	
Queen	1
Single	2
Bathrooms	**Qty**
Ensuite	1
Private	1
Guest Share	
Family Share	

DIRECTIONS:
30min. west of Nelson via
Coastal Highway 60, 30min. to
Abel Tasman National Park.

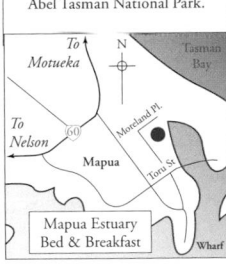

Mapua Estuary
Bed & Breakfast

Take a walk on the beach before breakfast after a superbly quiet good night's sleep. Relax over a delicious breakfast and take advantage of your host's 25 years of local knowledge to plan your day. Our attractive, comfortable home, overlooking the estuary with its interesting bird life is centrally located for all Abel Tasman Park, Kahurangi National Park, Nelson and Motueka River attractions. We would be pleased to make your bookings for these activities. Come back to an airy, spotless home right by the water. A 10-minute walk will take you to one of three character restaurants. Treat yourself to manuka-smoked fish while watching the sea birds and the sunset over the estuary. Quiet, comfortable and clean, with reasonable rates. Be assured of a warm welcome.

MAPUA "SEA VIEW" BED & BREAKFAST

40 Langford Drive, Mapua Village, Nelson
Ph (03) 540 2006. Fax (03) 540 2006
Mobile (025) 839 634
e-mail: *mapua.bb@paradise.net.nz*
http://www.mapua.co.nz

Features & Attractions

- *Abel Tasman Park 30min.*
- *Walk to restaurants/wharf*
- *Nelson City 30 min. drive*
- *Panoramic views - Peaceful*
- *Quality bedding/furnishings*
- *Off-street parking*

	Double	$85-99
	Single	$55-70
	Child	n/a

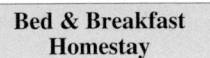
Bed & Breakfast Homestay

Bedrooms	Qty
Double	2
Twin	
Single	
Bed Size	**Qty**
King	
Queen	2
Single	
Bathrooms	**Qty**
Ensuite	2
Private	
Guest Share	
Family Share	

30 min. from Nelson, **Mapua "Seaview" Bed & Breakfast** is nestled in the coastal village of Mapua. Our new home offers uninhibited panoramic views overlooking the Waimea Estuary and the Richmond mountain vista beyond. A five minute stroll takes you to four picturesque waterfront licensed restaurants, to Leisure Park and popular beaches. Being central within the Nelson Bay's coastal region makes us an ideal base to explore Abel Tasman Park (30min), Farewell Spit and many other well known attractions. We have sought to create a homely friendly atmosphere with the accent on comfort. Our cosy guest rooms offer comfortable quality queen beds with feather duvets, TV and private bathrooms. Coffee/tea and home baking always available. Cooked or continental breakfast provided with fresh local fruit. The numerous leisure activities, sight-seeing highlights and sunshine should cater for everyone's interests and tastes. The regions vineyards, arts & craft studios surround us.

RUSH COVE

Westdale Road (PO Box 1068, Nelson), Nr. Mapua
Ph (03) 540 3635.
e-mail: *verbatim@xtra.co.nz*

Features & Attractions
- Tranquil estuary setting
- Friendly farm animals
- Stunning views
- Hearty country breakfast
- Family atmosphere
- Beaches, golf, wineries

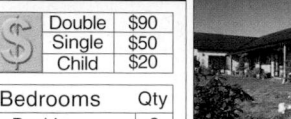

	Double	$90
	Single	$50
	Child	$20

Bedrooms	Qty
Double	2
Twin	
Single	

Bed Size	Qty
Queen	1
Double	1
Single	

Bathrooms	Qty
Ensuite	1
Private	
Guest Share	
Family Share	

Coastal Farmlet Bed & Breakfast

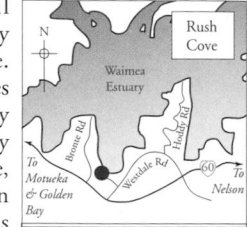

DIRECTIONS:
20 minutes from Nelson via
the Coastal Highway (SH60).
Turn right into Westdale Road,
11 km from Richmond. We
are two kilometres on right.

Wake up to a tranquil estuary setting and enjoy the relaxation of country life. At **Rush Cove**, we have 10 acres bordering the Waimea Inlet, home to a mob of friendly sheep and an ever-increasing menagerie. Our new family home has much of the character of an older, rustic farmhouse, with the guest bedroom opening up to the morning sun rising above the estuary. Guests are invited to make friends with the animals, canoe the estuary, enjoy an outdoor bath under the stars, or use **Rush Cove** as a base to explore the region. We are 20 min. from Nelson via the Coastal Highway and only minutes from wineries, restaurants and cafés, art and craft galleries and safe swimming beaches.

WESTLEIGH

Waimea West Road, Brightwater, Nelson
Ph (03) 542 3654. Fax (03) 542 3654
Mobile 025 - 608 8927
e-mail: *westleigh@paradise.net.nz*

Features & Attractions
- Secluded parklike setting
- Central for outdoor sports
- Country house atmosphere
- On wine and craft trails
- Wir sprechen deutsch
- Guided walks

	Double	$120
	Single	$60-80
	Child	

VISA MasterCard

Countrystay Bed & Breakfast

Bedrooms	Qty
Double	2
Twin	
Single	

Bed Size	Qty
King	
Queen	2
Single	

Bathrooms	Qty
Ensuite	1
Private	
Guest Share	
Family Share	

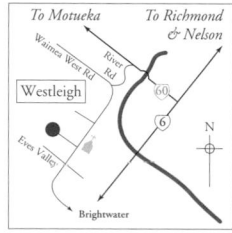

Westleigh is a very relaxing home, ideally located for you to use as a base to explore all that Nelson Province has to offer. Our home, set in the middle of 27 acres, has evolved from an old farm house. We are constantly expanding the garden and welcome suggestions.

The two guest rooms open onto a courtyard garden and we restrict numbers to one party of up to four people at a time, ensuring you can enjoy the ambience. You can choose privacy or join us. For the energetic we provide guided mountain biking and walks. There are more than ten good restaurants near **Westleigh**, but if you prefer it, delicious home cooked meals, shared with us, are available by arrangement. Breakfast is normally served 'al fresco'.

We look forward to sharing **Westleigh** with you.

THE LAST STRAW COTTAGE

Mt Heslington Road, Brightwater, Nelson
Ph (03) 542 3575, Fax (03) 542 3575
Mobile 025-305 020
e-mail: *laststraw@ts.co.nz*
http//:www.laststraw.co.nz

Tariff : N.Z. Dollars	
Double	$165
Single	$125
Extra person	$45

Bedrooms	Qty
Double	2
Twin	
Single	1

Bed Size	Qty
Super King	
King	
Queen	2
Single	1

Bathrooms	Qty
Ensuite	
Private	1
Guest Share	
Family Share	

Unique Self-contained Accommodation

DIRECTIONS:
From SH 6 turn into River Terrace Road, then first right onto Mt Heslington Road, approximately 3.5 km on right, look for sign.

Features & Attractions

- Peaceful country setting
- Private and independent
- Riding arena & stable facilities
- BBQ and brazier
- Rivers, beaches within short distance
- Wineries and award winning restaurants
- Arts, crafts, Nelson Saturday Flea Market
- Mountain bikes

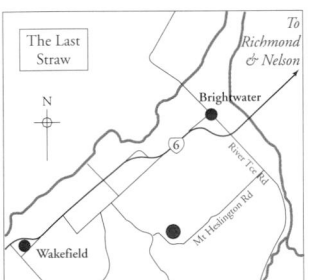

Our uniquely built straw bale cottage will be exclusively yours for the duration of your stay. Situated in a quiet, picturesque valley on a 16 acre farmlet, this cottage has all the features of a modern home but with the atmosphere and charm of an olde worlde cottage with wonderful thick walls, all natural materials and recycled timbers. It has its own private garden setting and courtyard with BBQ. The cottage is 5 minutes from 3 of Nelson's fine rivers which offer great swimming, fishing and picnicking. Rabbit Island beach is 10 minutes from your door. The cottage is a perfect honeymoon retreat or for anyone who wants total peace and privacy. An evening meal can be enjoyed at any one of our award winning cafés and restaurants or self-catered in your fully equipped kitchen. A breakfast hamper with provisions supplied for continental and cooked country breakfast will be delivered to you at the cottage each morning or evening as you prefer. Animals are welcome but outside only. We look forward to welcoming you for a memorable stay.

YOUR HOSTS: **Janice and Ray O'Loughlin**   Ph: (03) 544 6541

BAY VIEW BED & BREAKFAST

Bay View, 37 Kihilla Road, Richmond
Ph/Fax (03) 544 6541, Mobile 025-623 0252
e-mail: *bayview@ts.co.nz*

Bed & Breakfast & Self-contained Suite

Tariff : N.Z. Dollars		
	Double	$80-100
	Single	$65
	Child	

Bedrooms	Qty
Double	3
Twin	
Single	

Bed Size	Qty
Super King	1
King	
Queen	2
Single	

Bathrooms	Qty
Ensuite	1
Private	1
Guest Share	1
Family Share	

Features & Attractions

- *Spectacular views*
- *Quiet, peaceful setting*
- *Wine and craft trails*
- *Tasty, tempting breakfasts*
- *Award-winning restaurants nearby*
- *Close to great outdoor activities*

Bay View is a modern, spacious home, built on the hills above Richmond, with spectacular views of Tasman Bay and mountain ranges.

We offer rooms that are quiet, private and immaculately furnished with your complete comfort in mind. The large guest bathroom has shower and spa bath for two. To ensure your complete privacy we offer 'no share' accommodation if requested.

The lounge opens onto a sheltered deck where you can relax, enjoy a drink or sit and chat. The self-contained suite with off-street parking, private entrance, kitchen, laundry/bathroom, lounge area and queen

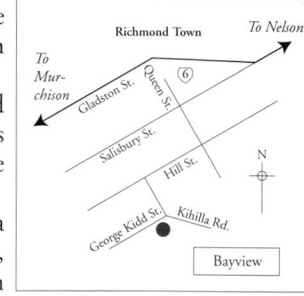

bed offers privacy and all home comforts. We have two miniature schnauzer dogs, a variety of birds in a large aviary, tend our colourful garden and enjoy meeting people from New Zealand and overseas.

By car, **Bay View** is 15 min. from Nelson and 2 min. from Richmond. National parks, golden beaches, vineyards and many crafts are close by.

Be assured of warm, friendly hospitality and a happy stay in our smoke-free home.

ALTHORPE

13 Dorset Street, Richmond, Nelson
Ph (03) 544 8117, Fax (03) 544 8117
e-mail: *rworley@voyager.co.nz.*

Tariff : N.Z. Dollars	
Double	$120-140
Single	$100-110
Child	

Bedrooms	Qty
Double	1
Twin	1
Single	

Bed Size	Qty
Super King	
King	
Queen/Double	1
King/Single	2

Bathrooms	Qty
Ensuite	1
Private	1
Guest Share	
Family Share	

VISA   MasterCard

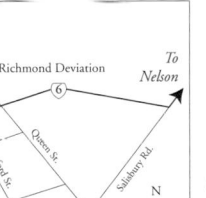

DIRECTIONS:
Please phone for easy directions

BA   **Boutique Accommodation
Bed & Breakfast**   BB

Features & Attractions

- *Special breakfast selection*
- *Large private gardens*
- *Swimming pool and spa*
- *Award winning restaurants*
- *Warm hospitality*
- *National parks & beaches*
- *Wineries, arts and crafts*
- *Trout fishing & kayaking*

Call us out of this world if you will. But with two intimate guest rooms **Althorpe** provides warm old fashioned fuss and care that defines the art of hospitality. An ensuite serves our double bedroom while a private bathroom is provided for the twin/king suite. Guests are afforded the quiet luxury of two relaxing lounge rooms while outside spacious gardens with their own swimming pool and spa invite a casual stroll or dip in summer.

Among the services that have our guests reluctant to leave us, you'll find a delightful, tasty gourmet breakfast. By arrangement guests may also enjoy an evening meal complimented by a local wine ($40.00 per person).

All this comes within the walls and grounds that carry the echoes of bygone colonial years. At the end of the day's journey you deserve nothing but a little pampering, personal attention and all the comforts of home. Bob, Jenny and Tackles, our cat, look forward to making your stay a special highlight of your holiday.

CEDARWOOD LODGE

18 Angelus Ave, Richmond, Nelson
Ph (03) 544 8551, Fax (03) 544 8551
Mobile 021-293 3588
e-mail: *cedarwoodlodge@xtra.co.nz*
http://www.cedarwoodlodge.co.nz

Tariff : N.Z. Dollars		
	Double	$150
	Single	$130
	Child	$20 + age

Bedrooms	Qty
Double	2
Twin	1
Single	

Bed Size	Qty
Super King	
King	
Queen	3
Single	1

Bathrooms	Qty
Ensuite	2
Private	1
Guest Share	
Family Share	

 Bed & Breakfast in Attractive Established Grounds

DIRECTIONS:
Please phone for simple directions.

Features & Attractions

- *Friendly and relaxed hospitality*
- *Central to all attractions*
- *Beautiful established grounds*
- *Panoramic sea views*
- *National parks and beaches*
- *Wineries, arts and crafts*
- *Award winning restaurants*
- *Pool and tennis court*

Cedarwood Lodge offers friendly, relaxed accommodation central to all that we Nelsonians treasure. Our beautiful beaches, fishing, rivers, national parks, cafés and crafts along with our award winning restaurants and vineyards await your exploration.

The natural cedar shingle lodge, with its rich native woods featured throughout, is set in a secluded two-acre established garden. Native plantings attract tuis, bellbirds and fantails, while pheasants and quail wander the trailing paths leading down to the large garden pond.

Our suites are spacious, having queen size bedrooms, private adjoining sitting room, walk-in wardrobe/ dressing room and full ensuite with bath and shower. The main guest lounge with its open log fire extends out to wisteria canopied decking, overlooking the garden, tennis court and pool area. Beyond, the superb views of Tasman Bay and the mountain ranges.

Whether your visit is for business or leisure, we assure you a warm welcome, personal service and wonderful memories of our beautiful province.

Minutes to airport – courtesy passenger transfer available.

KERSHAW HOUSE

10 Wensley Road, Richmond, Nelson
Ph (03) 544 0957, Fax (03) 544 0950
e-mail: *niels-sherry@clear.net.nz*

Tariff : N.Z. Dollars	
Double	$185-225
Single	$145-165
Child	

Bedrooms	Qty
Double	3
Twin	
Single	
Bed Size	**Qty**
Super King	
King	1
Queen	2
Single	
Bathrooms	**Qty**
Ensuite	3
Private	
Guest Share	
Family Share	

 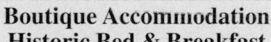

**Boutique Accommodation
Historic Bed & Breakfast**

Features & Attractions

- *Historic building (1929)*
- *Arts, crafts and glass blowing*
- *Award winning restaurants*
- *Golf course*
- *4 walking minutes to city centre*
- *Famous vineyards nearby*
- *National parks and beaches*
- *Deluxe breakfast*

Our historic **Kershaw House** is truly a character home with all the amenities you expect from a boutique bed & breakfast and more. The moment you enter the oak-panelled entrance hall, with its wooden staircase leading upstairs to the gallery, featuring Art Deco lead light window from 1929 and other original details, you will be transported back in time. Our house has been classified as New Zealand Historic Places Trust #2. This unique architecture, with great attention to details and small surprises, awaits the guests. Being so close to renowned Abel Tasman National Park, award winning vineyards and restaurants, arts, crafts, golf, fishing – only to mention a few attractions – Richmond is a must for every visitor to New Zealand. Sherida and Niels' aim is to provide hospitality with a difference.

A note from your hosts: "Enjoy the best wines from the Tasman Region in our very relaxing lounge and listen to your favourite tunes or music, while we serve some home-made canapes. Come and experience this part of the world, it is so beautiful."

DIRECTIONS:
Please phone for easy directions.

181

MAPLEDURHAM

8 Edward Street, Richmond
Ph (03) 544 4210, Fax (03) 544 4210
Mobile 025-226 2908
e-mail: *mapledurham@ts.co.nz*

Tariff : N.Z. Dollars	
Double	$185-215
Single	$145-180
Child	

Bedrooms	Qty
Double	2
Twin	1
Single	
Bed Size	**Qty**
Super King	
King	
Queen	3
Single	1
Bathrooms	**Qty**
Ensuite	2
Private	1
Guest Share	
Family Share	

 Boutique Accommodation and Bed & Breakfast   VISA MasterCard

Features & Attractions

- Warm hospitality
- Central location
- Peaceful setting
- Gourmet breakfasts
- National Parks and beaches
- Arts, crafts and glassblowing
- Award winning restaurants
- Wineries and superb seafoods

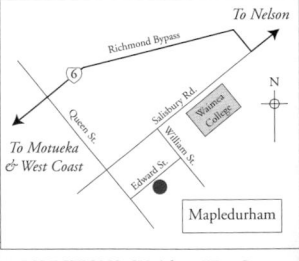

DIRECTIONS: SH 6 from West Coast, Murchison, Motueka **or** Nelson, Picton, Blenheim. Then follow map according to your direction.

In its peaceful setting, midway between the city and the wonders of Nelson Province, **Mapledurham** provides the perfect base from which to explore. It is a charming and elegant old home set in half an acre of tree-lined gardens and has a welcoming presence that enchants guests from the moment they arrive. Each guest bedroom has a style and character of its own; all are furnished with a greeting of fresh fruit and flowers and posture-sprung beds that are soft enough to offer the very best night's sleep, and for the morning, a tea-tray-with-everything plus home-made cookies. Once settled in, it's time for a welcoming drink, either in the comfortably furnished lounge with its varied art works and piano, or on one of the three verandahs. **Breakfast** is a real treat; eye-catching, healthy and satisfying, emphasising fresh, home-grown, home-made and gourmet.

Deborah, being a seasoned traveller with extensive local knowledge, will willingly help plan your Nelson itinerary. Those who wish simply to relax will find sanctuary in the vine-covered pergola with the scent garden nearby, or in winter a cosy log fire beckons in the lounge. Whatever has brought you to Nelson, your stay at **Mapledurham** will remain one of your treasured memories.

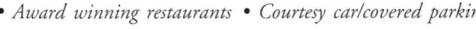

CHESTER LE HOUSE

39 Washbourn Drive, Richmond, Nelson
Ph (03) 544 7279, Fax (03) 544 7279
e-mail: *n.smith@xtra.co.nz*

MasterCard
VISA

Features & Attractions

- *Rural and sea views*
- *National parks and beaches*
- *Award winning restaurants*
- *Private, peaceful setting*
- *Wineries, arts & crafts nearby*
- *Courtesy car/covered parking*

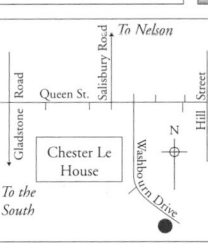

Bed & Breakfast & Self-contained Suite

Double	$80-90
Single	$50
Child	

If you are looking for something special and restful away from city noise yet conveniently located to Nelson City and Abel Tasman National Park, then **Chester Le House** beckons. Our lovely modern home has rural and sea views with safe walkways for evening strolls just a few steps away. Evening dinner featuring fine New Zealand wines or a typical Kiwi barbecue is available on request. Our outdoor living area is relaxing and welcoming. Our guest rooms are spacious, combining charm with modern facilities, warmth and comfort. Locked garaging, laundry facilities and a dryer are available for your convenience. We love to share our home with both business and leisure travellers. A courtesy car for pick-ups is available. Why not spoil yourself, extend your stay to relax and explore our beautiful province.

DIRECTIONS: SH 6 from West Coast, Murchison, Motueka or Nelson, Picton and Blenheim. Then please follow area map.

Bedrooms	Qty
Double	1
Twin	2
Single	
Bed Size	**Qty**
King	
Queen	1
Single	4
Bathrooms	**Qty**
Ensuite	1
Private	
Guest Share	1
Family Share	1

THE HERB HOUSE

42 Harts Road, Richmond, Nelson
Free Ph (0800) 437 832, Fax (03) 544 0953
e-mail: *info@herbaltea.co.nz*
http://www.herbaltea.co.nz

Features & Attractions

- *Pick your own herb tea*
- *Birdlife and friendly sheep*
- *NZ native tree collection*
- *Eat out or cook in*
- *Visitor Centre nearby*
- *Gateway to everything!*

Double	$80-100
Single	$70
Child	

F

Bed & Breakfast and Self-contained Unit

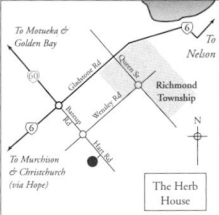

Bedrooms	Qty
Double	1
Twin	
Single	1
Bed Size	**Qty**
King	
Queen	1
Single	
Bathrooms	**Qty**
Ensuite	1
Private	
Guest Share	
Family Share	

We want to share our wonderful five acres with you. **The Herb House** is on our herbal tea farm - *"Harts Road Tea"*. Teas have names like Soothing Soreness, Tackling Tension, Digestive Delight, and Winter Wellness. See our website for more.

In Spring the raised herb gardens are a blaze of colour and inspiring smells - there is always something to pick! We're a little bit country, but close to Richmond township, and State Highway 6. You can really relax with us and do what you want, in your own time.

We are born and bred Nelsonians, so know the district well, its history, and the huge range of things to see and do. We'd love to meet you.

ALMOND COTTAGE

3/60 Songer Street, Stoke, Nelson
Ph/Fax (03) 547 9486, Mobile 025-233 0996
e-mail: *almond.cottage@paradise.net.nz*
http://www.travelwise.co.nz

Features & Attractions

* Special breakfast   * Agents Abel Tasman Ent.
* Airport pick-up   * Ample off-street parking
* 10 min. City centre   * Quiet location

Double	$80
Single	$55
Child	

Bedrooms	Qty
Double	1
Twin	1
Single	
Bed Size	**Qty**
King	
Queen	1
Single	2
Bathrooms	**Qty**
Ensuite	
Private	
Guest Share	1
Family Share	

Homestay Bed & Breakfast

A quiet, elegant cottage, with warm homely atmosphere, close to the lovely Monaco Peninsula, with wonderful mountain views, extending into Tasman Bay. Take a stroll down Grace Street and Ranier Avenue and see local potter, glass gallery and wood turner. Have dinner at the Honest Lawyer, our romantic olde English Pub and restaurant, overlooking Monaco Inlet, 200 metres away.
Relax and read the Guardian or Telegraph in our private lounge or conservatory with complimentary tea/coffee.
Our queen and twin rooms are tastefully furnished with warm cottage atmosphere.
Our modern guest bathroom with polished native timber floor has both bath and shower. We offer laundry facilities.
Almond Cottage is a wonderful starting point for you to explore this beautiful area.

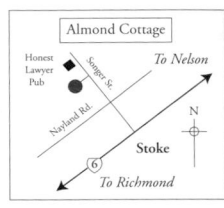

PARKSIDE BED & BREAKFAST

16 Centennial Road, Tahunanui, Nelson
Ph (03) 548 6629, Fax(03) 548 6621
Mobile 025-217 7811
e-mail: *parkside.nelson@xtra.co.nz*

Features & Attractions

* Beautiful spacious accommodation   * 5 min. walk to beach
* Abel Tasman National Park   * BBQ area
* Award winning seafood restaurants   * Private and peaceful

Homestay Bed & Breakfast

Double	$110
Single	$75
Child	

Bedrooms	Qty
Double	3
Twin	
Single	
Bed Size	**Qty**
King	
Queen	3
Single	2
Bathrooms	**Qty**
Ensuite	2
Private	1
Guest Share	
Family Share	

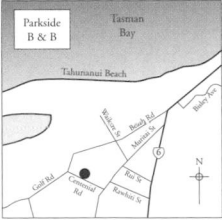

Our large well appointed B&B is situated minutes from the beach, restaurants, sporting grounds, golf courses and airport. Our separate guest area contains two large queen size bedrooms with ensuite and one double room with own bathroom. The guests have their own access to the separate guest lounge with all day tea and coffee making facilities. The private section is ideal for relaxing, is a safe place for children and has a shady private fernery. Have a delicious breakfast in private or join us on our large deck. Shopping in Nelson city is only 8 minutes away. Be sure of a warm friendly stay in our smoke free h ome with our two daughters aged 14 and 6 years and our friendly cat Mickey. There is secure lock-up garaging for all guests.

ARAPIKI

21 Arapiki Road, Stoke, Nelson
Ph (03) 547 3741. Fax (03) 547 3742
Mobile (021) 138 7535
e-mail: *wisechoice@nelsonparadise.co.nz*
http://www.nelsonparadise.co.nz

Features & Attractions

- *Centrally located in Nelson area*
- *Fully self-contained units*
- *Continental breakfast $7.50 pp*
- *Attractive garden setting*
- *Private deck or balcony*
- *Off-street parking*

Double	$65-$75
Single	$55-$60
Child	

Self-contained Homestay Units in Attractive Garden Setting

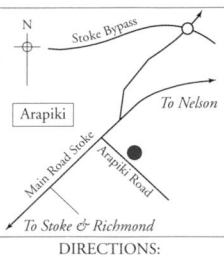

DIRECTIONS:
From the Stoke Shopping Centre Arapiki Rd is on the right approx. 1km north along the Main Rd Stoke. It is approx.6 km from Central Nelson.

Enjoy a relaxing holiday in the midst of your trip. The two self-contained smokefree units in our large home offer you comfort and privacy and are also very suitable for longer stays. These quality units in an attractive garden setting are centrally located in the Nelson area which has NZ's highest sunshine hours. Unit 1, which is larger, is in a pleasant and private garden setting. A ranchslider opens out to a deck with outdoor furniture for your use. It contains an Electric Stove, Microwave, TV, Auto Washing Machine and Phone.

Unit 2 has a balcony setting with seating to enjoy sea and mountain views. It contains a TV, Microwave and Phone.

At present our reasonable prices offer excellent value for money for the 'home away from home' accommodation provided.

Bedrooms	Qty
Double	2
Twin	
Single	
Bed Size	**Qty**
King	
Queen/Double	2
Single	1
Bathrooms	**Qty**
Ensuite	2
Private	
Guest Share	
Family Share	

TARATA HOMESTAY

5 Tarata Street, Stoke, Nelson
Ph (03) 547 3426, Fax (03) 547 3640
e-mail: *hosts@taratahomestay.co.nz*
www.taratahomestay.co.nz

Features & Attractions

- *Off-street parking*
- *Guest lounge*
- *Close to Isel Park*
- *Private facilities*
- *Very clean and quiet*
- *Generous breakfasts*

Double	$80
Single	$60
Child	$20

Homestay Bed & Breakfast

Bedrooms	Qty
Double	1
Twin	1
Single	
Bed Size	**Qty**
King	
Queen	1
Single	2
Bathrooms	**Qty**
Ensuite	
Private	1
Guest Share	
Family Share	

Tarata Homestay is located in Stoke in a lovely quiet street where you will find our comfortable home, surrounded by gardens and mature trees. Guests have their own private entrance to the house from a sealed off-street parking area. As we take only one group of guests at a time, you would have exclusive use of all facilities which include a private bathroom. A comfortable guest lounge with TV, video and complimentary tea and coffee is provided, and although we enjoy the company of our guests, we recognise your needs to relax and unwind in private after a day's travel.

There is a comprehensive selection of local information about activities, interests, crafts and restaurants, so that you can plan your stay with us in a relaxed environment. We are always available to help you with ideas, especially if time is limited. In the morning enjoy our sumptuous continental breakfast.

DIRECTIONS:
From Main Rd. Stoke turn into Maitland Ave. Take 3rd turn right then the next left. Our sign is out front.

39 RUSSELL

39 Russell St, (Postal: 41 Russell St.), Nelson
Ph (03) 548 4655, Fax (03) 548 4677
e-mail: janeevans@clear.net.nz
http://www.nelsonluxuryaccommodation.co.nz

Tariff : N.Z. Dollars	
Double	$350
Single	$350
Extra persons $35	

Bedrooms	Qty
Double	1
Twin	1
Single	
Bed Size	**Qty**
Super King	
King	
Queen	1
Single	2
Bathrooms	**Qty**
Ensuite	1
Private	1
Guest Share	
Family Share	

Boutique Accommodation
Fully Self-contained

Features & Attractions
- *Colour, harmony*
- *Privacy, independence*
- *Indoor/outdoor dining*
- *Complimentary goodies, incl. local wine*
- *Fully equipped kitchen*
- *Studio tour by appointment*

Situated in old Nelson, secluded and private, overlooking the sea, lies New Zealand artist Jane Evans' stylish, fully self-contained luxury cottage. '**39 Russell**' is much more than a B&B. You will find the fridge stocked with extra goodies and complimentary bottles of hand crafted local wines, and a generous fruit bowl. This is about colour, harmony, privacy and independence. You will not find a chocolate on your pillow! You will find instead a personalized gift of the Nelson Regional Guide Book,' ('Art In It's Own Place') and Jane will be happy to guide you in local information should you require assistance.

The cottage has a fully equipped kitchen. For the traveler the independence of separate washing machine and dryer. In winter a cozy studio wood fire to welcome you in the comfortably furnished and sunny open living space with wooden floors and colourful rugs. Cottage has phone/fax, TV/ video, CD/tape deck, CDs, books, current magazines. Bi-fold doors lead from the deck into a large courtyard garden beyond with long wooden table. The courtyard is theatrically lit at night creating a romantic ambience. Alternatively, you may wish to wander the few minutes along the waterfront to one of Nelson's award winning restaurants.

DIRECTIONS:	From the Nelson Information Center drive down Halifax Street past the post office. Turn right at the roundabout into Haven Road and follow until you see Russell St on your left. **39 Russell** is up the 'Private Rd' on your left Jane's house is behind the fairytale gate on the right.

ATAWHAI HOMESTAY MIKE'S B&B

4 Seaton Street,
Atawhai, Nelson
Ph (03) 545 1671, Fax (03) 545 1671
e-mail: *cooperkent@actrix.gen.nz*

Features & Attractions

- *Safe, quiet, comfortable*
- *Close to sea*
- *Panoramic views*
- *En route to West Coast*
- *Gateway to National Parks*
- *1¹/₂ hours to ferry*

Homestay
Bed & Breakfast

Double	$65	
Single	$45	
Child	neg.	

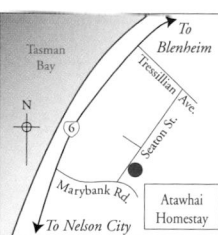

Bedrooms	Qty
Double	1
Twin	1
Single	
Bed Size	Qty
King	
Queen	1
Single	2
Bathrooms	Qty
Ensuite	2
Private	
Guest Share	
Family Share	

Only five minutes from Nelson City Centre we offer you quiet, comfortable, safe accommodation. Widely travelled ourselves, we know the importance of a hot shower, a clean, comfortable bed and helpful service.

Our guest accommodation is virtually self-contained on the ground floor of our two level home. The bedrooms each have ensuite facilities. The small guest lounge houses part of our large collection of books among which you are welcome to browse. Tea and coffee making facilities, a microwave oven and a washing machine are available for your use. Our interests include education, sea fishing and boating, veterans class running and canine obedience with our beautiful schnauzer dog. Breakfast is served in the conservatory, giving you superb views across Tasman Bay to the mountains beyond.

STANDING STONES BED & BREAKFAST

63 Marybank Road, Atawhai, Nelson
Ph (03) 545 1781
Mobile 025-678 6265
e-mail: *lorrainewakefield@xtra.co.nz*
http://www.standingstonesnz.com

Features & Attractions

- *Incredible views*
- *Backing onto bush reserve*
- *Home-made breads*
- *Espresso coffee*
- *E-mail and Internet access*
- *Massage therapist*

Bed & Breakfast
Panoramic Views

Double	$70-85
Single	$40
Child	neg.

Bedrooms	Qty
Double	3
Twin	1
Single	1
Bed Size	Qty
Queen	2
Double	1
Single	2
Bathrooms	Qty
Ensuite	
Private	
Guest Share	2
Family Share	

Wake up to bird song and breakfast above the trees, enjoy fantastic sea views across Tasman Bay to the mountains beyond.

Genuine hospitality, 5 minutes from downtown Nelson. This is a large 2-storey house with nice decks. Play petanque in my lovely garden or just sit and enjoy the peace and quite.

There is a gas BBQ available and dinners and packed lunches on request. I am a qualified chef and a massage therapist, so please take advantage of making a booking for a massage to unwind after a day's sightseeing. Being a traveller myself I know the benefits of good food and decent showers!! I have 2 great walk-in showers and laundry facilities are also available.

DRUMDUAN

148 The Glen Road, RD 1, Nelson
Ph (03) 545 0090, Fax (03) 545 0090
Mobile 021-545 009

Features & Attractions

- *11 km from Nelson City*
- *Safe, peaceful location*
- *Spa in garden setting*
- *19th century farm homestead*
- *Sea and mountain views*
- *Dinner by arrangement*

Bed & Breakfast
Countrystay

Double	$90
Single	$30-40
Child	

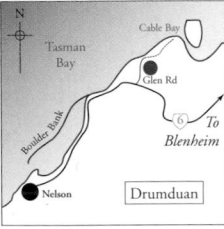

Bedrooms	Qty
Double	1
Twin	
Single	2
Bed Size	**Qty**
King	
Queen/Double	1
Single	2
Bathrooms	**Qty**
Ensuite	1
Private	
Guest Share	
Family Share	1

Drive 10 minutes north of Nelson to the start of the spectacular Boulder Bank and enjoy the peaceful views of farmland, Tasman Bay and the mountains beyond – all at **Drumduan's** doorstep. Experienced travellers ourselves, we also appreciate the value of peaceful, quiet and warm surroundings. With our friendly dog Tip we invite you to share this wealth with us during your stay in Nelson. Helen has a keen interest in gardening and there is a spa pool under the trees. Observe farm life first hand, wander along the Boulder Bank or take the Cable Bay Walkway. While dinner is by prior arrangement, Nelson boasts many fine cafés and restaurants, with local seafood a speciality. We are also equipped and happy to provide information on other acitivities in the Nelson Region. – *Please note: no credit card facilities.*

Waitaria Bay - Marlborough Sounds

"Stornoway House"

Four Fathom Bay, Private Bag, Marlborough
Ph (03) 579 8020, Fax (03) 579 8021
Mobile 025-372 631
e-mail: n.p.mccallum@xtra.co.nz
stornoway.co.nz

Tariff : N.Z. Dollars	
Double	$260-280
Single	$85
Child	$35

Bedrooms	Qty
Double	2
Twin	1
Single	
Bed Size	**Qty**
Super King	
King	1
Double	1
Single	3
Bathrooms	**Qty**
Ensuite	
Private	1
Guest Share	
Family Share	1

  Private Wilderness Retreat

Features & Attractions

- *Quiet, idyllic, private.*
- *Fish, swim, walk, relax*
- *Pure native bush drinking water*
- *Walks - bush, bluffs, ridgetops*
- *Piano, pool table, farm deer*
- *Single party bookings only*
- *Complimentary fishing gear, dinghy & a 1 hr scenic cruise*

DIRECTIONS: Four Fathom Bay is situated in the Pelorus Sound, just 35 min. boat travel from Havelock. Havelock is on the main highway between Blenheim and Nelson in the South Island.

Unique, idyllic touch of paradise, only 30 minutes from State Highway. Older style farm homestead set amongst large trees, native and exotic forest, 2 acres of lawns, native birds, wild animals, on waters edge and floating jetty.

Barbecue meals or formal dining with open fire Fish from jetty, snapper close by or the deep holes around the outer Marlborough Sounds.

23 km of easy/medium walking roads, through exotic and native forests, high bluffs and breathtaking ridge tops at 600 m. Viewing across a labyrinth of water ways. Hills, mountain,etc, offering you a genuine experience of nature's serene, unspoilt tranquility. No vehicles, no people, no noise, except native birds. Relax and unwind. 100% Pure New Zealand Freedom. Guided 4X4 transport available. Accommodation includes cruising 60 km of beautiful coastline. Visit Marine Farm and return to Havelock after farmstay. Your enjoyment is our pleasure. Hunting block available.

Season discounts apply. We supply all meals (extra charge for lunch and evening meal).

THE NIKAUS

86 Manaroa Road, Waitaria Bay, Kenepuru Sound
RD 2, Picton
Ph (03) 573 4432, Fax (03) 573 4432
Mobile 025-544 712

Tariff : N.Z. Dollars	
Double	$75-125
Single	$45-70
Child	

Bedrooms	Qty
Double	1
Twin	1
Single	

Bed Size	Qty
Super King	
King	
Double	1
Single	2

Bathrooms	Qty
Ensuite	
Private	
Guest Share	1
Family Share	

 Farmstay Bed & Breakfast

Features & Attractions

- Large country garden
- Central location in Kenepuru & Pelorus Sounds
- Scenic walks, panoramic views
- Hearty farm meals
- Friendly hosts and animals
- Golf, fishing, water taxis
- Genuine NZ farm experience

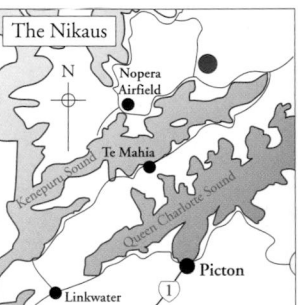

The Nikaus

The **Nikaus** sheep and cattle farm, situated in Waitaria Bay Kenepuru Sound, is two and half hours drive from Blenheim via Havelock or Picton. We offer friendly personal service in our comfortable spacious

DIRECTIONS: From Picton or Havelock travel along Queen Charlotte Drive to Linkwater, turn onto Kenepuru Rd and drive one and a half (1.5) hours to Waitaria Bay. Continue on Manaroa Rd, **The Nikaus** is 1 km on the right (Gate No 86).

home. The large gardens (in AA Garden Book) contain many rhododendrons, roses, camellias, lillies and perennials with big sloping lawns and views out to sea. We are a non-smoking houschold with interests in farming, boating, fishing and gardening.

We have 2 pet dogs. Other animals include the farm dogs, donkeys, pet wild pigs, turkeys, hens, peacocks a house cow, sheep and cattle. We offfer good hearty country meals using home grown produce.

Local operators are available for fishing trips, water and land taxis. For bookings and directions please phone/fax (03) 573 4432.

HOUSE OF GLENORA

22 Broadway cnr Wellington Street, Picton,
Ph (03) 573 6966, Fax (03) 573 7735
Mobile 025-224 0594
e-mail: *glenora.house@clear.net.nz*
www.glenora.co.nz

Tariff : N.Z. Dollars	
Double	$85-130
Single	$60-95
Child	

Bedrooms	Qty
Double	3
Twin	2
Single	1
Bed Size	**Qty**
Super King	1
King	1
Queen	1
Single	5
Bathrooms	**Qty**
Ensuite	2
Private	1
Guest Share	1
Family Share	

      Boutique Accommodation / Bed & Breakfast

Features & Attractions

- *Art, craft & wine trails*
- *Weaving workshops*
- *Great outdoor activities*
- *Secluded and peaceful*
- *Courtesy car*
- *Laundry facilities*
- *Off-street parking*
- *Magnificent views*

Picton (map)
Ferry Terminal
London Quay
High St.
Auckland St.
Wellington St.
Broadway
House of Glenora

Welcome to **House of Glenora**, one of Marlborough Sound's historical homes. Built in 1860 and surrounded by a sprawling garden, it is situated in the heart of Picton, yet very secluded and peaceful. Scandinavian creativity and New Zealand hospitality is blended into a colourful and vibrant home with a difference.

As Birgite is a master weaver, **House of Glenora** incorporates the International Weaving school, studio and gallery. The large bedrooms, extensive living areas, wide sunny verandahs and patios are decorated with a stunning mixture of antiques and contemporary pieces.

Enjoy the magnificent views of Picton Harbour and relax in the delightful garden with its 140 year old English oak tree.

Central heating, laundry facilities, courtesy car and off-street parking, fax and, of course, the Swedish-style "smorgasbord" breakfast together with the warm and vivacious feeling of **House of Glenora** and the beauty of Marlborough Sounds will surely make your stay here a memorable experience. We look forward to meeting you.

KARAKA POINT LODGE

312 Port Underwood Road, PO Box 586, Picton
Ph (03) 573 7700, Fax (03) 573 5444
Mobile (025) 614 3878
e-mail: *JandB@karakapointlodge.co.nz*
http://www.karakapointlodge.co.nz

Tariff : N.Z. Dollars		
	Double	$150-175
	Single	$135-160
	Child	

Bedrooms	Qty
Double	2
Twin	
Single	
Bed Size	**Qty**
Super King	
King	1
Queen	1
Single	
Bathrooms	**Qty**
Ensuite	1
Private	1
Guest Share	
Family Share	

Luxury Bed & Breakfast
Boutique Accommodation

Features & Attractions

- *Stunning views from all rooms*
- *Ferry 8 km (15 minutes drive)*
- *Delicious breakfasts*
- *Multiple night discounts*

- *Warm friendly hospitality*
- *Superior comfort beds*
- *Air conditioned rooms*
- *Spa under the stars*

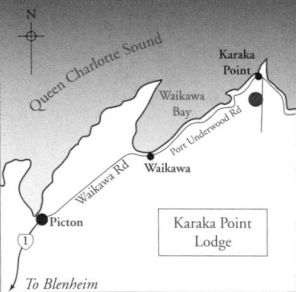

Our exclusive home is a rare gem in a gourmet paradise. A wonderful place to come and relax in comfort, either inside or on the spacious decks, which are directly accessed from lounge and bedrooms. You will love the relaxed atmosphere.

Karaka Point Lodge faces north, getting maximum all day sunshine and, being elevated, the panoramic views of the Queen Charlotte Sound are quite outstanding. Beaches where you can swim are about five minutes walk. Our exterior spa is in a secluded green area close to the house. Guests love to spa under the stars or with the festive lights at night.

Our beds are superb and our food delicious (dinner available by prior arrangement). Guest accommodation has all the necessities and more! Privacy or company is your choice. To sample some of the best delights of the area one night is not enough! We strive to give you an unforgettable stay. Bookings essential.

WHATAMONGA HOME STAY

425 Port Underwood Road, Picton
Ph (03) 573 7192, Fax (03) 573 7193
Mobile 025-430 834
e-mail: *info@whsl.co.nz*
www.whsl.co.nz

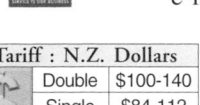

Tariff : N.Z. Dollars	
Double	$100-140
Single	$84-112
Child	

Bedrooms	Qty
Units	2
Double	2
Single	
Bed Size	**Qty**
Super King	2
King	1
Queen	
Single	2
Bathrooms	**Qty**
Ensuite	2
Private	2
Guest Share	
Family Share	

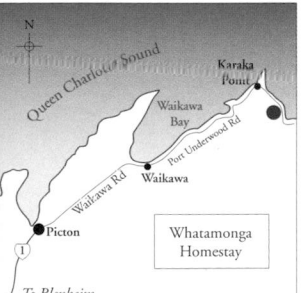

Luxury Self-contained Accommodation

Features & Attractions

- *Magnificent views*
- *Set in native bush*
- *Direct access to water*
- *20 min. to ferry terminal*
- *Self-contained seclusion*
- *Brand new luxury fit out*
- *Dinner by arrangement*
- *Extensive website www.whsl.co.nz*

Your hosts at **Whatamonga Home Stay** are Alex and Colette Wilson. The homestay offers accommodation in 2 brand new free standing secluded units, or in 2 separate bedrooms with own bathroom and deck under the main house. The home stay has been specifically designed by one of Marlborough's leading designers to face north for best sun and to allow guests to enjoy the view and their seclusion, or enjoy the interaction with the sea offered by accommodation with direct access to the water.

Evening meals are served in the main house as are cooked breakfasts. Continental breakfasts can be delivered to the units or downstairs bedrooms by prior arrangement. Bookings are essential, especially during the summer months of October to May.

DIRECTIONS:
From Picton take Waikawa Rd. From Waikawa shop take Port Underwood Rd. past Karaka Point. After 2 km **Whatamonga Homestay** sign is on left.

CHARMWOOD

158 Murrays Road, RD 3, Blenheim
Ph (03) 570 5409, Fax (03) 570 5110
Mobile 025-847 403
e-mail: *Charmwood@xtra.co.nz*
www.charmwood.co.nz

Tariff : N.Z. Dollars		
	Double	$110-145
	Single	$90
	Child	

Bedrooms	Qty
Double	2
Twin	1
Single	
Bed Size	Qty
Super King	
King	
Queen	2
Single	2
Bathrooms	Qty
Ensuite	2
Private	1
Guest Share	
Family Share	

**Rural Retreat
Bed & Breakfast**

Features & Attractions

- *Wine trails abound*
- *Queen Charlotte Walk*
- *Mussel farm tours*
- *Garden visits*
- *Craft trails*
- *Excellent fishing*

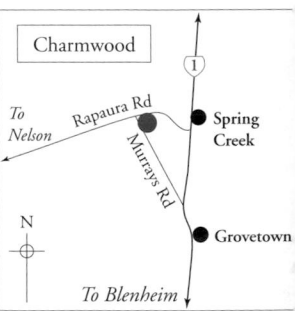

DIRECTIONS:
Turn off SH 1 at Spring Creek into
Rapaura Rd. Murrays Road
corner 700 m on left.

Peter and Lind a welcome you to **Charmwood** for a retreat in the countryside of Marlborough. Start your day with a country fare cooked breakfast while we would love to help you plan your itinerary, then stroll around our garden with Murdoch the cat, perhaps play some tennis, then cool off in the swimming pool. In the colder months curl up in front of the open fire or bubble away in the spa pool. Ask if our yacht 'Sunshine' is available - Peter may be able to take you sailing in the Queen Charlotte Sound. Linda's background is fashion and she enjoys handcrafts, gardening, music and sailing. Peter's background is construction. He is a keen yachtsman and also interested in olive growing and travel.

RHODODENDRON LODGE

SH 1, St Andrews, RD 4,
Blenheim
Ph (03) 578 1145, Fax (03) 578 1145

Features & Attractions

- *Large swimming pool*
- *Wine trails*
- *Purified water*
- *Fresh farm breakfast*
- *Local art and crafts*
- *Laundry available*

	Double	$80-100
	Single	$60
	Child	half price

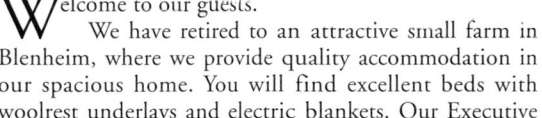

**Homestay
Bed & Breakfast**

Bedrooms	Qty
Double	2
Twin	1
Single	
Bed Size	**Qty**
King	
Queen/Double	2
Single	2
Bathrooms	**Qty**
Ensuite	1
Private	1
Guest Share	
Family Share	

DIRECTIONS:
1.5 km south from town on SH 1.
Large sign at gate. Twenty-five
minutes from Picton Ferry.

Welcome to our guests.

We have retired to an attractive small farm in Blenheim, where we provide quality accommodation in our spacious home. You will find excellent beds with woolrest underlays and electric blankets. Our Executive Suite has a "Bechstein" piano in it. If you like a full breakfast, we recommend delicious bacon, eggs and tomatoes produced on our farm. Outside a private courtyard with tree ferns and gardens surrounds a large swimming pool. Our house is set within extensive lawns and gardens with rhododendrons, roses and trees.

We are close to gourmet restaurants and have a selection of their menus. Marlborough has beautiful parks, wine trails, scenic sounds and walkways. Visitors travelling by train or bus will be met in Blenheim. We offer a courtesy phone call for your next homestay - "Happy Holidays!".

TAMAR VINEYARD

67 Rapaura Road, RD 3
Rapaura, Blenheim Region
Ph (03) 572 8408, Fax (03) 572 8405
e-mail: *tamar.vineyard@xtra.co.nz*
www.tamarvineyard.co.nz

Features & Attractions

- *A romantic retreat*
- *Four poster bed*
- *Sumptuous breakfast*
- *Heart of the wine trail*
- *15 minutes to Blenheim*
- *30 minutes to Picton*

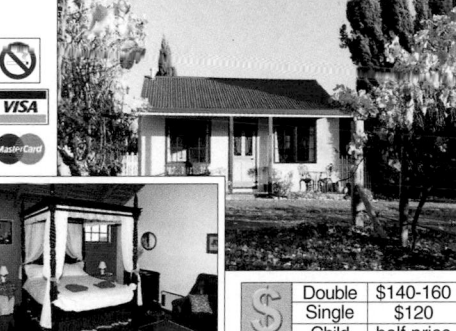

	Double	$140-160
	Single	$120
	Child	half price

**Self-contained
Vineyard Cottage**

Situated in the heart of the wine region, **Tamar** is one of Marlborough's oldest vineyards. Your newly-built cottage is a secluded, warm, romantic retreat with an ornately carved four-poster bed, featherdown duvet and classic leather couch. From the wide verandah you have breathtaking views through the vines to the Richmond Ranges. Our sumptuous three-course breakfasts feature homegrown produce and preserves. As we are an easy stroll from several wineries and restaurants you may choose to lunch or dine out, or cater for yourself in your full-equipped kitchenette. Clive and Yvonne enjoy showing you round the vineyard and we can help arrange winery tours or trips to the Marlborough Sounds (30 minutes drive) and Rainbow Skifield (1 hour's drive). We look forward to welcoming you for a memorable stay.

Bedrooms	Qty
Double	1
Twin	
Single	
Bed Size	**Qty**
King	
Queen	1
Single	1
Bathrooms	**Qty**
Ensuite	
Private	1
Guest Share	
Family Share	

OMAKA HEIGHTS
BED & BREAKFAST COUNTRYSTAY

199 Brookby Road, Omaka Valley, RD 2, Blenheim
Ph (03) 572 7402, Fax (03) 572 7403
e-mail: *omaka.heights@xtra.co.nz*
http://www.omakaheights.co.nz

Tariff : N.Z. Dollars	
Double	$120-160
Single	$85-115
Child	neg

Bedrooms	Qty
Double	2
Twin	1
Single	

Bed Size	Qty
Super King	
King	
Queen	2
Single	2

Bathrooms	Qty
Ensuite	3
Private	
Guest Share	
Family Share	

 Countrystay Bed & Breakfast

Features & Attractions

- Outstanding views
- Wine & sightseeing tours
- Art & Craft visits
- Scenic flights
- Golf, fishing, boating
- Whale & dolphin watching
- Skiing & tramping
- Excellent dining nearby

DIRECTIONS:
From Blenheim take Middle Renwick Rd after passing the airport take 1st left into Godfrey Rd. Then take 1st right into Dog Point Rd and 1st left into Brookby Rd.

Positioned in the picturesque Omaka Valley, just 12 kilometres from Blenheim City, our new purpose built hilltop Countrystay offers outstanding panoramic views over vineyards and farmland through to the Richmond Range in the distance. We are within a few minutes drive of over 30 wineries. There are numerous restaurants and cafés, offering world class cuisine, located within Blenheim City and the surrounding vineyard area.

Our self-contained Countrystay wing offers two guest rooms with private ensuite facilities and private decks plus a guest lounge. The twin room/ensuite is completely wheelchair accessible. The lounge provides tea/coffee making facilities, refrigerator and TV. The bedrooms are fully equipped with hairdryer and electric blankets. An additional guest room with private ensuite is available within the main house. Guests are offered a hearty breakfast and complimentary pre-dinner beverages. Evening meals are available by arrangement.

You may enjoy a stroll around our 8 ha property on which we farm alpacas and ostriches.

WYCOLLER

106A Maxwell Road, Blenheim, Marlborough
Ph (03) 578 8522
e-mail: *wycoller@travelwise.co.nz*

Tariff : N.Z. Dollars	
Double	$85-95
Single	$60-70
Child	

Bedrooms	Qty
Double	1
Twin	1
Single	
Bed Size	**Qty**
Super King	
King	
Double	1
Single	2
Bathrooms	**Qty**
Ensuite	1
Private	1
Guest Share	
Family Share	

**Homestay
Bed & Breakfast**

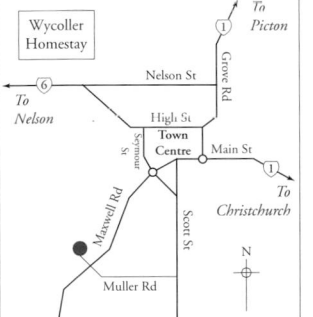

Features & Attractions

- *Open wood fire*
- *Lovely garden*
- *Art and craft trail*
- *Golf courses*
- *Sound's cruises*
- *Wine trails*

Set amongst 150 year old trees, **Wycoller** is architecturally designed to blend into its surroundings and is less than a ten minute walk to the town's centre. Our separate guest wing comprises all amenities, including tea/coffee making facilities.

A continental and/or generous cooked breakfast is provided.

The private patio is accessible from both rooms so you can enjoy lawns and fragrant gardens or relax in the hammock.

The town centre of Blenheim offers a diversity of restaurants and excellent cuisine. We have menus available.

Modern elegance, tranquility and exceptional location give **Wycoller** a special feel. A warm welcome awaits you. Non-smokers preferred. Please phone first.

BEACHFRONT FARMSTAY

Karamea, RD 1, Westport
Ph (03) 782 6762, Fax (03) 782 6762
Mobile 025-222 1755
e-mail: *farmstay@xtra.co.nz*
http://www.travelwise.co.nz

Tariff : N.Z. Dollars	
Double	$110-130
Single	$90
Child	neg.

Bedrooms	Qty
Double	2
Twin	
Single	1
Bed Size	**Qty**
Super King	
King	1
Queen	1
Single	1
Bathrooms	**Qty**
Ensuite	2
Private	
Guest Share	
Family Share	1

 Farmstay / Bed & Breakfast

Features & Attractions

- *2 min. walk to beach*
- *Peaceful surroundings*
- *Wonderful views*
- *Native forest walks*
- *Close to famous **Heaphy Track***
- *Generous cooked breakfast*
- *We offer horse trekking, hunting and fishing*

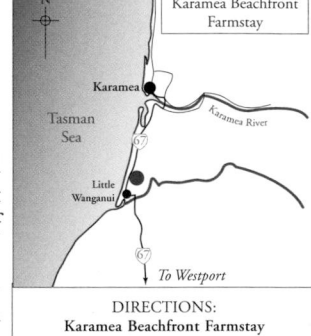

DIRECTIONS:
Karamea Beachfront Farmstay
is 84 km north of Westport
and 3 km north of Little Wanganui.

Karamea Beachfront Farmstay is 2 minutes walk from a deserted sandy beach. Come as far north as you can on the West Coast and relax for a few days. The only noise you will hear is the sound of the sea breaking on the shore.

We have a dairy farm with 320 milking cows. I enjoy cooking. Breakfasts are generous with fresh baked bread and pan-fried fish straight from the sea (if the tide is right). Dinners include farm-grown meat and vegetables and delicious desserts. New Zeland wine is complimentary.

For the more adventurous we can offer horse trekking, hunting, fishing and forest walks. Long stay rates are available. In Karamea you can see the spectacular Limestone Arch and Honeycomb Caves, Kahurangi National Park and wonderful scenery.

The famous **Heaphy Track** starts just north of Karamea.

198

AWAPIRITI
Highway 65, Murchison
Nelson Region
Ph (03) 523 9466, Fax (03) 523 9777

Tariff : N.Z. Dollars	
Double	$105-110
Single	$95
Child	n/a

Bedrooms	Qty
Double	2
Twin	1
Single	
Bed Size	**Qty**
Super King	
Queen	1
Double	1
Single	2
Bathrooms	**Qty**
Ensuite	2
Private	1
Guest Share	
Family Share	

 Farmstay - Bed & Breakfast

Features & Attractions

- Breathtaking scenery
- Native forest/farm walks
- River boundary/fishing
- Great night skys
- Cottage gardens
- Glow worms
- Fishing guides arranged
- Quiet peaceful surroundings

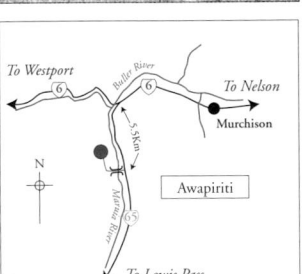

DIRECTIONS:
From north: 5.5km past
SH 65 turn-off, turn right over bridge.
From south: 5km from Maruia Falls turn
left over bridge. **Awapiriti** signposted.

To experience something different, visit **Awapiriti** nestled beside the Maruia River in the beautiful Maruia Valley. Share our comfortable homestead with its warm glow of native timber, log fires and colonial decor, providing the ultimate in comfort and relaxation. Here you can take time out in the cottage gardens, smell the roses and breathe the clean country air, take a farm walk and talk to the animals – elk/deer, bison, cattle and sheep.

Later enjoy a romantic candle light dinner with your hosts. We provide healthy country style meals that mostly consist of home-grown produce. Convivial pre-dinner drinks and wine is complimentary.

Breakfast is full or continental with fresh fruit and home made bread. Just 3 hours approximately from Picton/Christchurch/Hokitika, **Awapiriti** is a haven for adults, unsuitable for children.

Please telephone ahead for reservations.

HAVENLEE HOMESTAY

76 Queen Street, Westport
Ph (03) 789 8543, Fax (03) 789 8502
e-mail: *havenlee76@hotmail.com*

Features & Attractions

- *Great hospitality*
- *Lovely garden setting*
- *Generous breakfast*
- *Tranquil central location*
- *Nearby scenic attracions*
- *Two national parks nearby*

Rural Town Homestay

Double	$85
Single	$60
Child	neg.

Peace in Paradise - this is **Havenlee**, the perfect spot for those seeking tranquil, central location. We are both born and bred West Coasters - hospitality is part of our heritage. We welcome and invite you to share our modern, spacious home set amongst native and exotic trees and shrubs just 300 metres from the town centre. Breathtaking scenery is in abundance in the northern West Coast. Westport is sited between the Kahurangi and Paparoa National Parks - home to the magnificent towering rain forests with rare bird and plant life. In close proximity is the Tauranga Bay seal colony, Punakaiki Pancake Rocks and the scenic Charming Creek Walkway. As our guests, you will enjoy a continental - plus breakfast, warm, comfortable beds, a well appointed bathroom with a large bath tub and separate shower room, full laundry facilities, restaurants within walking distance, lots of local knowledge in a friendly, relaxed smokefree environment.

DIRECTIONS:
Along Palmerston St, right at Wakefield St, left at Queen St, 1st house on left.

Bedrooms	Qty
Double	2
Twin	1
Single	
Bed Size	**Qty**
King	
Queen/Double	2
Single	2
Bathrooms	**Qty**
Ensuite	
Private	
Guest Share	1
Family Share	

RIVER VIEW LODGE

SH 6 Lower Buller Gorge, PO Box 229, Westport
Ph/Fax (03) 789 6037, Mobile 025-249 1286
e-mail: info@rurallodge.co.nz
http://www.rurallodge.co.nz

Features & Attractions

- *Rooms with views*
- *Quiet & peaceful*
- *Close to Westport*
- *Full breakfast included*
- *One of NZ's "gardens to visit"*
- *Evening meal by arrangement*

Double	$145-174
Single	$106-127
Child	Half price

Boutique Accommodation Bed & Breakfast

Bedrooms	Qty
Double	3
Twin	1
Single	
Bed Size	**Qty**
King	
Queen/Double	3
Single	2
Bathrooms	**Qty**
Ensuite	4
Private	
Guest Share	
Family Share	

Situated above the Buller river, 'River View Lodge' was purpose-built in 1994 as a Bed and Breakfast accommodation lodge.

The rooms are spacious and open onto a large deck overlooking the garden. Facilities in the rooms include toiletries, hair dryers, heated towel rails, tea and coffee making facilities, TV, fresh flowers, clock radios. In addition each room has its own wardrobe and seating area.

Separate dining room lounge. Laundry available.
We are close to the seal colony and white water rafting, trout fishing, golf and underworld rafting. Come and enjoy our special place

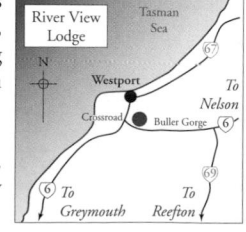

THE ROCKS HOMESTAY
Hartmount Place, PO Box 16, Punakaiki
Ph (03) 731 1141, Fax (03) 731 1142
Mobile 025-204 9833
e-mail: *therocks@minidata.co.nz*
www.minidata.co.nz/therocks/

Features & Attractions
- *Pancake Rocks, Blowholes*
- *Adjoins National Park*
- *Eco tours available*
- *Spectacular panoramas*
- *Relaxed and friendly*
- *Dinner by arrangement*

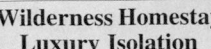

Double	$110-150
Single	$80-95
Child	

Wilderness Homestay
Luxury Isolation

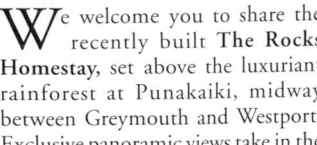

Bedrooms	Qty
Double	2
Twin	1
Single	
Bed Size	**Qty**
King	
Queen	2
Single	2
Bathrooms	**Qty**
Ensuite	3
Private	
Guest Share	
Family Share	

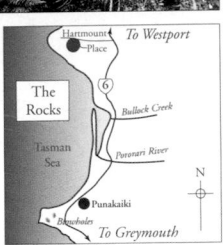

We welcome you to share the recently built **The Rocks Homestay**, set above the luxuriant rainforest at Punakaiki, midway between Greymouth and Westport. Exclusive panoramic views take in the Tasman Sea coast, the famous Blow Holes and Pancake Rocks, limestone cliffs, Paparoa National Park forest and magnificent sunsets. Heated towel rails, hairdryers, electric blankets, ensuites, conservatories and an extensive library of New Zealand books enhance your experience. Breakfast includes muesli, cereals, fresh yoghurt and home baking. We provide home-cooked evening meals with wine by prior arrangement. Our associated Green Kiwi Tours can take you on eco tours in the surrounding dramatic landscapes of the local area. Come share our interest in our environment, the outdoors, and in nature photography.

PAROA HOMESTAY
345 Main South Road, Greymouth
Ph (03) 762 6769, Fax (03) 762 6765
Mobile 025-685 6280
e-mail: *paroahomestay@hotmail.com*

Features & Attractions
- *Ensuite & private facilities*
- *Luxurious guest's lounge*
- *Special continental breakfast*
- *3 min. walk to beach*
- *Brilliant sunsets*
- *Bush walks, fishing*

Double	$99-105
Single	$75-79
Child	$30 u/12

Homestay
Bed & Breakfast

Bedrooms	Qty
Double	2
Twin	
Single	1
Bed Size	**Qty**
Super King	1
King	1
Double	1
Bathrooms	**Qty**
Ensuite	1
Private	1
Guest Share	1
Family Share	

Experience legendary West Coast hospitality in a modern, spacious, luxurious classic-style home. Experience an amazing seaview and incredible sunsets from the twin terraces – 3 minutes walk to the beach. Choose between ensuite or private facilities.
Punakaiki Pancake Rocks/Blowholes, rainforest bush walks and FREE Glow Worm Cave are all within 35 minutes drive radius. Excellent eating establishments are just 6 minutes away. Awake to a chorus of native birds nesting in towering Powhutakawa trees and shrubs. A superb continental breakfast is served.
Pam enjoys people, bush walking and collects antiques and fine china. She also enjoys everything associated with food.
Pam has been home hosting for 7 years and offers wonderful hospitality to everyone.

PINERS HOMESTAY

75 Main South Road, Karoro,
Greymouth
Ph (03) 768 5397, Fax (03) 768 5396

Tariff : N.Z. Dollars	
Double	$85
Single	$55-60
Child	neg.

Bedrooms	Qty
Double	1
Twin	1
Single	

Bed Size	Qty
Super King	
King/Single	
Queen	1
Single	2

Bathrooms	Qty
Ensuite	
Private	
Guest Share	1
Family Share	

 Homestay Bed & Breakfast

Features & Attractions

- *Wonderful West Coast hospitality*
- *Amazing mountain views*
- *Delicious food*
- *Off-street parking*
- *5 minutes walk to seaside*
- *Very comfortable beds*
- *Special diets no problem*
- *Budget price rental cars arranged*

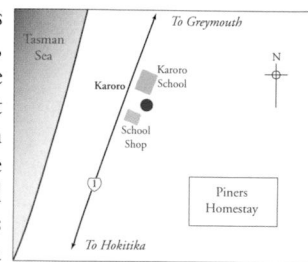

How would you like a legendary West Coast experience? West Coasters are famous world wide for their hospitality. Bev and Graham, born and bred Coasters, offer you an experience that you will long remember. We offer luxury at an affordable price. Enjoy amazing mountain views and watch the sun go down over the sea. We are nestled in the bush and plenty of bird life abounds. Graham, a goldminer until recently, has a wealth of knowledge about goldmining and enjoys fishing. Bev enjoys reading the many books in their home and is a real "foodie", so cooking great meals is no problem. Interior decorating and antiques are other interests and of course, we both love meeting people. We have two very spoiled "children" (our cats) sharing our home. Guests are welcome to smoke out on our terrace. Special diets are no problem - vegetarian, diabetic etc. We have courtesy pick-up from buses or Tranz Alpine. There is an extra toilet and hand basin adjacent to bedrooms. We take pleasure in helping arrange tours and things to do while in our lovely district.

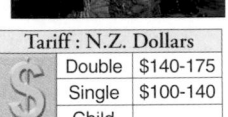

KINGFISHER LODGE
109 Cashmere Bay Road, Te Kinga, Lake Brunner
RD 1, Kumara, West Coast
Ph/Fax (03) 738 0822, Mobile 025 376 411
e-mail: *bjk@comauth.co.nz*
http://www.kingfisher-lodge-bed-breakfast-lake-brunner.co.nz

Tariff : N.Z. Dollars	
Double	$140-175
Single	$100-140
Child	

Bedrooms	Qty
Double	3
Twin	2
Single	
Bed Size	**Qty**
Super King	
King	
Queen	3
Single	4
Bathrooms	**Qty**
Ensuite	2
Private	
Guest Share	3
Family Share	

      Luxury Lakeside Retreat

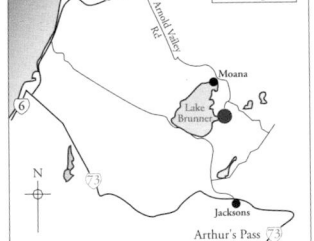

Features & Attractions

- *Secluded location*
- *Professional fishing guide host*
- *Tranquil lakeside setting*
- *Temperate rain forest*
- *Health spa and sauna*
- *Fully self-contained cottages*
- *Kayaks and Canadian canoes*
- *Internet and email facilities*

DISCOVER YOUR LAKESIDE HAVEN

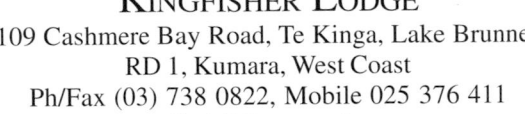

Kingfisher Lodge, nestled on the shore of Lake Brunner with its unspoilt wilderness surroundings, offers a wealth of water and nature recreational pursuits. Your host Ben Kemp, a professional fishing guide and knowledgeable local historian, will ensure you enjoy our friendly West Coast hospitality.

As our guest you will enjoy all the charm and cozy ambience of a personal fishing lodge with the additional luxuries of ensuite, health spa and sauna, kitchenette and laundry facilities. Only 2.5 hours drive from Christchurch or you can enjoy a scenic journey on the Tranz Alpine Express and alight a mere five minutes stroll away from our lakeside retreat. **Kingfisher Lodge** offers the perfect destination to relax and enjoy Westland's beautiful Lake Brunner.

Continental or full cooked breakfasts are available with complimentary morning and afternoon teas, Lunch and dinner can be catered for by arrangement with your host. At **Kingfisher Lodge** it's all here, the only thing missing is you.

AWATUNA HOMESTEAD ACCOMMODATION

Stafford Road (PO Box 25, Hokitika) Awatuna, Westland
Ph (03) 755 6834, Fax (03) 755 6876
Mobile 025-260 3171
e-mail: *awatuna@xtra.co.nz*
http://www.awatunahomestead.co.nz

Tariff : N.Z. Dollars	
Double	From $150
Single	$110
Child	$30

Bedrooms	Qty
Double	3
Twin	2
Single	

Bed Size	Qty
Super King	1
Queen	2
King Single	2
Single	2

Bathrooms	Qty
Ensuite	3
Private	1
Guest Share	
Family Share	

 Countrystay Bed & Breakfast & Self-contained Accommodation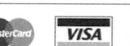

Features & Attractions

- *Cultural interest talks*
- *Garden walks & watching native birds*
- *Disabled/elderly facilities available*
- *Whitebaiting in season and canoeing*
- *Beach fossicking & fishing*
- *Vintage car rides*
- *Dinner by arrangement*
- *Closest town 10 min. away*

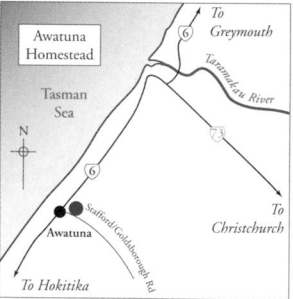

DIRECTIONS: From Hokitika, take SH 6 north for 13 km. At Awatuna, turn right into Stafford Road. Travel 90 m to number 9.

Awatuna Homestead offers you time to pause and enjoy the peaceful surroundings of gardens, featuring native trees and shrubs. French doors open onto wide verandahs from each well appointed guest room. Walk on the nearby wild West Coast beach, fossick, fish, or just sit and watch the awesome sunsets. On your return, Pauline, Hemi, Eleanor and Peter welcome you to experience wood stove warmth, country cooking and time spent sharing in your hosts' cultural and historic knowledge of the area. Masie, our small friendly stick retrieving dog, and Smudge, the pony, complete the family welcome. The Pipers Flat apartment has country charm and ambience, private access, exclusive deck, and expansive views of the sea, mountains and native bush. Sleeps 4 in 2 separate rooms, and another 2 on a fold out double sofa-bed in the lounge.

Fully self-contained for those that require more privacy. Apartment guests are offered the same activities as guests in the homestead. Tariff $140 double, $20 each extra person.

CRAIDENLIE LODGE

Blue Spur, PO Box 182, Hokitika
Ph (03) 755 5063, Fax (03) 755 8497
e-mail: *bruce@craidenlielodge.co.nz*
www.craidenlielodge.co.nz

Tariff : N.Z. Dollars	
Double	$160
Single	$160
Child	

Bedrooms	Qty
Double	6
Twin	2
Single	

Bed Size	Qty
Super King	
King	
Queen	6
Single	4

Bathrooms	Qty
Ensuite	3
Private	
Guest Share	2
Family Share	

 **Bed & Breakfast
Tour included in Tariff**

Features & Attractions

- *Quiet private surroundings*
- *Sheep - deer - cattle - dogs*
- *Rate includes minimum of one tour*
- *Farm setting*
- *Wonderful gardens*
- *Glow worm dell*
- *Lake Kaniere - Hokitika Gorge*

DIRECTIONS:
From Main St. into Hokitika turn east into Hampden St. Proceed straight for approximately 2km until sign on right.

Our visitors book has interesting entries.
John and Jane Adamson from the UK, 'Thank you, the best B&B and guided tour we ever had.'
Roy and Mary Watts from the UK, 'Outstanding in all respects, great conducted tours.'
We converted our 6500 square foot home into a lodge in 1999. Located on a 40 acre section, our home provides complete quiet and privacy. The native Kahikatea trees that surround the lodge are unique.
Bruce is a tennis nut, a born and bred fourth generation coaster and entrepreneur. He will delight you with his local knowledge and loves to take guests on guided tours which are complimentary. Most of our guests allow us to chauffeur them to the local restaurant in the evening, pick them up, take them to the glow worm dell and other local sights.
Hokitika is the centre of the West Coast. Most guests base themselves here for visits to the glaciers and the Punakaiki Pancake Rocks, allow two nights.

BRAESIDE

445 Lake Kaniere Road, Hokitika
Ph (03) 755 5151
Mobile 025-244 2398

Features & Attractions

- *Superb views*
- *Peaceful surroundings*
- *Fishing lakes 10 min.*
- *Close to Hokitika Airport*
- *Dinner by arrangement*
- *Beautiful Lake Kaniere*

 Farmstay Bed & Breakfast

DIRECTIONS: Please phone for simple directions

Double	$80
Single	$50
Child	$20

Relax and enjoy time out at **Braeside**, where the views are superb and peace is paramount. Where its only 10 minutes drive to anywhere, fishing, lakes, town, airport or any interests you may have.

If the season is right, try your luck at "Whitebaiting", a traditional fishing sport, enjoyed by many West Coasters.

Restaurants abound in Hokitika or by prior arrangement you can try our home cooked meal for an additional $24 per person.

We can advise you on places of interest to visit. Our home is warm and comfortable set on a hill overlooking our property and surrounding area.

You can find it by following the road to Lake Kaniere and looking for the swinging sign on your left just 1 minute from Kaniere Village.

Bedrooms	Qty
Double	1
Twin	1
Single	
Bed Size	**Qty**
King	
Queen	1
Single	2
Bathrooms	**Qty**
Ensuite	
Private	
Guest Share	1
Family Share	

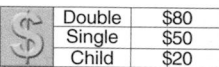

CARRICKFERGUS

Robertson Road, Harihari
Ph/Fax (03) 753 3124, Mobile 021-152 9406
e-mail: *info@carrickfergus.co.nz*
www.carrickfergus.co.nz

 FARM & HOME HOSTS

Features & Attractions

- *Fishing springfed streams*
- *Harihari coastal walkway*
- *Bushwalks/natural hot springs*
- *Mountain and rural views*
- *Peace and tranquility*
- *Dinner by arrangement*

 VISA MasterCard

Double	$140
Single	$85
ShareTwin	$135

Lifestyle Farm Homestay & Self-contained Suites

Bedrooms	Qty
Double	3
Twin	1
Single	
Bed Size	**Qty**
King	
Queen/Double	3
Single	2
Bathrooms	**Qty**
Ensuite	2
Private	1
Guest Share	
Family Share	

Our home is north facing, set in landscaped grounds, which adjoin a 32 acre sheep and Highland cattle farmlet with extensive mountain and rural views. Have breakfast at your self-contained suite which has private facilities or join us in our home for continental breakfast. We endeavor to make your stay comfortable. Stroll in our gardens or browse our West Coast book collection. Allow time to explore the Harihari Coastal Walkway, "a delight from start to finish, a two to three hour feast for the senses", or visit our natural hot springs and glowworms, or pit your skills against brown trout in local spring-fed streams. Leave time for a visit to the glaciers and the White Heron Colony. **Carrickfergus** – a comfortable midway rest between Christchurch/Wanaka or Nelson/Queenstown.

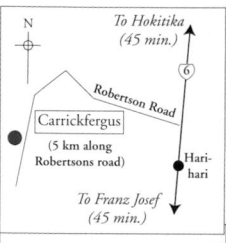

To Hokitika (45 min.)

Robertson Road

Carrickfergus
(5 km along Robertsons road)

Harihari

To Franz Josef (45 min.)

DIRECTIONS: Turn into Robertson Rd. Blue signpost on SH 6. 1.5km north of Harihari - follow map.

WAPITI PARK HOMESTEAD

State Highway 6, Harihari, South Westland
Ph/Fax (03) 753 3074
e-mail: *wapitipark@xtra.co.nz*
www.countrylodge.co.nz

Tariff : N.Z. Dollars	
Double	$125-235
Single	$100-165
Child	n/a

Bedrooms	Qty
Double	4
Twin	2
Single	
Bed Size	**Qty**
Super King	
King	2
Queen/Double	2
King/Single	3
Bathrooms	**Qty**
Ensuite	3
Private	2
Guest Share	
Family Share	

Country Lodge

Features & Attractions

- *Quiet, peaceful surroundings*
- *Superior comfort beds*
- *Dinner by arrangement*
- *Evening glow worm tour*
- *Large, spacious rooms & lounges*
- *Traditional hospitality*
- *Farm tour to feed Wapiti*
- *Guided hunting/fishing available*

Hosts Grant and Beverleigh invite you to discover the unique experience of staying at **Wapiti Park Homestead**, South Westland's premier hosted establishment for the discerning traveller. Enjoy a special combination of elegance and warm hospitality. Relax in complete comfort and affordable luxury. Set

DIRECTIONS: On the west side of SH 6 at southern approach to Harihari. Look for the sign.

in tranquil surroundings, the modern colonial-style lodge overlooks its own small farm which specialises in breeding Wapiti (Rocky Mountain Elk). The 6pm farm tour enables one to learn about and hand-feed the Wapiti. Enjoy the spacious living areas with two lounges and trophy/ games room, large, airy bedrooms with either ensuite or private facilities and superior comfort beds. Bountiful meals feature traditional country fare. Wander in the gardens, relax on the deck or stroll to the ornamental lake and settle in peace with a good book and a cool drink – the choice is yours. Located on SH6 ,the Lodge is the ideal stopover between the Picton/Nelson/ Christchurch and Wanaka/Queenstown areas. An increasing number of guests stay several nights, so they can explore this scenic wonderland of glaciers, national parks, rain forests and walkways at their leisure. Superb guided fishing for brown trout and salmon, and hunting for all New Zealand species is available. A warm welcome awaits you at **Wapiti Park**. Not suitable for young children. Advance booking recommended. Booking discounts available.

MATAI LODGE

Whataroa, South Westland, South Island
Ph/Fax (03) 753 4156, Mobile 021-155 2506
e-mail: *jpurcell@xtra.co.nz*

Features & Attractions

- *Glacier flights*
- *Forest & glacier walks*
- *3-course dinner 30pp*
- *Fishing - salmon and trout*
- *White heron bird sanctuary*
- *Golf, kayaking, horse riding*

Farmstay Bed & Breakfast

Double	$140
Single	$80
Child	half price

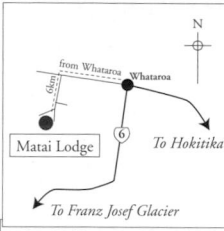

DIRECTIONS: Whataroa – 20min. north of Franz Josef Glacier. 3km west of SH 6: Blue B & B sign.

If you are coming to see the **Glaciers**, walk in the **World Heritage Park**, the coastal track at Okarito or visit the **White Heron Bird Sanctuary** in **Whataroa**, you are warmly welcomed to share with us our tranquil, rural retreat in our modern, spacious home on a 400 acre farm of sheep, cows and a farm dog. Upstairs is a suite of two bedrooms, conservatory and private bathroom and downstairs a king size ensuite. You are welcome to join us for a home-cooked dinner with NZ wine ($35.00 per person). Our motto is: "A stranger is a friend we have yet to meet". Glenice speaks Japanese and has taught felting, spinning and weaving in Japan. We both play tennis and golf.

Bedrooms	Qty
Double	2
Twin	1
Single	
Bed Size	**Qty**
Super King	1
King	1
King/Single	2
Bathrooms	**Qty**
Ensuite	1
Private	1
Guest Share	
Family Share	

KNIGHTSWOOD BED & BREAKFAST

State Highway 6 (PO Box 70) Franz Josef Glacier
Ph (03) 752 0059. Fax (03) 752 0061
e-mail: *knightswood@xtra.co.nz*
http://www.knightswood.co.nz

Features & Attractions

- *Mountain and rural views*
- *Situated on a deer farm*
- *Peaceful surroundings*
- *Scenic glacier flights*
- *Guided hunting/fishing*
- *Fresh home baking*

Double	$120-150
Single	$90-120
Child	neg.

Bed & Breakfast Deer Farm

Bedrooms	Qty
Double	2
or Twin	2
Single	
Bed Size	**Qty**
King	2
Queen	
Single	
Bathrooms	**Qty**
Ensuite	2
Private	
Guest Share	
Family Share	

Welcome to tranquility, surrounded by mountains, rain forest and birdlife at **Knightswood**. Rusty built our home from local materials in true pioneering spirit. Being north facing, rooms offer spectacular views of the Southern Alps. Jackie is a paediatric nurse from England, Rusty a local helicopter pilot of 20 years and keen deer farmer. We have over 200 deer here! We would love to help you experience the breathtaking, abundant attractions accessible in this World Heritage Area. Allow a hearty breakfast to set you up for the day, enjoying amazing scenic flights over the glaciers, hiking on glaciers, through temperate rainforest or around mirror lakes. We, and our daughter Amy, look forward to helping you discover the magical qualities of the West Coast.

DIRECTIONS: On main SH6, 3 km south of Franz Josef. Travelling from the north we are on the right, from the south on the left side.

OKURU BEACH
Okuru, Haast, South Westland
Ph (03) 750 0719, Fax (03) 750 0722
e-mail: *okurubeach@xtra.co.nz*
http://www.okurubeach.co.nz

Features & Attractions
- *Walking distance to beach*
- *Fiordland Crested Penguins*
- *Enjoyable forest walks*
- *Good trout fishing*
- *Craft shop for guests*
- *Friendly and relaxed*

Double	$70-75	Self-contained: $80.00 per night	
Single	$45	Extra person: $10.00, sleeps 4	
Child	$20	Continental breakfast: $8.00 p.p.	

H

**Homestay
Bed & Breakfast**

Bedrooms	Qty
Double	3
Twin	2
Single	
Bed Size	**Qty**
King	
Double	3
Single	4
Bathrooms	**Qty**
Ensuite	1
Private	1
Guest Share	1
Family Share	

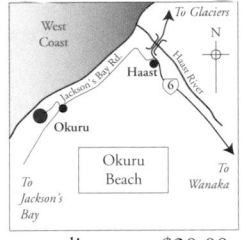

Okuru Beach gives you the opportunity to stay in a unique part of our country, where time moves slowly. Enjoy the coastal beaches with interesting driftwood and shells. On a walk in the rainforest a variety of native birds can be viewed. In the season, Fiordland Crested Penguins can be seen, within walking distance along a rocky beach, near Jackson's Bay, a 30-minute drive away. We and our friendly labrador dog enjoy sharing our comfortable home and local knowledge of the area. With prior notice we can serve dinner at $20.00 per person, BYO, vegetarian is available. Our interests are handcrafts, photography, fishing, shooting and tramping. We enjoy the chance to meet new people from New Zealand and overseas. Complimentary tea or coffee on arrival. Laundry facilities available (minimal charge).

Magic beaches – endless and unspoiled.

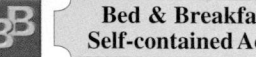

Ardara Lodge
233 Schoolhouse Road, Kaikoura
Ph (03) 319 5736, Fax (03) 319 5732
e-mail: *aemboyd@xtra.co.nz*
www.ardaralodge.com

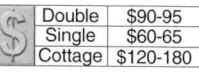

Features & Attractions

- *Spectacular mountain views*
- *Whalewatch/Dolphins 5 min.*
- *Quiet & tranquil – lovely gardens*
- *Bush and coastal walks*
- *Walk to 'Donegal House',*
  Irish restaurant and bar

Bed & Breakfast and Self-contained Accomm.

Double	$90-95
Single	$60-65
Cottage	$120-180

We welcome you to our modern home and cottage on 11 acres of farmland, which Ian's Great Great Uncle bought in 1882 after emigrating from Ardara, Ireland in 1876. You can experience the magic of the beautiful Kaikoura Mountains from our viewing decks. Walk over to 'Donegal House', Ian's brother's Irish Restaurant, and have a meal of locally caught fish or crayfish (lobster) and a glass of Guinness. We are five minutes from Whalewatch, Dolphins, Seal Swimming, horse riding, bush and coastal walks. Our timber cottage is popular with groups, families and honeymoon couples. All ensuite rooms have tv, fridge, hair dryer and coffee/tea making facilities. We look forward to meeting you and sharing our local knowledge of Kaikoura with you. – *For our Christchurch apartment – check our website:* www.ardaralodge.com/flat.html

Bedrooms	Qty
Double	6
Twin	1
Single	
Bed Size	**Qty**
King	
Queen	6
Single	3
Bathrooms	**Qty**
Ensuite	5
Private	
Guest Share	
Family Share	

DIRECTIONS: Driving north from Kaikoura on SH.1 (Atheney Rd.), turn left into **Schoolhouse Rd**. drive 1.5 km to **Ardara Lodge**.

Dillondale
RD 4, Kaikoura 8280
Ph (03) 319 5205
Mobile 025-295 0363
e-mail: *acton.adams@actrix.co.nz*

Features & Attractions

- *Warm, friendly hospitality*
- *Wonderful scenery*
- *Separate guest wing*
- *Experience farming life*
- *Dinners by arrangement*
- *Flexible mealtimes with hosts*

A Genuine Farmstay Excellent Accommodation

Double	$115-125
Single	$95-105
Child	neg.

Lynda and Percy welcome you to **Dillondale**, a 486 hectare (1200acres) sheep and beef farm with some forestry, set in the midst of a valley with panoramic views of the Seaward Kaikoura Mountains. We offer a friendly, peaceful and very comfortable atmosphere for guests to relax and yet be close enough to enjoy Kaikoura's whale watching, dolphin swimming and many other activities. On site activities include experiences observing farm activities as they occur and farm walks. Farm tours are also available for an extra charge – $15-$20 per person. We enjoy good food, wine and conversation with our guests. Hearty two course dinners are available with prior arrangement at $30 per person.

Bedrooms	Qty
Double	1
Twin	1
Single	
Bed Size	**Qty**
Queen	1
Double	1
Single	1
Bathrooms	**Qty**
Ensuite	1
Private	1
Guest Share	
Family Share	

DIRECTIONS: Reservations are essential to avoid disappointment. Easy directions will be given. on booking. **Kaikoura** 35 min., **Christchurch** 2¼ hrs., Hanmer Springs 1¼ hrs.

BALLINDALLOCH
95 Long Plantation Road, Culverden, RD 2
North Canterbury
Ph/Fax (03) 315 8220, Mobile 025-373 184

Features & Attractions

• *Quiet, peaceful surroundings* • *Magnificent mountain views*
• *Complimentary farm tour* • *Dinner by arrangement,$30pp*
• *Excellent trout/salmon fishing* • *30 min. to Hanmer Springs*

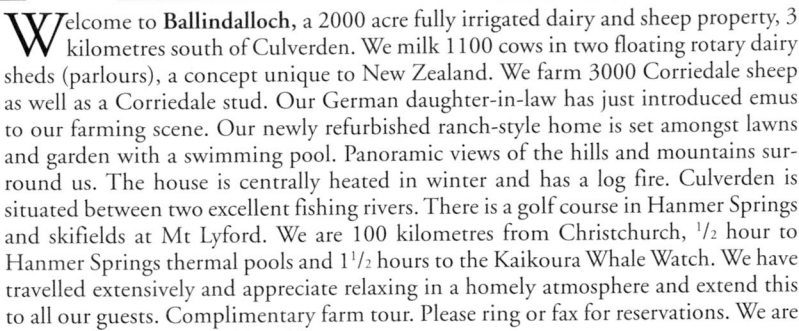

Double	$105
Single	$55
Child	half u/14

**Farmstay
Bed & Breakfast**

Bedrooms	Qty
Double	1
Twin	1
Single	
Bed Size	**Qty**
King	
Queen	1
Single	2
Bathrooms	**Qty**
Ensuite	
Private	
Guest Share	1
Family Share	

Welcome to **Ballindalloch**, a 2000 acre fully irrigated dairy and sheep property, 3 kilometres south of Culverden. We milk 1100 cows in two floating rotary dairy sheds (parlours), a concept unique to New Zealand. We farm 3000 Corriedale sheep as well as a Corriedale stud. Our German daughter-in-law has just introduced emus to our farming scene. Our newly refurbished ranch-style home is set amongst lawns and garden with a swimming pool. Panoramic views of the hills and mountains surround us. The house is centrally heated in winter and has a log fire. Culverden is situated between two excellent fishing rivers. There is a golf course in Hanmer Springs and skifields at Mt Lyford. We are 100 kilometres from Christchurch, $1/2$ hour to Hanmer Springs thermal pools and $1^1/2$ hours to the Kaikoura Whale Watch. We have travelled extensively and appreciate relaxing in a homely atmosphere and extend this to all our guests. Complimentary farm tour. Please ring or fax for reservations. We are a non smoking household and have one cat.

HANMER VIEW BED & BREAKFAST
8 Oregon Heights, Hanmer Springs 8273,
North Canterbury.
Ph (03) 315 7947 Fax (03) 315 7958
Free Ph (0800) 920 800
e-mail: *lawsurv@xtra.co.nz*

Features & Attractions

• *Panoramic views of forest,*
  village and mountains beyond
• *Warm hospitality*

• *Lovely forest walks*
• *Walking distance to hot pools*
• *Delicious food*

Double	$110-150
Single	$80-120
Child	n/a

**Bed & Breakfast
Boutique Accommodation**

Bedrooms	Qty
Double	2
Twin	1
Single	
Bed Size	**Qty**
King	1
Queen/Double	2
Single	2
Bathrooms	**Qty**
Ensuite	3
Private	
Guest Share	
Family Share	

Come and relax in the ambience of our purpose built Bed & Breakfast. Enjoy the privacy of your own studio room, designed with TV and ensuite and tastefully decorated with your comfort in mind. Laze on the deck or in our guest lounge absorbing the fantastic views while watching the native birds that are frequent visitors to our garden. Your needs are well provided for at **Hanmer View**. Tea, coffee and home baking are always available. Our generous breakfasts set you up for the day. Special evening dinner is available by prior arrangement. The Village Centre and Hot Thermal Pools are a short walk away. Jet boating, rafting, mountain biking, horse trekking, bungy jumping and skiing in the winter are for the energetic. You may just wish to walk in the forest or play a round of golf at our picturesque 18-hole course or simply soak in the hot pools.

ALBERGO HANMER

88 Rippingale Road, Hanmer Springs,
P.O. Box 79, North Canterbury
Ph (03) 315 7428 Fax (03) 315 7428
e-mail: *albergohanmer@hotmail.com*
http://www.albergohanmer.com

Tariff : N.Z. Dollars	
Double	$120-220
Single	$100
Child - on request	

Bedrooms	Qty
Double	3
Twin	
Single	

Bed Size	Qty
Super King/twin	2
King	1
Queen	
Single	

Bathrooms	Qty
Ensuite + Spa	2
Ensuite	1
Guest Share	
Family Share	

 Fine Accommodation

Features & Attractions

- *Newly created outdoor sunken courtyard*
- *Underfloor heating, double glazing*
- *2 min. drive to Centre*
- *Across from 18 hole golf course*
- *3-course gourmet breakfast (10 choices)*
- *Dinners by prior arrangement*
- *European service - attention to detail*
- *Large ensuites with double spa baths*

'True hospitality without compromise!'

Albergo **Hanmer** is set in a magic mountain arena, offering peace, privacy and all day sun. The interior styling is modern European, creating a fresh, light and comfortable feel. The guest wing features spacious double rooms with large ensuites. Unwind under a wonderful hot shower (high pressure), or take a spa, then relax in the private guest lounge. **Check out the new designer suite!**

DIRECTIONS: At junction before main village, 300m past Shell Garage, take **Argelins Rd.** (Centre Branch), go past Hanmer Golf Club, take first road on left **Rippingale Rd.** (no exit). **Albergo Hanmer** is 900 m down at the very end of this country lane.

Albergo's renowned 3-course gourmet breakfast, served in the sunny conservatory, presents you with more than 10 choices to start your day: Fresh fruit platter or Swiss Birchermuesli, then scrumptious Eggs Benedict on fresh Hollandaise, full English Breakfast or go Spanish with a Frittata, all topped off with a crunchy Swiss mini-loaf.

Dedicated hosts, Bascha and Beat Blattner, are a young couple (NZ & Swiss origins) with 15 years experience in Hospitality and Tourism. Languages spoken: English, Swiss, German, French, Italian and Spanish. The private atmosphere of the candle-lit dining room, combined with our European and Pacific Rim cuisine will give you a unique experience: Prime NZ beef medallions, baby lamb, venison tenderloins enveloped with Italian and Asian entrées and Swiss surprise desserts.

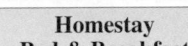
BREDON DOWNS

Bredon Downs, Amberley, RD 1,
North Canterbury
Ph (03) 314 9356, Fax (03) 314 8994
e-mail: *lucy.lucy@xtra.co.nz*

Features & Attractions
- *Amidst English style garden*
- *Dinners by arrangement*
- *Delicious & filling breakfast*
- *Visit our ostriches*
- *Start of Waipara wine trail*
- *2 hours to whales at Kaikoura*

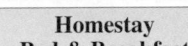

Double	$110
Single	$60
Child	$30

Homestay Bed & Breakfast

Bedrooms	Qty
Double	1
Twin	1
Single	1
Bed Size	Qty
King	
Queen	1
Single	3
Bathrooms	Qty
Ensuite	1
Private	1
Guest Share	
Family Share	

Our drive leads off SH 1, so we are conveniently located en route to and from the Inter-Island Ferry and just 40 minutes north of Christchurch – very easy to find. The house is a very comfortable hundred-year old farmhouse, extensively renovated and restored, and surrounded by an English-style garden with swimming pool which guests are welcome to use. We are close to the Waipara Wine Trail, the beach and an attractive golf course – the hot thermal pools at Hanmer are only an hour away. We breed ostriches, which we are pleased to show visitors, and we have chicks hatching each week during the summer.
We have travelled extensively and lived in Africa before coming from England to live here 35 years ago and enjoy welcoming local and overseas visitors into our home. We share our live with a Labrador, two geriatric donkeys and Rupert, the cat.

ROSSBURN

Spark Lane, Rangiora
Ph (03) 313 7427, Fax (03) 313 7421
Mobile 025-300 420
e-mail: *sparkfarm@xtra.co.nz*

Features & Attractions
- *Town-supply dairy farm*
- *Extensive Colonial Museum*
- *Country hospitality*
- *Hanmer Springs 1¼hrs drive*
- *Rangiora 1 kilometre*
- *Christchurch 25 min.*

Double	$80
Single	$60
Child	

Farm & Museum Bed & Breakfast

Bedrooms	Qty
Double	2
Twin	
Single	
Bed Size	Qty
Queen	1
Double	1
Single	1
Bathrooms	Qty
Ensuite	1
Private	
Guest Share	1
Family Share	

We are a town-supply dairy farming family and Kindergarten teacher. Our home **Rossburn** is a large two storied colonial homestead with the addition of cats, dogs, and cockatoo.Included in our tariff is an opportunity for guests to view our extensive colonial museum, which is visited by numerous overseas and local tourists. We assure, guests will be amazed by what there is to see – it could be the highlight of your trip. Available to guests is a sitting room (conservatory, TV).In our spacious park-like gardens is an all-weather tennis court (racquets provided).We love entertaining people from all walks of life and sharing travel experiences. Our interests evolve around our family of six grown-up children, farm and church life. Beaches and wineries are close by. We'd love you to share an evening meal with us ($20.00 pp). Please advise us at time of booking (also please phone for easy directions).
A warm welcome is assured.

WAIMAKARIRI LODGE

45 Depot Gorge Road, RD 1, Oxford
Ph (03) 312 3662, Fax (03) 312 3662
Mobile 025-371 096
e-mail: *sharonian@xtra.co.nz*

Tariff : N.Z. Dollars		
	Double	$130
	Single	$90
	Child	neg.

Bedrooms	Qty
Double	2
Twin	1
Single	
Bed Size	Qty
Super King	
King	
Queen	2
Single	2
Bathrooms	Qty
Ensuite	2
Private	1
Guest Share	
Family Share	

**Farmstay
Bed & Breakfast**

Features & Attractions

- *Spectacular gorge & mountain views*
- *Brand new purpose-built home*
- *Close to ski fields*
- *Christchurch/Airport 30 minutes*
- *Dinner by arrangement*
- *Trout fishing*
- *18 hole golf course*
- *Spa pool and home gym*

Waimakariri Lodge is situated on Route 72 and very easy to find. A Farmstay with panoramic views of gorge and mountains.

Enjoy our home-made mueslis, warm hospitality, home gym, relaxing private spa and quiet location.

This is the place for you! An 18 hole golf course is adjacent to our property, golf clubs are available. A scenic tour can be arranged in our vintage car, with picnic lunch provided.

Private guest lounge with tea and coffee making facilities, home-baking, e-mail facilities, complimentary guest laundry and private entrance. All bedrooms have warm, cosy beds and French doors opening out to verandah.

With our telescope in the turret, view the mountains and wonder at the evening sky!

You will also be welcomed by our two Jack Russells. Our home is your home, we welcome you to **Waimakariri Lodge!**

OHOKA PARK TRUFFIERE

708 Tram Road (RD 2, Kaiapoi, 8252) Ohoka
Ph (03) 312 6072, Fax (03) 312 6073
Mobile 025-292 9859
e-mail: *bmitch@xtra.co.nz*

Tariff : N.Z. Dollars	
Double	$110-130
Single	$80
Child	

Bedrooms	Qty
Double	2
Twin	
Single	
Bed Size	**Qty**
King	
Queen	1
Double	1
Single	
Bathrooms	**Qty**
Ensuite	
Private	1
Guest Share	
Family Share	

**Countrystay
Bed & Breakfast**

Features & Attractions

- *New home in park setting*
- *Separate guest wing*
- *Self-contained facilities*
- *Close to vineyards, ski fields*
- *Peaceful environment*
- *Christchurch Airport - 20 min.*

Our home, the first to be built in this new truffiere, offers a unique stay in the North Canterbury countryside. Just 10 km from Rangiora and 22 km  from Christchurch Airport, **Ohoka Park Countrystay** provides single party guest accommodation for up to 4 people in fully self-contained smoke free guest facilities.
We are close to the finest Canterbury wineries and neighbouring olive groves.
Winter ski fields at Mount Hutt are 1.5 hours drive away. Our guest wing has its own private entrance, kitchenette facilities with full continental breakfast, living room with separate dining table, TV, bathroom and under-floor heating.
Come and stay with us in this unique country environment. We look forward to meeting you.

Darfield - Christchurch	YOUR HOSTS: **Brian and Michelle**	Free Ph: 0800-181 144

MEYCHELLE MANOR

Main West Coast Road, SH 73, PO Box 162
'S' Bends, Kirwee, Canterbury
Ph (03) 318 1144, Fax (03) 318 1965
e-mail: *meychelle.m@inet.net.nz*
www.farmstaynewzealand.com

Tariff : N.Z. Dollars	
Double	$170
Single	$110
Child	neg.

Bedrooms	Qty
Double/Twin	2
Twin	
Single	
Bed Size	**Qty**
Super King/Twin	2
King	
Queen	
Single	
Bathrooms	**Qty**
Ensuite	2
Private	
Guest Share	
Family Share	

Luxury Farmstay
Bed & Breakfast

Features & Attractions

- *Easy to find on SH 73*
- *Shopping, restaurants, train 3 min.*
- *Skiing, golf courses, wineries very close*
- *Astronom. telescope, DVD home theatre*
- *Delicious breakfast*
- *Private beautiful rooms*
- *E-mail, fax, laundry avail.*
- *Exotic & farmyard animals*

We warmly welcome you to our family home, **Meychelle Manor**, a deer farm 25 minutes from Christchurch International Airport, 35 minutes from the city, right on SH 73. You can enjoy a seat beside our lake and feed the ducks and fish or putt on our golf green, play pentonque or swim in our indoor heated pool. Our private luxiourious ensuite rooms offer comfortable super-king/twin beds, central heating, hair dryers, clock radios and balconies. For breakfast we offer a delicious continental and/or cooked kiwi-style selection. An evening meal can be enjoyed at a variety of local restaurants/cafés or by arrangement with us. After dinner you may want to enjoy our digital home surround sound theatre, listen to music or play puzzles in our entertainment room, have a night swim in our softly lit pool room or star-gaze through our 8" Newtonian telescope. Next day you could connect to the Tranz Alpine train excursion (one of the top train rides in the world) or by appointment we can arrange hunting and fishing trips and more.

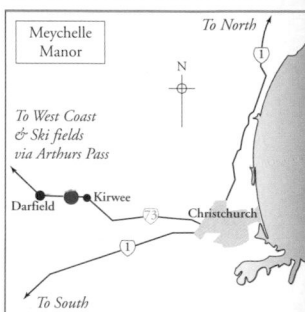

DIRECTIONS: From **Christchurch**: On SH 73 on the left after S-Bends after Kirwee. From **Darfield**: 3 min. from township on SH 73 on right, just before 'S' bends at Kirwee.

BRAMASOLE

Genesis Drive, West Melton, Christchurch
Ph (03) 318 1688 . Fax (03) 318 1338
Mobile 021 - 137 7789
e-mail: *samacd@xtra.co.nz*

Features & Attractions

- *Christchurch Airport 15min.*
- *Tennis court & swimming pool*
- *City centre 30 min.*
- *Quality home cooking*
- *Peaceful rural setting*
- *Winery nearby*

H **Luxury Self-contained Homestay Accommodation** **S^C**

Double	$120
Single	$80
Child	neg.

Bedrooms	Qty
Double	1
Twin	1
Single	
Bed Size	**Qty**
King	
Queen	1
Single	2
Bathrooms	**Qty**
Ensuite	
Private	1
Guest Share	
Family Share	

We will be delighted to collect you from Christchurch International Airport and whisk you to rural West Melton, at the heart of Canterbury's wine region. The best of the South Island's fishing, golf and skiing is easily accessible, while **Bramasole** is an ideal base for sightseeing and shopping in Christchurch or for excursions further afield. Or you can relax in the privacy of your own elegant and comfortable self-contained suite and enjoy swimming, tennis and croquet in a beautiful garden setting.
Sally is an accomplished and imaginative cook, using our own eggs, fruit and vegetables and organic produce wherever possible. Other family members include our two teenage children, two friendly long-haired dachshunde and Beckie the cat.

GARDEN VINEYARD HOMESTAY

Torlesse Road, West Melton, RD 1, Christchurch
Ph (03) 347 7556, Fax (03) 347 7558
e-mail: *drewann@ihug.co.nz*
www.gardenvineyard.co.nz

Features & Attractions

- *Superb independent unit*
- *Christchurch Airport 15 min.*
- *Golf - 10 courses nearby*
- *Special long stay rates*
- *Wine tasting*
- *Relaxing garden setting*

VISA
MasterCard

C **Self-contained Country Vineyard Stay** **S^C**

Double	$80-125
Single	$60-110
Child	

If you want to do "your own thing" but still experience a "Kiwi" homestay holiday in the countryside, a stay on our vineyard is for you. Our comfortable self-catering unit is in a peaceful garden setting, surrounded by trees, amidst 5 acres of grapevines. We are situated 15 minutes from Christchurch Airport and 25 minutes from the city centre.

Our unit is particularly suited to one or two couples, or a family of up to 4 members. Being keen golfers we can advise clients on the 10 courses nearby. All linen is supplied and a continental breakfast is provided daily.

Bedrooms	Qty
Double	1
Twin	1
Single	
Bed Size	**Qty**
King	
Queen	1
Single	2
Bathrooms	**Qty**
Ensuite	
Private	1
Guest Share	
Family Share	

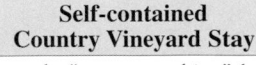

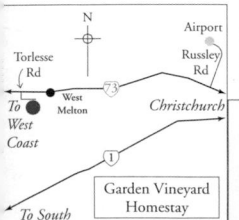

DIRECTIONS: From airport, turn right Russley Rd. At next roundabout. Turn right SH 73. 13 km to West Melton. Torlesse Rd. 3 km on left past West Melton Hotel. We are approx. 1 km on the right.

Complimentary tea and coffee. If you do not wish to cook, there are several local restaurants nearby, or a meal can be provided by arrangement from your hosts.

DEVONDALE HOUSE

66 Johns Road, Belfast, Christchurch
Ph (03) 323 6616, Fax (03) 323 8723
Mobile 025-200 7236
e-mail: *sfox@xtra.co.nz*

Tariff : N.Z. Dollars	
Double	$165-210
Single	
Child	

Bedrooms	Qty
Double	2
Twin	
Single	
Bed Size	**Qty**
Super King	
King	1
Queen	1
King/Single	
Bathrooms	**Qty**
Ensuite	2
Private	
Guest Share	
Family Share	

 Bed & Breakfast Boutique Accommodation

Features & Attractions

- *Peace, tranquillity & views*
- *Personal, friendly hospitality*
- *Large garden with tennis*
- *Security gate*
- *The ultimate B & B experience*
- *Farm & wildlife reserve walk*
- *Pre dinner drinks with hosts*
- *Cavalier King Charles Spaniel*

Devondale House is a lovely rural retreat, only minutes from the airport and city, yet quiet behind security gates with a relaxing walkway through adjacent farmland. This tranquil haven, set in expansive gardens, with tennis court and country walks, offers guests warm hospitality in elegant surroundings. An unbeatable location from which to explore the Canterbury area, from Hanmer to Kaikoura and the whale watch. Take an evening stroll through the adjacent farm to the beautiful Groynes, an area with fish-filled waterways and abundant bird life. Close by, enjoy an evening meal at the **Willowbank** restaurant, followed by a tour to see the **Kiwis**. The Antarctic Centre takes you on a snow and ice experience to the South Pole. At **Devondale House** you will be treated to a memorable stay with comfortable, gracious rooms, and warm friendly hospitality. Two especially large elegant bedrooms with ensuites and rural mountain views featuring writing desks, quality linen, fresh flowers, and tea & coffee making facilities. A traditional English breakfast is served in the sunny breakfast room or al fresco on the terrace.

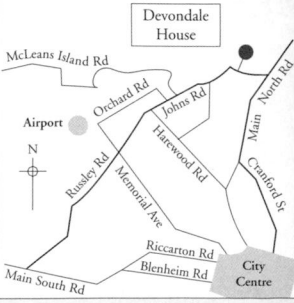

DIRECTIONS: Johns Rd. is the main road between Airport and Main Rd.North, 15 min. from City Centre. Look for statue at gate.

FAIRLEIGH GARDEN GUEST HOUSE

411 Sawyers Arms Road, Harewood, Christchurch
Ph (03) 359 3538, Fax (03) 359 3548
Mobile 025-224 3746
e-mail: *fairleighgardenbb@xtra.co.nz*
http://www.fairleighgarden.co.nz

Tariff : N.Z. Dollars		
Double	$135-165
Single	$110
Child	$45

Bedrooms	Qty
Double/Triple	2
Twin	1
Single	
Bed Size	**Qty**
Super King	1
King/Single	2
Queen	2
Single	1
Bathrooms	**Qty**
Ensuite	3
Private	
Guest Share	
Family Share	

Boutique
Bed & Breakfast

Features & Attractions

- *Airport 4 min./city 10 min.*
- *Large cottage garden*
- *Ample onsite parking*
- *Laundry available*
- *Fresh home baking & great coffee*
- *Courtesy car to organic restaurant 'Untouched World'*
- *Dinner options available by arrangement*

DIRECTIONS:
Turn off State Highway 1 at the Sawyers
Arms Road/Casebrook Roundabout.
You will find **Fairleigh Garden** on the
right - 800 m along Sawyers Arms Rd.

Dear Travellers,
We are staying at **Fairleigh Garden Guest House** and we just have to tell you about this wonderful place. A piece of 'country' so close to the airport and to the city. Berry fields and sheep grazing just next door. Garden views from every window and the smell of homebaking greets you in the mornings. The breakfast table is laden with fresh fruits, juices, homemade breads, muffins, jams and the omelettes are something special. It's just perfect! Valerie and Allan have helped us with our planning. Day trips to Akaroa, Hanmer Springs, Kaikoura, Mt Hutt Ski Fields, 15 golf courses in 15 minutes, restaurants, shops, arts, crafts, gardens and New Zealand wildlife. The list could go on forever. The warmth and friendliness is great, a real home away from home. We are coming back for two more nights before we fly out in three weeks. Do contact Valerie and Allan, they will be happy to meet you at the airport. True New Zealand hospitality. Don't miss it – we love it. See you soon. P.S.: The beds are firm and oh! so comfortable! And you will meet Zambie and Santa, two lovable black cats!

CASTLEREAGH

368A Yaldhurst Road, Russley, Christchurch
Ph (03) 342 5201, Fax (03) 342 3030
Mobile 025-464 951

Features & Attractions

- *Restful, friendly atmosphere*
- *Easy city/airport access*
- *Russley Golf Course 5 min.*
- *Bus route to city*
- *Quiet garden setting*
- *All meals with hosts*

Homestay
Bed & Breakfast

Double	$80
Single	$50
Child	$15

Bedrooms	Qty
Double	1
Twin	1
Single	1
Bed Size	**Qty**
Queen	1
Double	1
Single	2
Bathrooms	**Qty**
Ensuite	1
Private	
Guest Share	1
Family Share	

Welcome to our home. Our single storey 5 bedroom, 3 bathroom home is situated on a main route to the city, within 5 minutes of the International Airport, and easy access to the West Coast and main routes both north and south of Christchurch. We offer free pick-up and delivery from the airport, or from any other public transport you request. Cooked and continental breakfast is included in your tariff, includes fresh New Zealand products. Dinner by request. Our home is set in an English-style garden with outdoor privacy. We have off-street parking. Our spacious bedrooms offer electric blankets, heaters and hair dryers. Laundry facilities available. Guest lounge with TV.

Barry and I are retired from farming and horticulture and would enjoy helping you plan your South Island experience – starting in our lovely city. Barry is a fourth generation New Zealander with a wide knowledge of the South Island. Tariff – $80.00, Twin, Queen or double. $50.00 – single.

LAVENDER TOWERS

11 Kedleston Drive, Avonhead, Christchurch
Ph (03) 358 4387, Mobile 021-134 7161
e-mail: *sandy@inet.net.nz*

Features & Attractions

- *Friendly family home*
- *Beautiful cottage garden*
- *Continental breakfast*
- *Dinner by arrangement ($25 pp)*
- *Free pickup*
- *Close transport to city*

Homestay
Bed & Breakfast

Double	$95
Single	$65
Child	

Bedrooms	Qty
Double	1
Twin	
Single	1
Bed Size	**Qty**
King	
Queen/Double	1
Single	1
Bathrooms	**Qty**
Ensuite	
Private	1
Guest Share	
Family Share	1

Welcome to our Garden City. We would like to make your holiday as comfortable and memorable as possible. Situated in the northwest in a quiet, safe suburb with off-street parking. 7 km to city/2 km to airport. Short walk to shopping mall and beautiful parks. Interests – boating, gardening, doll-making, sport, travel and animals. We have travelled throughout New Zealand and are happy to help you with your sightseeing/garden tours. Continental breakfast includes yoghurt, homemade muffins/jam. Barbecue area in summer/warm fire in winter. Guest lounge available. Free tea, coffee/cookies. Laundry/e-mail facilities at small cost. Two of our three children are at home. We have two adorable samoyed dogs and one cat. A very warm **Kiwi** welcome awaits you.

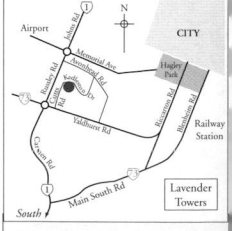

DIRECTIONS: Travel south on Riccarton Rd. turn right into Yaldhurst Rd. After 2 km turn right into Cutts Rd/Apsley Dve. Then 3rd. street on left.

FLEUR LODGE

67 Toorak Avenue, Avonhead,
Christchurch
Ph (03) 342 5473, Fax (03) 3425475

Tariff : N.Z. Dollars	
Double	$85
Single	$65
Child	n/a

Bedrooms	Qty
Double	1
Twin	1
Single	

Bed Size	Qty
Super King	
King	
Double	1
Single	2

Bathrooms	Qty
Ensuite	
Private	
Guest Share	1
Family Share	1

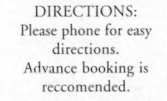

Bed & Breakfast
Homestay

Features & Attractions

* *Quiet, peaceful surroundings*
* *Excellent cooked breakfast*
* *3-course dinner available*
* *5 min. City Bus - 10 min.Airport*
* *Free pick-up for city tour*
* *Close to Antarctic Centre*
* *Only 20 min. to city*
* *Guest lounge and conservatory*

DIRECTIONS:
Please phone for easy directions.
Advance booking is reccomended.

Our home is in a quiet residential street and has been built to catch all-day sun. For winter warmth we have a cosy log burner. Guest bedrooms are bright and have comfortable firm beds complete with electric blankets, while the adjacent guest bathroom houses a luxurious spa bath. Tea, coffee and homemade cookies are always available.

As we also enjoy good food, we invite you to sample our three-course dinner, made with local fresh produce. A delightful selection of breakfast dishes is available together with freshly made bread and muffins and homemade jams.

There is an excellent network of city bus routes throughout Christchurch which can be easily accessed from our area. The city centre is 9 km away - however, it's only 3 km to good shopping malls.A warm welcome awaits you at **Fleur Lodge**.

We are very happy to help with your onward travel bookings or to give you local information. **Fleur Lodge** is smoke free - outdoors smoking is fine. You are welcome to use our garden setting with table and chairs.

AMBIENCE ON AVON
9 Kotare Street, Fendalton, Christchurch
Ph (03) 348 4537 Fax (03) 348 4837
Mobile 025-333 627
e-mail: *lawsonh@amcom.co.nz*
http://www.ambience-on-avon.co.nz

Tariff : N.Z. Dollars		
	Double	$120-135
	Single	$90-110
	Child	

Bedrooms	Qty
Double	2
Twin	
Single	
Bed Size	**Qty**
King	
Queen	1
Double	1
Single	
Bathrooms	**Qty**
Ensuite	
Private	2
Guest Share	
Family Share	

**Homestay Bed & Breakfast
Boutique Accommodation**

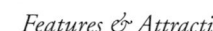

Features & Attractions

- Centrally located airport city shops
- Tranquil peaceful garden
- Gracious guest lounge
- Courtesy transfers
- Email & laundry facilities
- Home preserves and baking

Ambience on Avon in a private, picturesque garden on the Avon River. We enjoy welcoming guests into our home with its elegant comfortable understated furnishings, guest lounge with a large open fire, TV. Enjoy complimentary coffee, tea, home baked cookies and muffins under the large elm tree or down at the river garden with friendly ducks, birds or relax in special leather therapeutic chairs in our family room opening into the garden.

New Zealand art, comfortable beds, fine linen, electric blankets, room heaters, all modern conveniences for a relaxing, friendly stay. We enjoy travel home and abroad, art, walking, garden, fine food, wine and a merry singalong around our vintage pianola. We look forward to welcoming you to our beautiful garden city and helping to make your stay memorable.

BRYNDWR HOMESTAY

89A Aorangi Road, Bryndwr, Christchurch
Ph (03) 351 6092, Fax (03) 351 6092
e-mail: *wclancey@xtra.co.nz*
http://www.geocities.com/w_clancey/

Features & Attractions

- *Family home atmosphere*
- *Sheltered, quiet location*
- *Near visitor attractions*
- *Friendly, helpful service*
- *Dinner by arrangement*
- *Free pick up*

Homestay
Bed & Breakfast   H

Double	$100-110
Single	$80-85
Child	neg.

W e welcome you to our spacious and comfortable home set in quiet park-like gardens. The ensuite room, with queen-size double bed, opens onto a balcony overlooking a secluded outdoor swimming pool area. The twin bedroom has shared facilities. All rooms are electrically heated. The large lounge, which opens into the garden, has a log burner also. A sun room/TV room is available as a private lounge. Tea, coffee, juice and home baking are always to hand and dinner can be pre-arranged for the evening with us. We have both travelled, have a wide range of interests and enjoy meeting people. If needed, we are happy to help with travel plans. Laundry facilities and off-street parking are available.

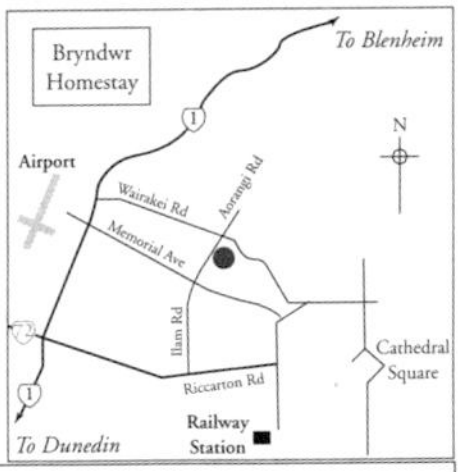

DIRECTIONS: Take SH 1, by-passing Christchurch, (Russley Rd). At Wairakei Rd roundabout (close to airport) drive towards Bryndwr, east along Wairakei Rd. At second group of shops, turn right along Aorangi Rd. 89A is soon on the left.

Bedrooms	Qty
Double	1
Twin	1
Single	
Bed Size	**Qty**
King	
Queen	1
Single	2
Bathrooms	**Qty**
Ensuite	1
Private	
Guest Share	
Family Share	1

Vintage tram – Christchurch.

"VILLA VICTORIA"
27 Holly Road, Merivale, Christchurch
Ph (03) 355 7977, Fax (03) 355 7977
Mobile 025-397 376
e-mail: *villa.victoria@xtra.co.nz*
http://www.villavictoria.co.nz

Tariff : N.Z. Dollars	
Double	$160-175
Single	$110-125
Child	

Bedrooms	Qty
Double	2
Twin	
Single	1
Bed Size	**Qty**
Super King	
King	
Double	2
Single	1
Bathrooms	**Qty**
Ensuite	3
Private	
Guest Share	
Family Share	

Boutique Accommodation
Bed & Breakfast

Features & Attractions

- *Peace and tranquility*
- *Romantic, restful garden*
- *Not suitable for children*
- *Centrally located*
- *Off-street parking*
- *Smoke free inside house*

Enter a world of elegance, romance, great hospitality, fine food. Built in 1901, **Villa Victoria** is situated in one of Christchurch's historic, quiet suburbs just minutes from city activities. Authentically restored, it reflects the elegance and charm of yesteryear.

Kate aims to recreate the lifestyle of the Victorian/Edwardian era, where old traditions and gracious living still linger. This tranquil haven has been designed to be a home away from home – it is small and intimate with personalised hospitality. Delectable breakfasts are a speciality using fresh local seasonal produce served in the formal dining room or during summer on the verandah overlooking the picturesque private garden – served at guests convenience. Wine and cheese is served early evening or a port and coffee after dining out. **Villa Victoria** is only a short stroll to exclusive Merivale Village which offers fine restaurants, wine bars, antique and boutique shopping. City centre is 5 minutes by car, 20 minutes walk or bus at corner of the street. Fifteen minutes from airport.

DIRECTIONS:
From the Airport take Memorial Ave, Fendalton Rd, turn left into Harper Avenue, Bealey Ave. Turn left into Papanui Rd, third street on the right is Holly Rd.

VILLA 121

121 Winchester Street
Merivale, Christchurch
Ph (03) 355 8128, Fax (03) 355 8126
e-mail: *gt@hagley.school.nz*

Tariff : N.Z. Dollars		
$	Double	$100
	Single	$80
	Child	$20

Bedrooms	Qty
Double	2
Twin	
Single	

Bed Size	Qty
Super King	
King	1
Queen	1
Single	

Bathrooms	Qty
Ensuite	
Private	1
Guest Share	
Family Share	1

  Homestay
Bed & Breakfast

DIRECTIONS:
From Papanui Road turn into
Office Road. Winchester Street is
the first street on your left.
Villa 121 is on the corner.

Features & Attractions

- *Friendly hosts*
- *Centrally located*
- *Delicious breakfast*
- *Merivale Mall 2 min.*
- *Golf course nearby*
- *Dinner by arrangement*
- *Old-world garden*
- *Tennis court 3 min.*

We are well travelled, fun loving and really enjoy meeting people. We provide a relaxing atmosphere and look forward to making your stay a happy and memorable one.

Villa 121 is a tastefully and stylishly restored villa set in a lovely old-world garden - only 2 minutes walk to Merivale Mall - 4 minutes by car to the central city (or a 20 - 25 minute walk). Delicious continental and/or cooked breakfast is available at a time to suit you and complimentary tea & coffee and homebaking is available at any time.

Your hosts are Trish (school teacher) and Barry (consultant surveyor). We are very keen sports people and love especially tennis, golf and skiing. We are happy to help you organise your sporting activities. Closest golf course and tennis courts are only 3 minutes away.

Relax in the sun on the wisteria and vine clad verandah in summer and enjoy the open fire in the winter.

🚫

GREATSTAY BED & BREAKFAST

43b Kilmarnock Street, Riccarton, Christchurch
Ph/Fax: (03) 343 1377, Mobile 025 - 622 0788
e-mail: ruske.greatstay@xtra.co.nz
www.greatstay.co.nz

Tariff : N.Z. Dollars		
	Double	$110
	Single	$80
	Child	

Bedrooms	Qty
Double	1
Twin	1
Single	
Bed Size	**Qty**
Super King	
King	
Queen	1
Single	2
Bathrooms	**Qty**
Ensuite	1
Private	1
Guest Share	
Family Share	

Bed & Breakfast
Homestay

Features & Attractions

- *Courtesy pickup*
- *Off-street parking*
- *Quiet, restful environment*
- *Close large shopping complex*
- *Vicinity to Westpac Centre*
- *Close to city centre*

Our four year old Mediterranean home offers spacious and comfortable accommodation. We have sought to create a friendly atmosphere with the accent on comfort and luxury. "Home away from home." Our house is back from the road and is quiet and restful. Off-street parking. Breakfast can be as healthy or wicked as you wish. **Greatstay** is 25min. walk to the city centre through Hagley Park, Botanic Gardens, Art Centre and Museum. Beautiful walks, golf course and shopping complex only minutes away.

We are close to the Public Hospital, University, Airport, Railway Station and restaurants. City bus at gate. We have courtesy pickup for your convenience. We are 50+ with three grown children and now grandchildren. We would be pleased to assist planning your holiday.

"Come as a guest. Leave as a friend."

CROYDON HOUSE BED & BREAKFAST HOTEL

63 Armagh Street, Christchurch
Ph (03) 366 5111, Fax (03) 377 6110
Free Ph (0800) 276 936
e-mail: *welcome@croydon.co.nz*
http://www.croydon.co.nz

Tariff : N.Z. Dollars		
Double	$120-135	
Single	$85-99	
Child	$20	

VISA MasterCard

Bedrooms	Qty
Double	7
Twin	4
Single	
Bed Size	**Qty**
Super King	1
Queen	5
Double	4
Single	5
Bathrooms	**Qty**
Ensuite	9
Private	2
Guest Share	
Family Share	

 Bed & Breakfast - Guest House

Features & Attractions

- *Charming accommodation*
- *Delightful garden*
- *On historic tram route*
- *Personal service*
- *Five minutes walk to City Centre*
- *Booking inf. & Internet access*
- *Gateway to the South Island*
- *German, English spoken*

Croydon House is a charming, small hotel offering fine accommodation in the heart of New Zealand's Garden City.

All bedrooms are tastefully refurbished with private or ensuite bathroom

Start your day with our scrumptious buffet and indulge yourself in a deliciously cooked breakfast prepared especially for **you**.

Explore the city – perhaps a ride on the tram that passes by **Croydon House's** front door, or a punt on the nearby Avon River.

Major attractions for the more ambitious: great restaurants, conference venues, Art Centre and the famous Botanical Gardens are within easy walking distance.

For more information, visit our Home Page on the Internet.

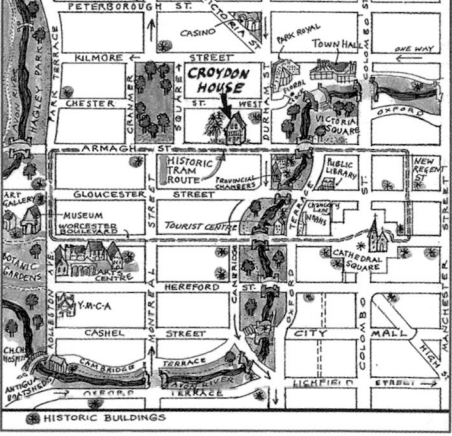

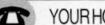

THE GRANGE GUEST HOUSE
56 Armagh Street, Christchurch
Ph (03) 366 2850, Fax (03) 374 2470
Mobile 021-366 608
e-mail: *reservations@thegrange.co.nz*
http://www.thegrange.co.nz

Features & Attractions
- City Centre 5 min. walk
- On tourist tram route
- Art Centre & gardens close
- Full cooked breakfast
- On-site car park
- Friendly service

 Bed & Breakfast Guest House

Double	$115-125
Single	$85-95
Child	$15-25

The Grange Guesthouse – a gracious Victorian mansion – is situated within walking distance from most of Christchurch's favourite spots, including Cathedral Square, the Art's Centre, Art Gallery and Museum, also the Botanic Gardens, Hagley Park and Mona Vale. Built before the turn of the century, and now tastefully refurbished **The Grange Guesthouse** offers a high standard of accommodation. You can relax in the guest lounge or in the garden. During your stay you will be treated to comfortable accommodation, complimentary tea and coffee, multi-channel TV, off-street parking, laundry service. Sightseeing tours and onward travel can be arranged. Non-smoking is encouraged. Banks, shops, restaurants, night clubs and cafés are all in easy walking distance. Paul and Marie Simpson are a mother and son team whose hospitality will ensure your stay is a pleasurable and pleasant one. All our tariffs include GST and full cooked breakfast. Please enquire about our winter rates, 1st June through 1st October.

Bedrooms	Qty
Double	6
Twin	2
Single	3
Bed Size	**Qty**
King	2
Queen/Double	6
King/Single	6
Bathrooms	**Qty**
Ensuite	6
Private	
Guest Share	1
Family Share	

AVON PARK LODGE
144A Kerrs Road, Avonside, Christchurch
Ph (03) 389 1904, Mobile 025-641 9692
e-mail: *avonparklodge@zfree.co.nz*

Features & Attractions
- Spacious and private
- Warm, friendly atmosphere
- Close to parks & Avon River
- Quiet, beautiful garden
- Large, comfortable rooms
- 5-minute drive to city

Homestay Bed & Breakfast

Double	$85
Single	$55
Child	

A pleasant surprise awaits you at the end of our drive, when you see our lovely house and hidden garden. Our home offers a spacious, relaxed atmosphere where you are assured of a warm, friendly welcome and excellent accommodation at affordable prices. Our two large upstairs guest bedrooms are furnished with your comfort in mind and include tea and coffee making facilities, electric blankets and heating. Our modern guest-share bathroom includes heating and the use of a hair dryer. Off-street parking available. After a scrumptious cooked or continental breakfast enjoy walks along the Avon River or through nearby parks. Eat at local restaurants or family meals can be arranged. Close to a golf course and beaches. With the city being just a short 5 minute drive away and very close to frequent public transport, we are ideally sited for exploring Christchurch and surrounding areas. Complimentary pickup.

Bedrooms	Qty
Double	1
Twin	1
Single	
Bed Size	**Qty**
King	
Queen	1
Single	2
Bathrooms	**Qty**
Ensuite	
Private	
Guest Share	1
Family Share	

Directions: Driving east from city turn left into Fitzgerald Ave. At end of Avenue turn right into Avonside Drive, continue into Woodham Rd. Turn left into Kerrs Rd.

WILLOW LODGE

71 River Road, Richmond, Christchurch
Ph (03) 389 9395, Fax (03) 381 5395
e-mail: *willow@inet.net.nz*

Tariff : N.Z. Dollars	
Double	$100-140
Single	$70-80
Child	$25

Bedrooms	Qty
Double	2
Twin	1
Single	1

Bed Size	Qty
Super King	1
Queen	2
King Single	2
Single	1

Bathrooms	Qty
Ensuite	1
Private	2
Guest Share	
Family Share	

         Homestay - Bed & Breakfast

Features & Attractions

- *Friendly atmosphere*
- *Beautiful river setting*
- *Family suite*
- *Spacious bedrooms*
- *1928 Art Deco style home*
- *Central City: walk – 20 min.*
- *Airport/Rail: car – 20 min.*
- *Central City: car – 5 min.*

"You really can live by the river! What a jolly life ....." 'Wind in the Willows'.

Your perfect end to a wonderful journey – relax and unwind, read or chat, make yourself at home. Enjoy a choice of one large suite or two large rooms.

We value our home's 1920/30's architecture and style, and mix it with plenty of contemporary art and books. Excellent large, firm beds.

Breakfast is fresh and generous – organic bread, cereals, fresh fruit, eggs, good coffee and teas.

And it is 'jolly' here ..... Christchurch is bulging with good things – food and wine, bookshops, clothes, antiques and a lively arts scene. We are happy to add our personal experience to enhance your stay. Sam is our elderly black Labrador. Shuttle or taxi service to gate from air/rail/coach.

Also available: mountain bike, off street parking and laundry.

DIRECTIONS:
Drive to eastern end of
Bealey Avenue (City), right into Fitzgerald
Avenue, then fourth left into River Road.

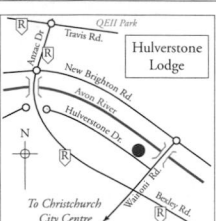

VISA
MasterCard

HULVERSTONE LODGE
18 Hulverstone Drive, Avondale,
Christchurch
Ph (03) 388 6505, Fax (03) 388 6025
Mobile 025-433 830
e-mail: *hulverstone@caverock.net.nz*

Features & Attractions

- *Complimentary pick-up*
- *Long stay discounts*
- *Diane spricht deutsch*
- *Visa/Mastercard accepted*
- *Fax facilities*
- *Diane parle francais*

Bed & Breakfast Accommodation		Double	$80-120
		Single	$60-90
		Child	

racing the bank of the Avon River in a quiet suburb, yet only 10 minutes from the city, stands picturesque **Hulverstone Lodge**. Watch the sun rise over the river, or catch glimpses of the Southern Alps and Port Hills from our charming guest rooms. Delightful walks pass the door. There are golf courses and other recreational facilities nearby, while frequent buses provide convenient access to the city. A stroll along the riverbank leads to New Brighton's restaurants, sandy Pacific Ocean beach and pier. An ideal base for a year-round holiday, **Hulverstone Lodge** is within a couple of hours' drive of Akaroa, Hanmer Hot Springs, skifields and Kaikoura, each with its own attractions. We guarantee you warm hospitality, quality accommodation and delicious breakfasts. Come and experience the ambience of Hulverstone Lodge!

DIRECTIONS: Follow the Ring Road, marked with an R on the big blue road signs, until it crosses the Avon River. Then turn left and left again.

Bedrooms	Qty
Double	3
Twin	3
Single	1
Bed Size	**Qty**
Super King	2
King	1
Queen	
Single	1
Bathrooms	**Qty**
Ensuite	1
Private	1
Guest Share	1
Family Share	

LOCARNO GARDENS APARTMENT
25 Locarno Street, St. Martins, Christchurch
Ph/Fax (03) 332 9987, Mobile 025-399 747
e-mail: *locarno@xtra.co.nz*

FARM & HOME HOSTS

Features & Attractions

- *5 min. drive to city centre*
- *Quality furnishings and décore*
- *Fish and watergarden, laundry facilities*
- *Breakfast optional extra*
- *Off-street parking*
- *Shops, Lyttelton, Gondola, Jade Stadium close*

Two Self-catering Apartments		Double	$85-95
		Single	$85-95
		extra person	$20

ileen and David invite you to their fine 80 year old character villa, with stained glass windows, surrounded by mature trees and established gardens.

Choose between the **Studio** apartment with private verandah entrance, super king bed, ensuite, TV, microwave, fridge and if required, adjoining twin bedroom (extra $20 per person) or the **Stand-alone** architecturally designed Apartment with separate lounge, queen bed, ensuite, bed-settee, TV microwave and fridge.

Relax in the picturesque garden courtyard by the goldfish pond. River walks and a tennis court close by.

Aileen's knowledge of restaurants is extensive and David enjoys diving, deer hunting and outdoor activities.

3 minutes walk to bus.

DIRECTIONS: Locarno Street is opposite St Marks Anglican church near 99 Opawa Road.

Bedrooms	Qty
Double	2
Twin	1
Single	
Bed Size	**Qty**
Super King	1
Queen	1
Single	2
Bathrooms	**Qty**
Ensuite	2
Private	
Guest Share	
Family Share	

KLEYNBOS & THE GRAND COTTAGE

59 Ngaio Street, St. Martins, Christchurch
Ph (03) 332 2896, Fax (03) 332 2896
e-mail: *bandb@voyager.co.nz*

Tariff : N.Z. Dollars	
Double	$70-85
Single	$45-70
Child	neg.

Bedrooms	Qty
Double	2
Twin	
Single	1
Bed Size	**Qty**
Super King	
King	
Queen	2
Single	1
Bathrooms	**Qty**
Ensuite	2
Private	
Guest Share	1
Family Share	

     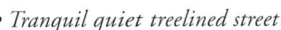
Homestay & Self-contained Accommodation

To City Centre — Barbadoes St — Moorehouse Ave — Brougham St — Waltham Rd — Gamblins Rd — Ngaio St — Wilsons Rd — Kleynbos B & B

4 km city centre – 6 km railway station
15 km airport

Features & Attractions

• *Tranquil quiet treelined street*   • *City centre 4 kilometres*
• *Art, oil paintings, native wood*   • *Discounts for self-catering*

KLEYNBOS **B&B** HOMESTAY – Away from the 'hustle and bustle', close to the city centre, in an easy to find street. That's us! As travelling is rather wearing on your body and mind, your room is generous in size, has an ensuite (or guest share) bathroom and - very important - a comfortable bed. We have enjoyed the privilege to live in New Zealand for almost 15 years and having guests is a little like family who have come to stay.
Hans and Gerda look forward to meeting you.

THE GRAND COTTAGE:
This lovely, spacious, free-standing and totally private 1920 character quality holiday home has 2 living areas, 2 toilets, 3 double bedrooms and a garden. It is fully equipped. Situated next to Kleynbos B&B, 4km from the city centre. Close to parks, hills and walkways.
Self catering $ 85.00 per night for 2.
Extra person $ 10.00 per night.
Breakfast $ 10.00 per person per night.
Sleeps 6 comfortably.

BLOOMFIELDS BED & BREAKFAST

105 Lyttelton Street, Hoon Hay - Spreydon
Christchurch
Ph (03) 332 5360, Fax (03) 332 5362
e-mail: *bloomfield@clear.net.nz*

Tariff : N.Z. Dollars		
Double		$75
Single		
Child		$10

Bedrooms	Qty
Double	1
Twin	1
Single	
Bed Size	**Qty**
Super King	
King	
Queen	1
Single	2
Bathrooms	**Qty**
Ensuite	
Private	1
Guest Share	
Family Share	

Bed & Breakfast
Self-contained Accommodation

Features & Attractions

- *Quiet, peaceful surroundings*
- *Continental breakfast*
- *Raceway Addington close by*
- *Close to large shopping mall*
- *Close to indoor swimming pool*
- *Westpac Trust Centre*
- *Close to railway station*
- *Off-street parking*

Bloomfields B & B

Christchurch

DIRECTIONS:
Between Addington
Raceway and Centennial Park.

① Addington Raceway
② Centennial Park
③ Railway Station

If you would like peace and quiet in our lovely city, our two-bedroom apartment is ideal. Our apartment, adjoining our home, has a large lounge and fully self-contained kitchen, washing facilities, phone and TV. For your privacy and enjoyment you have your own front lawn to sit and relax on. If we can be of any assistance to make your holiday more enjoyable, wc are only too pleased to help. Children are welcome and there is a cot and highchair available if needed.

We provide a comprehensive style continental breakfast. This is prepared and placed in your apartment, so you can breakfast at your leisure. If you prefer, you may do your own catering (discount tariff).

Bev and Kerry wish you a safe journey!

232

OVERTON

241 Kennedys Bush Road, Halswell,
Christchurch
Ph (03) 322 8326, Fax (03) 322 8350
Mobile 025-623 0831
e-mail: *brizzell.accom@xtra.co.nz*

Features & Attractions

- *Rural hill setting*
- *20 min. to city centre*
- *Panoramic views*
- *Adjacent Akaroa Highway*
- *Easy off-street parking*
- *Sole use of independent unit*

Double	$80-95	
Single	$45-80	
Child	$10-15	

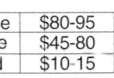 **Bed & Breakfast &
Self-contained Accomm.**

Bedrooms	Qty
Double	1
Twin	2
Single	
Bed Size	Qty
King	
Queen	1
Single	4
Bathrooms	Qty
Ensuite	
Private	1
Guest Share	
Family Share	1

Only 20 minutes from the Cathedral – our ¹/₂ acre landscaped garden on the Port Hills overlooking the rural setting of the Canterbury Plains on to the Southern Alps. Choose the completely self contained Garden Lodge (yours for exclusive use), with one double bedroom and one twin, TV, toilet, shower and cooking facilities or share the very comfortable home with a New Zealand family experienced in tourist requirements. Fibre arts, gardening and walking are some of Judi's interests in which guests are welcome to indulge. Joe is happy to share his love of angling at local rivers and lakes. New Zealand cuisine by Judi is available, featuring home grown produce. Tranquil, cosy and convenient to city amenities or rural pursuits.

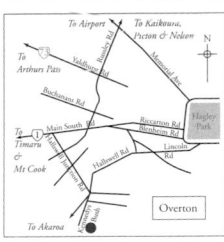

DIRECTIONS: Please
phone for easy directions.

SOUTHSHORE HOMESTAY

71A Rockinghorse Road,
Southshore, Christchurch
Ph (03) 388 4067
e-mail: posmerch@posmerch.co.nz

Features & Attractions

- *Direct beach access*
- *Private and peaceful*
- *Varied bird-life on estuary*
- *Miles of sandy beach nearby*
- *Lovely views from both rooms*
- *Only 20 minutes from City*

Double	$75-95	
Single	$60-75	
Child	n/a	

DIRECTIONS:
Please phone for easy directions.
City and airport pick-up if required.

**Homestay
Bed & Breakfast**

Bedrooms	Qty
Double	1
Twin	1
Single	
Bed Size	Qty
King	
Queen	1
Single	2
Bathrooms	Qty
Ensuite	1
Private	
Guest Share	
Family Share	1

Share with us an environment unique to Christchurch - Southshore. Only 20 minutes from the city, Southshore is situated between the ocean and the estuary of the Avon River. This seaside enclave offers walkways to enjoy the open water views of the estuary and its varied bird-life, or miles of sandy beach for strolling or swimming. Our house is situated down a private driveway with access to the beach. A large double room with ensuite and a smaller twin room are available to guests. Both rooms are warm and welcoming and overlook the dunes wilderness. We are in our sixties and together enjoy gardening, music and collecting antiques. Jan is a keen embroiderer and Graham a member of the Vintage Car Club. We are non-smokers - including Jaffa the cat. Dinner by arrangement, $25pp, includes wine. Please phone for reservations.

CAVENDISH HOUSE

10 Ross Terrace, Lyttelton
Ph (03) 328 9505, Fax (03) 328 9502
Mobile 025-616 0266
e-mail: *gsorell@xtra.co.nz*

Tariff : N.Z. Dollars	
Double	$130-150
Single	$110
Child	neg.

Bedrooms	Qty
Double	1
Double/Twin	1
Single	

Bed Size	Qty
Super King/Twin	1
King	
Queen	1
King/Single	

Bathrooms	Qty
Ensuite/Spa	1
Ensuite/Shower	1
Guest Share	
Family Share	

**Bed & Breakfast
Boutique Accommodation**

Features & Attractions

- *Dramatic scenery of ships and the sea*
- *Charming old world garden*
- *Spacious areas for relaxation*
- *Luxury spa bath*
- *Generous breakfast*
- *Fabulous walks*

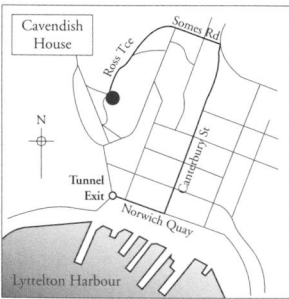

Nestled high in the hills above the Port of Lyttelton, this gracious Edwardian villa offers you spectacular views and unequalled hospitality in a charming old world atmosphere with the comforts of modern living. It is quiet, spacious and private. Could you ask for more?

The elegantly appointed Venice Room has a most comfortable queen-sized bed, and luxurious ensuite spa bath. It's just the place for that special romantic occasion, be it honeymoon, anniversary or plainly indulgent holiday making.

The Tasman Room is tastefully furnished, has a super-king/twin bed (s), and brand new ensuite facilities.

The Chart-Room Lounge is set aside for you to relax, and to enjoy tea, coffee or soft drink while you watch the ships. As evening approaches, complimentary drinks are served on the adjoining verandah before you venture down the quaint laneways to the cafés and restaurants.

Although this historic Port of Lyttelton is still a working port, it has retained that special romance of ships and the sea. Explore its history in the Maritime Museum, visit the timeball, take the self-guided historic walk. For the more energetic, walk in the footsteps of the pioneers up the Bridle Path and enjoy the panoramic views from Mt Cavendish, then take the Hornbrook Track home.

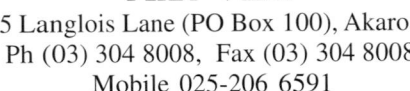

AKA-VIEW

5 Langlois Lane (PO Box 100), Akaroa
Ph (03) 304 8008, Fax (03) 304 8008
Mobile 025-206 6591
e-mail: *aka-view@xtra.co.nz*
http://www.aka-view.co.nz

Tariff : N.Z. Dollars	
Double	$165-205
Single	$125-155
Child	

Bedrooms	Qty
Double	2
Twin	1
Single	

Bed Size	Qty
Super King	
King	
Queen	2
Single	2

Bathrooms	Qty
Ensuite	2
Private	1
Guest Share	
Family Share	

**Luxury
Bed & Breakfast**

DIRECTIONS: Rue Lavaud - main village street - turn left at BNZ corner into Rue Balguerie - up to Langlois Lane, fifth on right, just before end of 50 kph zone.

Features & Attractions

- *Breathtaking view from all guest rooms*
- *Phone, fax and email available*
- *10 min. walk to shops & restaurants*
- *Scrumptious breakfast*
- *Quality bed linen*
- *Toiletries, hairdryers, robes*
- *Bedtime port and chocolates*
- *Romantic Akaroa*

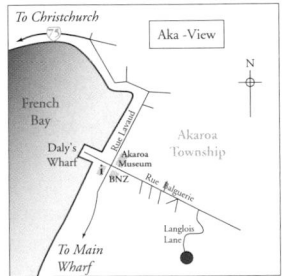

*Do you dream of a place "with a view"?
Elegant bedrooms, just made for two
Comfortable study - still "with a view"
Books, music, good coffee too -
A gourmet breakfast - sheer delight
Perfect - after a restful night
In a large country house
That's just all "brand new"
Fulfill your dreams at - "AKA-VIEW".*

Opening early summer 2001 after two years planning **Aka-View** is designed by an architect as a purpose-built Country Bed & Breakfast. The upper level features two queen suites, one twin, private guest study, all with unprecedented harbour views. In addition, guests have use of the ground floor lounge, with cosy fire, stylish but comfortable furnishings.

Gourmet breakfast is served either in the large kitchen, formal dining room with balcony, or alfresco, weather permitting. Fine teas, superb coffee, tasty treats are available in the guest study.

We share our home with many "teddy bears" who together with Rosanne and Kelvin welcome our guest to **Aka-View**. Our dreams come true!

BLYTHCLIFFE

37 Rue Balguerie, Akaroa, Canterbury
Ph/Fax: (03) 304 7003
e-mail: blythcliffe@xtra.co.nz
www.blythcliffe.co.nz

Old World Ambience

Tariff : N.Z. Dollars	
Double	$145-150
Single	$120
Child	

Bedrooms	Qty
Double	3
Twin	
Single	1
Bed Size	Qty
Super King	
King	
Queen	3
Single	1
Bathrooms	Qty
Ensuite	2
Private	1
Guest Share	
Family Share	

DIRECTIONS:
Turn left up Rue Balguerie,
(Museum cnr.) approximately
200 metres on left.

 **Bed & Breakfast
Luxury self-contained Cottage**

Features & Attractions

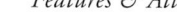

- *200m from town centre*
- *Internet and e-mail facilities*
- *5th generation local knowledge*
- *Vast range of NZ native trees*

- *Croquet, pétanque, full size billiard table*
- *Help with interests & activities freely given*
- *Cat.1 listing, NZ Historic Places Trust*
- *Restful & quiet garden environment*

ANYONE FOR CROQUET?

Just 200 m from the centre of Akaroa village, the walled street frontage of **Blythcliffe** belies what awaits you beyond the gate. The house was built in 1858 and has a category 1 listing with the New Zealand Historic Places Trust. A shelled path leads around the edge of the lawn to a shady pavillion that provides guests with the perfect place to enjoy special continental and/or cooked breakfast outdoors. Croquet mallets and pétanque boules are housed here just in case you feel like a little light recreation. Or cross a bridge over the stream bordering this garden and stroll through an acre stand of native bush. Two quaint double guest rooms overlooking different portions of the garden are freshly decorated in blue, yellow and greens. Both have private bathrooms, one ensuite. A small upstairs guest lounge opens onto the upper balcony and provides guests with tea and coffe making facilities and a television. Beyond, a modern self-contained cottage providing accommodation for two, sits in its own private garden and has its own streamside BBQ area. Inside is spa bath, fully featured kitchen, TV, Video and CD-player. The privacy and understated elegance of this charming bed and breakfast is waiting for you. Just lift the latch and wander into the secret garden.

ROSSLYN ESTATE

SH 75, Rapid # 5797, Main Christchurch - Akaroa Road
(Barry's Bay, RD 2, Akaroa)
Ph (03) 304 5804, Fax (03) 304 5804
e-mail: *Rosslyn@xtra.co.nz*

Tariff : N.Z. Dollars	
Double	$110-120
Single	$90
Child	

Bedrooms	Qty
Double	2
Twin	
Single	

Bed Size	Qty
Super King	
King	
Queen	2
Single	

Bathrooms	Qty
Ensuite	2
Private	
Guest Share	
Family Share	

**Historic Farm Homestead
Bed & Breakfast**

DIRECTIONS:
State Highway 75, **Rosslyn Estate** sign
behind white picket fence (left travelling
to Akaroa) in Barry's Bay.

Features & Attractions

- *Working dairy and deer farm*
- *Situated in extinct volcano*
- *Bush-lined streams*
- *Abundant bird life*

- *Share NZ family table*
- *Refreshments on arrival*
- *5 km to winery and restaurants*
- *70 km to Christchurch*

Embrace the tranquility of farm life while conveniently situated on the main road between Christchurch and Akaroa, at the French Farm/Wainui intersection, allowing you to explore this intriguing volcanic peninsula with ease. Our home is set amid rolling hills 400 m along a meandering driveway, overlooking the Akaroa Harbour. **Rosslyn** is a large historic homestead built in the 1860's. It has been our family home for four generations. The homestead and farm buildings are rich in history, including the original building that milled timber for the Christchurch Cathedral. We take pride in offering quality homegrown and prepared produce, from vegetables and fruit to preserves. We invite you to join us for diner ($25 pp), served in the farm-style kitchen. Breakfast ranges from fresh fruit to full cooked with homemade bread toasted on the embers. While with us you will have a large ground floor bedroom, firm queen bed, ensuite bathroom, antiques, central heating and screened windows for your comfort. A spa room, laundry, e-mail and phone/fax are also available. We look forward to welcoming you with a fresh pot of tea/coffee or cool drink served with home baking.

MENTEITH COUNTRY HOMESTAY

Rapid No. 961, Springs Road, RD 6, Christchurch
Ph (03) 325 2395, Fax(03) 325 2469
Mobile 021-131 5523
e-mail: *menteith@clear.net.nz*

Tariff : N.Z. Dollars	
Double	$95-105
Single	$70
Child	neg.

Bedrooms	Qty
Double	2
Twin	1
Single	

Bed Size	Qty
Super King	
King	1
Queen	1
Single	2

Bathrooms	Qty
Ensuite	2
Private	1
Guest Share	
Family Share	

 Quality Country Homestay

Features & Attractions

- Indoor swimming/spa pool
- Easy city/airport access
- Peaceful rural setting
- Secure off-street parking
- Golf course, University 3 km
- Moggy named Muffin
- Try your hand at spinning!
- Email facilities

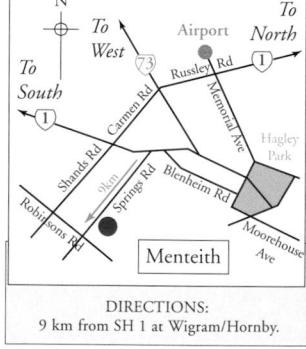

DIRECTIONS:
9 km from SH 1 at Wigram/Hornby.

Our tranquil 10 acre farmlet nestles among mature trees with spectacular mountain views and easy 15 minute city/airport access. It supports a lucerne crop, a small flock of sheep (to provide specialist fleeces for Fay's spinning - you're welcome to try your hand!) and two beehives (to maintain Stephen's interest and expertise in this fascinating industry).

Menteith, so named after an ancient Graham clan in Scotland, is an alpine-style home built from local riverbed stone, complemented in the interior with a collection of imported timbers and brick, offering a warm atmosphere. Relax in our warm indoor spa/swimming pool conservatory (robes provided) before your busy day of sightseeing. Spacious rooms offering cosy firm beds, TV, tea/coffee facilities and cookies, electric blankets, heating and hairdryer. Laundry facilities available.

Hearty breakfasts served from home-grown produce - the time is your choice.

Delightful reasonably priced restaurants nearby. Lincoln golf course and university 3 km. Our retirement interests include golf, Rotary, skiing, genealogy and travel.

Smoking welcome outside.

RYTON STATION

Harper Road (RD 2, Darfield) Lake Coleridge, Canterbury
Ph (03) 318 5818, Fax (03) 318 5819
e-mail: *ryton@xtra.co.nz*
http://www.ryton.co.nz

Tariff : N.Z. Dollars	
Double	$200
Single	$120
Child	neg.

Bedrooms	Qty
Double/Twin	7
Twin	
Single	

Bed Size	Qty
Super King	
Queen	6
Double	1
Single	

Bathrooms	Qty
Ensuite	7
Private	
Guest Share	
Family Share	

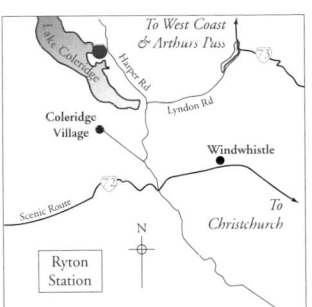

DIRECTIONS: Follow Ryton signposts from either SH 72 at Windwhistle or SH 73 at Lake Lyndon, approximately ¹/₂ hour. On the north side of Lake Coleridge, 10 min. once on Harper Rd.

 High Country Station Stay
Ensuite, Dinner, Bed & Breakfast

Features & Attractions

- *High country merino sheep station*
- *37,000 acres (14,000 hectares)*
- *Superb views overlooking Lake Coleridge*
- *Dinner included in tariff*
- *Trout, salmon fishing*
- *Farm walks/horse riding*
- *Ensuite chalets*
- *Horse trekking*

Adventure and hospitality in the South Island high country. Ryton Station is a wonderful place for a personal experience of home hospitality on a 37,000 acre high country merino sheep station.

The scenery is magnificent, overlooking Lake Coleridge, the air and water crystal clear. 1¹/₂ hours inland from Christchurch, accessible all year round. Abundance of fishing, walks, tramping, station activities. Jet boat and 4X4 trips available. Skiing at Mt Hutt (1 hour away), Porter Heights and Mt Olympus. Local golf courses nearby.

Relax and enjoy the native flora and fauna in the peacefulness of our environment. Office, TV and laundry facilities available in the homestead. Ensuite chalets accommodation includes dinner with the family. Self-catering lodge accommodation also, next to the homestead.

YOUR HOSTS: **Colleen & Roger Mehrtens**   Free Ph: 0800-466 093

GREEN GABLES DEER FARM

Waimarama Road, Methven
Ph (03) 302 8308, Fax (03) 302 8309
e-mail: *greengables@xtra.co.nz*
www.nzfarmstay.com

Tariff : N.Z. Dollars	
Double	$130-155
Single	$80-100
Child	$35-55

Bedrooms	Qty
Double	2
Twin	1
Single	

Bed Size	Qty
Super King	2
King	
Queen	
SuperKing Single	2

Bathrooms	Qty
Ensuite	2
Private	1
Guest Share	
Family Share	

 Farmstay - Bed & Breakfast

Features & Attractions

- *Fishing, golf, hot air ballooning*
- *Country cuisine - dinner $40 pp*
- *Skiing Mt Hutt, horse riding*
- *5 hours from Queenstown*

- *1 hour to Christchurch - International Airport*
- *Scenic bush walks - open gardens*
- *Restaurants nearby*

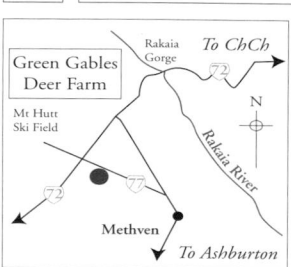

Awarm welcome awaits you at **Green Gables**, which is minutes from Methven - Mount Hutt, a beautiful, picturesque village, which has to offer an impressive range of summer and winter activities. This is an area of freshness, adventure and enjoyment, situated one hour from Christchurch, the garden city of New Zealand and its international airport. Relax in our peaceful farmhouse, which is the closest accommodation to Mt Hutt Skifield. The tastefully appointed guest wing is complete with ensuite facilities, super king beds, wool underlays, electric blankets, heaters, hair dryers and clock radios. French doors opening from all bedrooms provide private access. **Green Gables** presents magnificent views of Mount Hutt and the surrounding mountains. Hand-feed pet deer "Lucy" and her lovely fawn in a tranquil setting with white doves, Royal Danish White Deer, "Max" the golden labrador and "Harry" the silver-grey cat. Dine in the evening with delicious New Zealand country cuisine and wine – $40pp. Relax by the open fire with TV in our comfortable sitting room. We delight in sharing our knowledge of this fascinating area, its history and its wide range of all season activities.

TYRONE DEER FARM

Methven/Rakaia Gorge Alternative Route,
No.12 RD, Rakaia, Mid Canterbury
Ph (03) 302 8096. Fax (03) 302 8099
e-mai: *tyronedeerfarm@xtra.co.nz*

Tariff : N.Z. Dollars	
Double	$100-110
Single	$75
Child	

Bedrooms	Qty
Double	2
Twin	1
Single	
Bed Size	
Super King	
King	
Queen	2
Single	2
Bathrooms	Qty
Ensuite	2
Private	1
Guest Share	
Family Share	

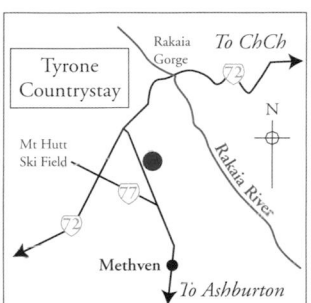

Countrystay
Bed & Breakfast

Features & Attractions

- *Centre of South Island*
- *Evening meal $30 p.p.*
- *Skiing MtHutt & heli-skiing*
- *Jet boating/hot air ballooning*
- *1hour Christchurch Airport*
- *Tramping alpine & bush walks*
- *Fishing, hunting guides avail.*
- *Golf 18-hole courses, club hire*

Welcome to **Tyrone Deer Farm**, centrally situated in the Mt Hutt Methven Rakaia Gorge area in the middle of the South Island, 5 km from the Inland Tourist Route (Highway 72) and one hour from Christchurch International Airport making **Tyrone** an ideal stopover if heading south to Queenstown etc, north to Picton/Nelson or Highway 73 to the West Coast. Positioned on the farm our home has views of the mountains (Mount Hutt) which also builds the back-drop of grazing deer a few metres away. As our family have left home, we have plenty of room for guests with electric blanket, and duvets on beds, heaters and hair dryers in the bedrooms, a lounge with open fire, TV, tea/coffee facilities and guest fridge.

Come and meet Guz, our pet deer, her daughter $$ and 10.30, our cat. Laze in the garden or swim in our pool. By arrangement, join us for a home-cooked evening meal served with New Zealand wine.

We are able to arrange professional guides for fishing salmon and trout, and for hunting: especially Tahr, Red Deer and Chamois

Ashburton

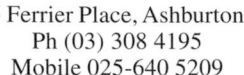 YOUR HOSTS: **Shona and Colin Thomas**　　Ph: (03) 308 4195

TREWINT HOUSE

 5 Ferrier Place, Ashburton
Ph (03) 308 4195
Mobile 025-640 5209
e-mail: *trewint@ashburton.co.nz*

Features & Attractions

- Quiet cul-de-sac
- Pool table
- Farm garden tour
- Christchurch Airport 1hr.
- Mt Hutt ski field
- Horse riding, golf course

Double	$100
Single	$50
Child	$20

 Bed & Breakfast Homestay H

Bedrooms	Qty
Double	1
Twin	2
Single	
Bed Size	**Qty**
King	
Queen	1
Single	4
Bathrooms	**Qty**
Ensuite	1
Private	1
Guest Share	
Family Share	

Retired farming couple Shona and Colin Thomas invite international travellers to stay at **Trewint House** and look forward to offering you luxury Kiwi hospitality in our new retirement home. With 12 years experience in the farmstay business and having travelled extensively ourselves, we know the pleasure of meeting people in a warm, friendly home atmosphere. Arrive as strangers – leave as friends. Our home is situated in a quiet cul-de-sac, 2 minutes off the main State Highway. Ashburton offers all the usual amenities of a large town and the centre is 4 minutes by car. Colin's interests include Rotary, rugby and farming. Shona's interests include Probus, dollmaking, golf and showing the beautiful farm garden to those who are interested (3 minutes by car).

Geraldine

YOUR HOSTS: **Jean and David McRae**　　Ph: (03) 693 9589

MCRAE'S

47 Cox Street, Geraldine
Ph (03) 693 9589　Fax (03) 693 9589

Features & Attractions

- Ensuite accommodation
- 2 golf courses
- Christchurch 2 hrs.
- 5 min. to town & bush walks
- Tea & coffe making facilities
- Private entrance, laundry

 Homestay Bed & Breakfast

Double	$120
Single	$60
Child	

Bedrooms	Qty
Double	1
Twin	
Single	
Bed Size	**Qty**
King	
Queen	1
Single	1
Bathrooms	**Qty**
Ensuite	1
Private	
Guest Share	
Family Share	

We've recently moved to Geraldine from Gore in Southland, where we did home-hosting for several years. The enjoyment we had from hosting guests from many different countries around the world, has encouraged us to continue offering guest accommodation here in lovely Geraldine. We are close to ski fields and fishing and rafting on the Rangitata River. If you like walking through native bush, we have walks right here on the town boundary, or you can explore lovely walkways in Peel Forest with native trees.

David is a retired farmer and still works part time on a farm. He enjoys rugby and horse trekking. Jean loves gardening and golf. We have five adult children and 7 grand children. The boss in the house is "Bobby Mac", a Bichon Frise dog, who is visitor friendly.

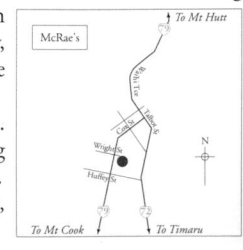

THE BRAE

156 Patrick Road, Gapes Valley, RD 21
Geraldine, South Canterbury Region
Ph (03) 697 4809, Fax (03) 697 4809
Mobile 025-244 4269
e-mail: john.val@xtra.co.nz

Tariff : N.Z. Dollars	
Double	$100
Single	$50
Child	neg.

Bedrooms	Qty
Double	1
Twin	2
Single	

Bed Size	Qty
Super King	
King	
Queen	1
Single	4

Bathrooms	Qty
Ensuite	
Private	1
Guest Share	
Family Share	1

**Farmstay
Bed & Breakfast**

Features & Attractions

- *Panoramic views*
- *Country cuisine*
- *Laundry facilities*
- *Phone, fax, e-mail*
- *2 hrs Christchurch/Mount Cook*
- *Geraldine's 'Barkers'*
- *Peel Forest Reserve*
- *Rangitata Rafting*

Val and John, farm hosts since 1987, warmly invite you to stay at 'The Brae', our 205 hectare accredited deer, cattle and lamb fattening property. Travel 14 km (15 minutes) from the well known picturesque village of Geraldine to Gapes Valley. **The Brae** is centrally positioned 1.5 km west of State Highway 79, halfway between Christchurch and Mount Cook - Queenstown. Our home has an inviting atmosphere, pool, BBQ area set in an attractive garden. Guest rooms have a superb outlook, restful décor, beds with duvets, electric blankets, hair dryers and toiletries for your comfort. John has resided all his life in the area, interests are farm related, gardening and all sports. Val enjoys golf, all crafts and cooking. Her experience as a resthome/hospital cook ensures guests of very high standards in food preparation and hygiene (NZQA Certificates). A three course meal using fresh, locally grown produce is available by prior arrangement – wine included, $25pp. Be assured of warm and friendly hospitality at **The Brae.**

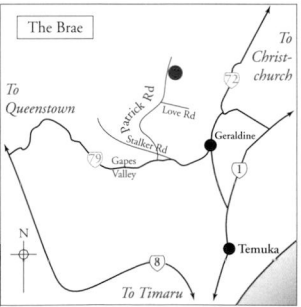

DIRECTIONS: 14 km from Geraldine on SH 79, to Stalker Road on your right, just before Gapes Valley Hall. Then right on Patrick Road for 1.5 km. From Fairlie turn left off SH 79 onto Patrick Road at Gapes Valley Hall and follow above directions.

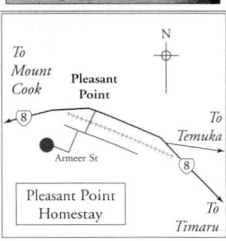

PLEASANT POINT BED & BREAKFAST
21 Ameer Street, Pleasant Point
South Canterbury
Ph (03) 614 7221, Fax (03) 614 7231

Features & Attractions
- *On road to Mount Cook, & the Southern Lakes*
- *18 hole golf course*
- *Steam train*
- *"Richard Pearse First Flight Memorial"*

 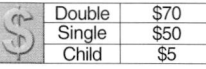

Homestay & Self-contained Accomm.

Double	$70
Single	$50
Child	$5

Bedrooms	Qty
Double	1
Twin	1
Single	
Bed Size	Qty
King	
Queen/Double	1
Single	2
Bathrooms	Qty
Ensuite	1
Private	1
Guest Share	
Family Share	

Pleasant Point is located 20 km south of Timaru on State Highway 8 - one of the main roads to Mount Cook, the Southern Lakes and the Hydro Electric Dams. An excellently maintained steam train operates through the township regularly. Another nostalgic trip can be made at the "Richard Pearse First Flight Memorial". We have a top class 18 hole golf course and only 8 km towards the historical landmark of Hanging Rock, you can wine and dine at the new Opihi Vineyard and Café. Shirley and Murray extend a warm welcome and look forward to your custom. We have a fully self contained, modern unit with complete bathroom/kitchen/laundry facilities and lock-up garage. Alternatively you can join us in a comfortable homestay and enjoy the spectacular mountain views from your upstairs bedroom/ensuite, family lounges and outside decking.

Charming
Bed & Breakfast
in
New Zealand
www.bnbnz.com

RIVENDELL LODGE

Stanton Road, Kimbell, RD 17, Fairlie
Ph (03) 685 8833. Fax (03) 685 8825
Mobile 027-4819 189

e-mail: *rivendell.lodge@xtra.co.nz*
http://fairlie.co.nz/rivendell

Tariff : N.Z. Dollars	
Double	$95
Single	$55
Child	neg.

Bedrooms	Qty
Double	2
Triple	1
Single	

Bed Size	Qty
Super King	
King	
Queen/Double	2
Single	3

Bathrooms	Qty
Ensuite	
Private	2
Guest Share	
Family Share	1

             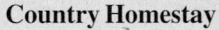

Country Homestay

Features & Attractions

- *Peaceful rural retreat*
- *Great home cooking*
- *Skifield 5 km*
- *Spa bath available*
- *Magnificent alpine scenery*
- *Guided walking & tramping*
- *Families welcome*
- *Internet/ e-mail access*

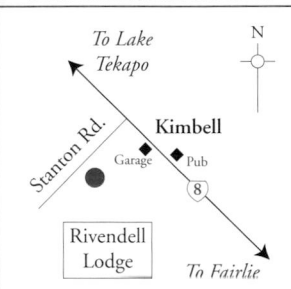

DIRECTIONS: 100m up Stanton Rd. at Kimbell on SH 8, 8km west of Fairlie.

"They stayed long in Rivendell and found it hard to leave. The house was perfect whether you liked sleep, or work, or storytelling, or singing, or just sitting and thinking best, or a pleasant mixture of them all. Everyone grew refreshed and strong in a few days there. Merely to be there was a cure for weariness, fear and sadness." - Tolkien.

Welcome to my one acre paradise; a haven of peace and tranquility offering quality country comfort and hospitality. I am a well travelled writer with a passion for mountains, literature and good conversation. I enjoy cooking and gardening and use home grown produce wherever possible. Evening meals, with local wines, are available by arrangement. Take time out from the Christchurch-Queenstown route and enjoy our magnificent country-side. Fishing, skiing, walking, golf and water sports nearby. Relax in our beautiful garden, complete with stream and cat, or come with us to some of our favourite places.

Complimentary refreshments on arrival. Laundry facilities available.

245

BELLBIRD COTTAGE

121-125 Noema Terrace, Lake Hawea, Ctrl. Otago
Ph (03) 443 7056, Fax (03) 443 1807
or Ph (03) 443 8678
e-mail: *marge@xtra.co.nz*
http://mysite.xtra.co.nz/~marge/

Tariff : N.Z. Dollars		
	Double	$110
	Single	$110
	Child	n/a

Bedrooms	Qty
Double/Twin	1
Twin	
Single	1
Bed Size	**Qty**
Super King	
King	
Queen/Double	1
Single	1
Bathrooms	**Qty**
Ensuite	1
Private	
Guest Share	
Family Share	

Self-contained Luxury Accommodation

Features & Attractions

- *Seven-day-dining close by*
- *Microwave & dishwasher*
- *Two television sets*
- *Fully equipped kitchen*

- *Full private laundry*
- *Log fire, stereo, video*
- *Central to activities*
- *Co-operative hosts*

Our modern, self-contained cottage is situated in beautiful Lake Hawea village, surrounded by majestic mountains, We are just 12 kilometres from Lake Wanaka in the centre of the Lakes District of Central Otago. With Queenstown just an hour away, less

DIRECTIONS:
Please telephone for easy directions.
Advance booking is recommended.

than 2 hours to Mount Cook, you are close to all attractions. We are located about 30 minutes from two major ski fields – Treble Cone and Cadrona. Lake Hawea is renowned for fishing with guides available. Horse riding, nature walks, adventure trips, canoeing, paragliding are just some of the local attractions. The cottage construction is timber and rammed earth. The bedroom has a double and single bed and there is a double sofa sleeper in the lounge. If required we have a double self-contained bedroom adjacent complete with ensuite. A typical comment from our guest book is: "This is an outstanding cottage, cosy, tastefully decorated and thoughtfully well equipped. Together with warm hospitality this has perfected our holiday in New Zealand." Hosts are Majorie Goodger, who has had a career in hotel management, and her sister Sheila McCaughan from a farming background. Should you wish, your log fire will be burning on your return from skiing. Dinner by arrangement hosted by Majorie, Sheila and Brian McCaughan. Easy to find – Noema Terrace leads off the main road, Capell Avenue, where you are welcome at 121 & 125.

LARCHWOOD LODGE

Dublin Bay, 2 RD, Wanaka
Ph (03) 443 7914. Fax (03) 443 7910
Mobile 025-239 6123
e-mail: *larchwood@xtra.co.nz*
www.larchwood.co.nz

Tariff : N.Z. Dollars	
Double	$125-170
Single	$110
Child	neg.

Bedrooms	Qty
Double or Twin	5/4
Twin	
Single	
Bed Size	**Qty**
Super King	
King	3
Queen/Double	1
King/Single	2
Bathrooms	**Qty**
Ensuite	5
Private	
Guest Share	
Family Share	

Homestay - Bed & Breakfast

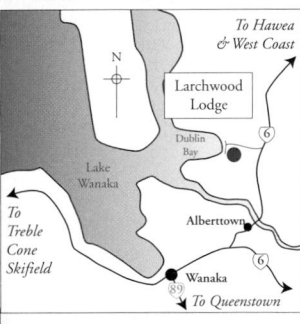

Features & Attractions

- *Tranquil rural atmosphere*
- *3 minute walk to lake*
- *Extensive private gardens*
- *Fishing at your door-step*
- *Full-size tennis court*
- *Kayaks & mountain bikes avail.*
- *Disabled/elderly facilities avail.*
- *Outdoor bath in garden*

To Hawea & West Coast

Larchwood Lodge

Dublin Bay

Lake Wanaka

Albertown

To Treble Cone Skifield

Wanaka

To Queenstown

DIRECTIONS:
7km north of Wanaka on SH 6.
turn left into Dublin Bay Road -
3km to **Larchwood** sign
on the left.

Why stay with us… unless our secret hideaway, meandering down to the shores of Lake Wanaka, to walk, kayak, swim, fish or relax by, sounds like **you**. Explore our tranquil gardens, trees framing the majestic mountains, or use the tennis court and mountain bikes, to expend any energy, left over from skiing, golfing, tramping or enjoying a good book. Maybe the 'olde-worlde' rustic charm of the Lodge, wide doors opening to summer's heat, or crackling fires on cold winter nights, has appeal. To others, a room to dry clothing and sportsgear may be of interest, or where the good fishing spots might be found! A choice of five bedrooms, with king sized zip-to-single beds, all overlook Lake Wanaka and the mountains and open onto outdoor balconies. TVs are banished to bedrooms, leaving the lounge for soft music, exchanging good yarns and sharing our life in Central Otago with you. Our kids have left the nest, so our golden retriever 'Mac' helps form the 'Welcoming Committee', (the cat's more elusive). Dan's a professional fishing guide.

HUNT'S HOMESTAY

56 Manuka Crescent, Wanaka
Ph (03) 443 1053, Fax (03) 443 1355
Mobile 025-265 0114
e-mail: *hunts.homestay@xtra.co.nz*
http://www.inow.co.nz/hunts.homestay

Features & Attractions

- New house in large garden
- Access to many activities
- Free laundry facilities
- Safe off-street parking
- Farm visits available
- Complimentary tea/coffee

Homestay
Bed & Breakfast

Double	$100	
Single	$60	
Child	neg.	

Bedrooms	Qty
Double	1
Twin	1
Single	
Bed Size	**Qty**
King	
Queen	1
Single	2
Bathrooms	**Qty**
Ensuite	
Private	
Guest Share	1
Family Share	

DIRECTIONS: From town take Lakeside Rd. to Beacon Point Rd., right to Manuka Crescent. We are opposite Manuka Crescent Motels.

Once settled in our roomy ground floor bedroom and lounge, our guests remark on the beauty of the lake and mountain views and how they change throughout the day. It was this aspect that drew us to this peaceful ¹/₂-acre section, when we left farming near Wanaka six years ago.

Our architecturally designed house has two spacious bedrooms and 360° views of lake and mountains. By chance we became involved in homestay activities and have greatly enjoyed the experience. We realised we had a great wealth of information about the area that we could pass on to our guests. Through our membership of "Lake Wanaka Tourism" we are kept informed of all tourist activities in the area. Whatever you want to do, we are happy to organise it.
We look forward to enjoying your company in our beautiful area.

NORTHRIDGE

11 Botting Place (PO Box 376) Wanaka
Ph (03) 443 8835, Fax (03) 443 1835
Mobile 025-950 436
e-mail: *s.atkinson@xtra.co.nz*

Features & Attractions

- Excellent, stunning views
- Generous breakfast
- Landscaped gardens
- Quiet and peaceful
- Warm hospitality
- Next to golf course

Bed & Breakfast
Homestay

Double	$120-140	
Single	$85	
Child		

Bedrooms	Qty
Double	2
Twin	1
Single	
Bed Size	**Qty**
King	
Queen	2
Single	2
Bathrooms	**Qty**
Ensuite	1
Private	1
Guest Share	1
Family Share	

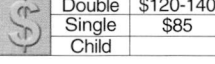

Northridge is situated on a ridge with spectacular views of Lake Wanaka and the Alps and within walking distance to restaurants, shops and the lakefront. Our quality stone and natural timber home lends itself to indoor/outdoor living, where you can have refreshments served whilst taking in the breathtaking views or amble through the garden. All rooms have the same stunning views, are large and the beds are complete with wool underlays, electric blankets, feather/down duvets and quality linen. Our home is centrally heated and has a fireplace to ensure warmth and comfort for those cosy winter evenings. We serve a substantial cooked or continental breakfast at a time that suits our guests. Wanaka has plenty to offer and we will be only too pleased to be able to offer suggestions. Come and share our piece of paradise with us.

DIRECTIONS: State Highway 84 continues on to Ardmore Street, drive down the lakefront and turn left at the end of the park MacDougall Street (State Highway 89). Botting Place is the 5th street on the left.

ASPIRING IMAGES HOMESTAY

26 Norman Terrace, Wanaka
Ph (03) 443 8358, Fax (03) 443 8327
e-mail: *grussell@xtra.co.nz*

Tariff : N.Z. Dollars	
Double	$100-110
Single	$60-75
Child	$25

Bedrooms	Qty
Double	2
Twin	
Single	

Bed Size	Qty
Super King	
King/Twin	1
Double	1
Single	

Bathrooms	Qty
Ensuite	1
Private	1
Guest Share	1
Family Share	·

Homestay - Bed & Breakfast

Features & Attractions

- *Stunning views*
- *Close to the lake*
- *Adjacent to large park*
- *4WD eco & photo tours*
- *Two mountain bikes*
- *Wide range of activities*
- *Help with travel plans*
- *e-mail & internet facilities*

"We'll be back!"

Wanaka, with its dramatic lake and mountain scenery, is a magical, unforgettable place which draws people back again and again. Our architect designed home has captivating lake and mountain views, a sunny aspect and a peaceful parkside setting. Secure within the natural stone exterior, guest rooms enjoy the warmth and rich restfulness of heart Rimu timber, sunny sheltered patios, quality furnishings and really comfortable beds.

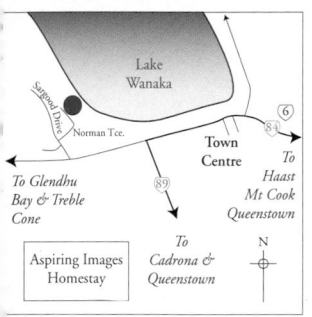

There is a wealth of activities and attractions offered here, using the lakes and rivers, the glacier-planed countryside and the sharply clear air above. Perhaps you'd like to settle down with a book from our library or browse through our collection of New Zealand books and maps while you consider your next move. We're qualified to help if you wish.

We've travelled widely ourselves, been involved in education, played and coached many sports and sung in a lifetime of choirs. We came under Wanaka's spell many years ago, and enjoy sharing with our guests **"Life the way it should be!"**

LAKE WANAKA HOME HOSTING
19 Bill's Way, Rippon Lea, Wanaka, Central Otago
Ph (03) 443 9060, Fax (03) 443 1626
Mobile 025-228 9160
e-mail: *lex.joy@xtra.co.nz*
http://www.lakewanakahomehosting.co.nz

Tariff : N.Z. Dollars	
Double	$100-125
Single	$65
Child	$25

Bedrooms	Qty
Double	2
Twin	1
Single	

Bed Size	Qty
Super King	1
King	
Queen	1
Single	2

Bathrooms	Qty
Ensuite	
Private	2
Guest Share	
Family Share	

 Homestay - Bed & Breakfast

Features & Attractions

- *Spacious, relaxing decor*
- *Mountain and lake views*
- *15-20 min. walk to shops*
- *A little luxury*
- *Peaceful lake walks*
- *Close to Rippon Vineyard*
- *Meals on request*
- *Lovely patio garden*

 We welcome visitors to Lake Wanaka and enjoy sharing our natural surroundings with others. We have a large, peaceful home where our guests can experience not only the awesomeness of the lake and mountains around, but also experience the ambience of Wanaka itself. The picturesque 20–30 minute walk to Wanaka Town is very worth while.
Our guest room upstairs has the super king size bed with an adjoining lounge with tea and coffee making facilities, fridge and T.V. and a private bathroom. Our double guestroom also has a private bathroom. We have smoke alarms, central heating and electric blankets in all beds. Good laundry facilities. We have no children living at home and no pets. Our interests are sport, gardening, boating, farming and good cuisine. Lex and I enjoy your company.

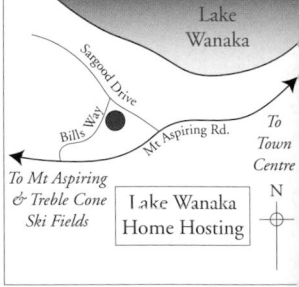

OAK RIDGE - LAKE WANAKA

Cnr Cardrona Valley Rd. / Studholme Rd.
Postal: PO Box 220, Wanaka, Central Otago
Ph (03) 443 7707. Fax (03) 443 7750
e-mail: *info@oakridge.co.nz*
www.oakridge.co.nz

Tariff : N.Z. Dollars	
Double	$150-240
Single	$135-216
Child	neg.

Bedrooms	Qty
Double	12
Twin or	12
Single or	12
Bed Size	**Qty**
Super King	12
Queen	
King/Single	2
Single	26
Bathrooms	**Qty**
Ensuite	12
Private	
Guest Share	
Family Share	

   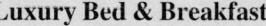

Luxury Bed & Breakfast

DIRECTIONS: From Queenstown via SH 89 (Cardrona Valley), **Oak Ridge** on the left just before entering Wanaka. Arriving in Wanaka from any other direction, proceed along Ardmore St. turn into Mac Dougall St. and as you breast the hill at Wanaka Golf Course, you look directly at the red roofs of **Oak Ridge**.

Features & Attractions

- *Quiet, peaceful surroundings*
- *Superb golf, fishing, hunting*
- *Spa baths ensuite*
- *Bush and mountain walks*
- *Fully licensed restaurant and bar*
- *Tennis court, swimming pool and spa*
- *Open log fire*
- *Downhill and nordic skiing*

Only 2 minutes drive from the centre of Lake Wanaka township, the careful blending of the old and the new create at **Oak Ridge** a holiday experience unique in terms of location, design, comfort and ambience. Set against a backdrop of the majestic mountain peaks of the Southern Alps amidst sweeping lawns, gardens and open woodland, **Oak Ridge** offers guests sumptuous hosted accommodation. A tennis court, spa, swimming pool, golf practice area, petanque terrain and sunken garden are available on site for your enjoyment. A large new dining room has been constructed with contemporary furnishings and housing an extensive collection of modern New Zealand art. Our new restaurant and bar offers superb a la carte dining, utilizing the very best of New Zealand's produce. In accordance with guest preference, our rooms can provide the following comforts: super-king or twin beds, ensuite with spa or shower, private patios, writing desk, complimentary tea and coffee in your room and satellite television. All rooms have 180° unobstructed views towards the Southern Alps. All rates are inclusive of a buffet continental breakfast.

PARKLANDS LODGE

Ballantyne Road, RD 2, Wanaka
Ph (03) 443 7305, Fax (03) 443 7345
Mobile (025) 955 160
e-mail: *parklandslodge@xtra.co.nz*
http://www.parklandswanaka.co.nz

Tariff : N.Z. Dollars		
	Double	$165-210
	Single	$135-185
	Child	$25

Bedrooms	Qty
Double	5
or Twin	1
Single	
Bed Size	**Qty**
Super King	2
King	1
Queen	2
Double	1
Bathrooms	**Qty**
Ensuite	4
Private	
Guest Share	1
Family Share	

 Bed & Breakfast / Luxury Accommodation

Features & Attractions

- *Spectacular mountain views*
- *Relaxing rural environment*
- *Swimming pool & barbecue area*
- *Ski fields nearby*
- *Continental/cooked breakfast inclusive*
- *Spa pool and guest lounge*
- *Dine with hosts an option*

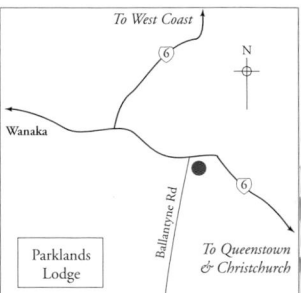

Parklands Lodge has been created to give guests a tranquil, relaxing experience. Your hosts Margaret and Lawrence offer warm, friendly hospitality, a retreat from the hustle and bustle of urban life. Relax in the spa, enjoy the swimming pool and BBQ area, play a 5 hole round of golf, or simply enjoy the spectacular mountain views. Fishing guide available.

What better way to start the day than with a superb breakfast including freshly brewed coffee, home-made bread and jams and a selection of fresh fruits and cereals, followed by a cooked breakfast of your choice.

Parklands Lodge is nestled on 10 acres of rural land, 6 kilometres south of Wanaka Lake and alpine resort and a 45 minute drive from Queenstown.

We also have a two bedroom self-contained apartment.

THE MAPLES WANAKA

68 Totara Terrace, Wanaka
Ph (03) 443 6633, Fax (03) 443 6634
Mobile (025) 602 7669
e-mail: *squires@paradise.net.nz*
http://www.the-maples-wanaka.co.nz

Tariff : N.Z. Dollars	
Double	$100
Single	$70
Child	$20

Bedrooms	Qty
Double	1
Twin	1
Single	
Bed Size	**Qty**
Super King	
King	
Queen	1
Single	2
Bathrooms	**Qty**
Ensuite	
Private	1
Guest Share	
Family Share	

Self-contained Bed & Breakfast & Pottery Studio

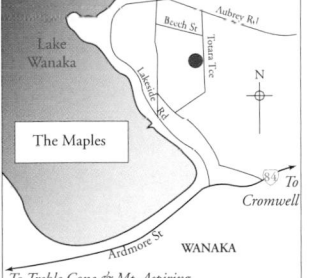

Features & Attractions

- *Guided fishing by arrangement*
- *Close to town and restaurants*
- *Privacy plus hospitality*
- *Delicious continental breakfast*
- *E-mail and Internet access*
- *Pottery studio on site*
- *Single-party booking only*
- *Lovely tree-clad section*

We welcome you to "The Maples" where our property includes our home, a two bedroom self-contained unit and our pottery studio, all nestled into a lovely tree-clad garden setting. Our smoke-free guest unit allows you to have as much privacy as you desire and yet the opportunity to socialize with us whenever you wish. It is warm and inviting with a queen size bed-sitting room plus an extra twin bedroom should your party require it. Comfortable beds, complimentary tea and coffee, TV, iron and hairdryer are just a few of the items on hand.

Feel free to wander around the gardens or visit our pottery studio to watch us at work . We have been potting professionally for over 20 years and enjoy socializing, music, wining, dining, reading and walking. Wanaka is handy to two major ski-fields and offers you New Zealand at its unspoiled best. We are happy to help you with bookings and information about the area and look forward to enjoying a delicious continental breakfast with you.

WANAKA SPRINGS BOUTIQUE LODGE

21 Warren Street, PO Box 25, Wanaka
Ph (03) 443 8421, Fax (03) 443 8429
Mobile 025-223 8959
e-mail: *relax@wanakasprings.com*
www.wanakasprings.com

NEW ZEALAND TOURISM AWARDS
2001/2002 FINALIST

Tariff : N.Z. Dollars		
	Double	$190-250
	Single	
	Child	

Bedrooms	Qty
Double	5
Twin	3
Single	

Bed Size	Qty
Super King	
King	
Queen/Double	5
Single	6

Bathrooms	Qty
Ensuite	8
Private	
Guest Share	
Family Share	

   Boutique Lodge

Features & Attractions

- *Peaceful in-town retreat*
- *Private native gardens*
- *Fine furniture & fabrics*
- *3-min stroll to shops*
- *Special Honeymoon room*
- *Business facilities*
- *Powerboat & garden spa*
- *Full activity service*

Wanaka Springs is the Township's newest boutique lodge, featuring local timbers and stone. Bringing you a fresh approach to comfort away from home, this 'in-town retreat' is your base for relaxation or for

DIRECTIONS:
Take SH 84 to Wanaka. At Caltex Service Station turn left into Brownston St. Take third left into Helwick St. and second left into Warren St. **Wanaka Springs** is at the end of the cul-de-sac on the left.

countless outdoor activities and adrenalin sport in and around Mt. Aspiring National Park - yet you'll be only a three-minute stroll from Wanaka's excellent shops, restaurants and bars.

Eight elegant ensuite guestrooms feature natural timber queensize and single beds along with occasional furniture. Delight in imported linens and fine fabrics – unwind in the sumptuous lounge with its open log fire, splendid furnishings and library. The large decks are ideal for relaxation and sundowners, with magnificent views views of Lake Wanaka and the surrounding mountians. Rejuvenate in our 8-seater garden spa pool or climb aboard our luxury powerboat on a scenic, sport or fishing charter.

Wanaka Springs: supreme comfort, informal sophistication and superior facilities for the discerning traveler.

VILLA AMO

Shine Lane, Pisa Moorings, No 3 RD, Cromwell
Ph (03) 445 0788, Fax (03) 445 071
Mobile 025-286 8316
e-mail: *VillaAmo@xtra.co.nz*

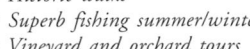

Features & Attractions

- *Situated on Lake Dunstan*
- *Rugged mountain scenery*
- *Skifields within an hour*
- *Historic walks*
- *Superb fishing summer/winter*
- *Vineyard and orchard tours*

Double	$120
Single	$105
Child	n/a

 Homestay Bed & Breakfast

Bedrooms	Qty
Double	2
Twin	
Single	
Bed Size	**Qty**
King	
Queen/Double	2
Single	
Bathrooms	**Qty**
Ensuite	
Private	1
Guest Share	
Family Share	

Welcome to **Villa Amo** in its tranquil setting on the shore of Lake Dunstan. Built in late 1996 it is the ideal base from which to explore the delights of beautiful Central Otago. We have superb fishing and water sports at our doorstep and many other activities only a 10 minute drive away in Cromwell. Queenstown, Wanaka and Alexandra all within 45 minutes. Our two spacious guest rooms are private and quiet and the well appointed bathroom is private – single party booking only. To start the day enjoy a substantial breakfast, cooked or continental, at a time that is convenient to you. After a day exploring the many wonderful attractions of the region relax on our sunny patio or in the outdoor therapeutic spa pool.

DIRECTIONS: Please phone for easy directions.

HIBURN FARMSTAY

Hiburn, RD 2, Cromwell
Ph (03) 445 1291, Fax (03) 445 1291
e-mail: *hiburn@xtra.co.nz*

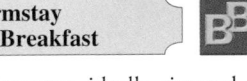

Features & Attractions

- *Peaceful setting*
- *Outstanding views*
- *Hill walks*
- *A real farmstay*
- *Share farming activities*
- *Amazing sheepdogs*

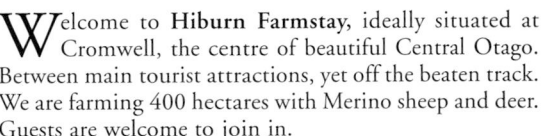

Double	$90
Single	$60
Child	$30

Farmstay Bed & Breakfast

Bedrooms	Qty
Double	1
Twin	1
Single	
Bed Size	**Qty**
King	
Queen/Double	1
Single	2
Bathrooms	**Qty**
Ensuite	
Private	
Guest Share	1
Family Share	

Welcome to **Hiburn Farmstay**, ideally situated at Cromwell, the centre of beautiful Central Otago. Between main tourist attractions, yet off the beaten track. We are farming 400 hectares with Merino sheep and deer. Guests are welcome to join in.

Farm activities are always included and working sheepdogs are a speciality. We encourage our guests to come to dinner and enjoy time chatting over a meal. Dinner is available by arrangement. Home produce is used as much as possible. Our interests include sport, curling, sheepdog competitions, gardening and handcrafts. **Hiburn Farmstay** is an ideal place to explore this region, children are welcome. We treat our guests as friends and invite you to relax with us and enjoy our wonderful farmstay.

DIRECTIONS:
Hiburn is 10 km north from Cromwell off State Highway 6. Please phone for further details. Best time to catch us in is mealtimes or evenings.

WALNUT GROVE
SH 6, Lowburn, RD 2, Cromwell
Ph (03) 445 1112, Fax (03) 445 1115
Mobile 025-774 695
e-mail: *walnut.grove@xtra.co.nz*
http://www.walnutgrove.co.nz

Tariff : N.Z. Dollars		
	Double	$120
	Single	$105
	Child	

Bedrooms	Qty
Double	2
Twin	
Single	
Bed Size	Qty
Super King	1
King	
Queen/Double	1
Single	
Bathrooms	Qty
Ensuite	2
Private	
Guest Share	
Family Share	

Countrystay - Bed & Breakfast

Features & Attractions

- *Historic gold mining area*
- *Beautiful scenery*
- *Queenstown/Wanaka 45 min.*
- *Close to Lake Dunstan*
- *Spacious home and garden*
- *Cromwell 4 min. drive*
- *Orchard on boundary*
- *Fishing, golf, sightseeing*

Relax and enjoy our world! A place for all seasons – with a dry climate, wonderful scenery, fine fishing in Lake Dunstan and rivers, excellent golf course, historic gold mining sites and towns, orchards, vineyards, wineries, the adventure activities of nearby Queenstown and Wanaka, it is unforgettable. The spring and autumn colours are magical. Comfortable non-smoking guest bedrooms have TV, clock radio, coffee/tea making facilities and ensuite bathrooms. (The super king is also available as two single beds.) We have a large lounge with wood burner fire for winter and separate dining room.

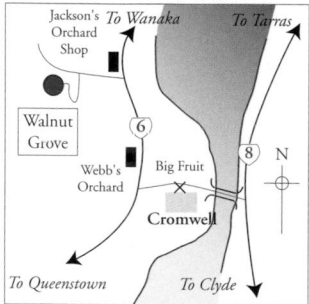

Breakfast is served when it suits you and we would be delighted to help plan your stay. A laundry is available. Our home is set in 4 acres with large garden and shady walnut trees in the grounds. With views of the valley and mountains and a working orchard beside us, it is a lovely setting. We have two siamese cats and a labrador dog. We have travelled extensively, just love meeting people and would like you to make our home your home when in Central Otago. Please ring for directions and reservations.

QUARTZ REEF CREEK

Rapid 349, SH 8, RD 3 Northburn,
Cromwell
Ph (03) 445 0404, Fax (03) 445 0404

Features & Attractions

- *Quiet, peaceful surroundings*
- *Lakeside setting*
- *Private deck & entrance*
- *Architecturally designed home*
- *Christchurch/Queenstown Highway*
- *Stunning lake & mountain scenery*

Double	$100
Single	$60
Twin	$90

Homestay Bed & Breakfast

Bedrooms	Qty
Double	1
Twin	1
Single	

Bed Size	Qty
King	
Queen/Double	1
Single	3

Bathrooms	Qty
Ensuite	1
Private	1
Guest Share	
Family Share	

Quartz Reef Creek is situated in the mountains and lakes of Central Otago, a dry climate with high average sunshine hours, in a rapidly expanding wine-growing area. Your sunny room has a panoramic views of mountains and lake, and total privacy. Also tea making facilities, fridge, microwave and TV. Another room has twin beds and a private bathroom.

Enjoy a walk along the lake front, a trip to local goldmining areas or visit local wineries. I have a pottery studio on site and supply local galleries. I also have a friendly black cat called Tom and a dog named Guinness. My home is the first house north of the bridge on the lake front.

DORNOCH

Chapman Road, Alexandra, R.D.1
Central Otago
Ph (03) 4492 760, Fax (03) 4492 760
e-mail: *dornoch@travelwise.co.nz*

Features & Attractions

- *Peaceful rural surroundings*
- *Central to adventure activities*
- *Meals on request*
- *Fishing, golf, sightseeing*
- *Fine local restaurants*
- *Vineyards and orchards*

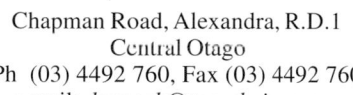

Double	$100
Single	$75
Child	

Homestay Bed & Breakfast

Bedrooms	Qty
Double	2
Twin	1
Single	

Bed Size	Qty
Queen	
Double	2
Single	2

Bathrooms	Qty
Ensuite	
Private	
Guest Share	1
Family Share	

Dornoch is situated in rural Alexandra, the gateway of exciting Central Otago, with its broad range of winter and summer activities, vineyards, orchards and alpine adventure enterprises and splendours. It is admirably sited to be the base from which you may tour and sample the southern wonderland, traversing the area from Mount Cook to Fiordland. **Dornoch** is seven acres of open fields, fruit trees, willows and roses.

With our personal interests in gardening and classic cars, we will be able to ensure you gain the optimum benefits from your well-earned holiday.

DIRECTIONS:
Property name is on post at boundary. Entrance is flanked by large cartwheels.

257

MONTEVUE HOMESTAY
13 Bodkin Road, Alexandra
Ph (03) 448 8993
Mobile 025-995 060
e-mail: *enquiries@montevue.co.nz*
http://www.montevue.co.nz

VISA
MasterCard

Features & Attractions
- Privacy plus hospitality
- Off-street parking
- Laundry facilities
- Dinner by arrangement
- Outdoor activities
- Courtesy transport

**Homestay
Bed & Breakfast**

	Double	$100-120
	Single	neg.
	Child	

Bedrooms	Qty
Double	2
Twin	1
Single	
Bed Size	**Qty**
Super King	1
Queen	1
King Single	1
Bathrooms	**Qty**
Ensuite	1
Private	1
Guest Share	
Family Share	

A warm welcome awaits you at **Montevue** Homestay. **Montevue**, as the name suggests, has wonderful mountain views. We offer cosy, comfortable, single party accommodation. Extras in king/twin room include, tea and coffee making facilities, sky television and a private outdoor balcony. If you are looking for adventure, eg: off-road walking, mountain biking, kayaking or canoeing, we have it and so much more here in Alexandra. If you are looking to tour award-winning vineyards, try our Grape Escape. You may just want an environment in which you can relax - you will find it here! The area and the experiences offered make this a magical place.

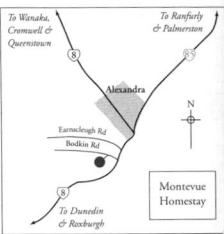

DIRECTIONS: Heading to Dunedin Bodkin Rd. is second right over the bridge and first road left coming from Dunedin.

"THE INN AT 670"
670 Lake Hayes - Arrow Junction, Lake Hayes,
RD 1, Queenstown
P (03) 442 0730, Fax(03) 442 0731
Mobile 027-433 6304
e-mail: *opm@xtra.co.nz*

Features & Attractions
- 4 skifields within region
- Golf courses nearby
- Very quiet location
- Electric blankets, feather down duvets
- Beautiful lake - fish or swim
- Close to Queenstown and Arrowtown

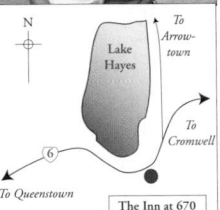

**Bed & Breakfast
Homestay**

	Double	$130-160
	Single	$65-80
	Child	Half price

Bedrooms	Qty
Double	1
Twin	1
Single	1
Bed Size	**Qty**
King	
Queen/Double	1
Single	3
Bathrooms	**Qty**
Ensuite	
Private	1
Guest Share	1
Family Share	

Garry and Marie invite you to stay with us at our home, The Inn at 670. –The whole of this majestic mountain area is a photographer's dream. Breathtaking magic views are continuously mirrored by Lake Hayes. We provide privacy, with comfort and top quality beds, individual heating and double-glazed windows. Enjoy a sumptuous buffet breakfast with home-made jams, fresh fruit and yoghurt, cereals, breads, freshly brewed coffee, and special teas. Our home is 15 minutes from Queenstown and 5 minutes from Arrowtown. There is a choice of four golf courses, 4 skifields, fishing and so many other exciting things to do.
Long stayers most welcome.

DIRECTIONS: From Queenstown or Cromwell take SH 6 to Lake Hayes.

BRIDESDALE

Walnut Lane, Ladies Mile, Queenstown, Otago
Ph (03) 442 0864, Fax (03) 442 0860
Mobile 025-360 403
e-mail: *Bridesdale@xtra.co.nz*

Tariff : N.Z. Dollars	
Double	$130-180
Single	$100
Child	$30-40

Bedrooms	Qty
Double	2
Triple	
Single	
Bed Size	**Qty**
Super King	
King	
Queen	1
Single	2
Bathrooms	**Qty**
Ensuite	
Private	1
Guest Share	
Family Share	

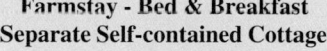
Farmstay - Bed & Breakfast
Separate Self-contained Cottage

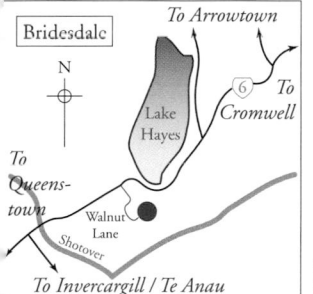

Features & Attractions

- *Cattle Farm*
- *Trout fishing*
- *Close to Skifields*
- *Mountain views*
- *Close to unlimited Queenstown Adventures and Attractions*
- *Peaceful and private*

Our farm is midway between Queenstown and Arrowtown, one kilometre off SH 6, 10 minutes to Queenstown and 8 minutes to Arrowtown. The farm boundaries the Kawarau River and the Hayes Creek where there is excellent private fly fishing. We have beef cattle, a few sheep and a farm dog.

If you ski you can be on two out of three local ski fields in half an hour. The cottage is yours exclusively and is fully self-contained with kitchen, electric blankets, hair dryers, TV, stereo, BBQ, washing machine, dryer and your own private area with beautiful mountain views. (Each additional adult $30-40). If preferred you can join us for breakfast as we enjoy meeting people.

Our prices include a continental breakfast. We have a shy cat called "Fergus" and a friendly little Fox Terrier called "Trouble". No smoking inside please.

Arrowtown - Queenstown ☎ YOUR HOSTS: Sheila and Lex Emslie   Ph: (03) 442 1518

RIVERBANK COTTAGE

Rapid 1350, SH 6, RD 1 Queenstown, PO Box 1093
Ph (03) 442 1518, Fax (03) 442 1519
Mobile 021 - 347 804
e-mail: *cottage@riverbank.co.nz*
http://www.riverbank.co.nz

Tariff : N.Z. Dollars	
Double	$185
Single	$165
Child	

Bedrooms	Qty
Double	2
Twin	
Single	
Bed Size	**Qty**
Super King	1
King	1
Queen	
Single	
Bathrooms	**Qty**
Ensuite	2
Private	
Guest Share	
Family Share	

 Boutique Accommodation Bed & Breakfast   🚭

Features & Attractions

- 4 Ski fields
- Golf courses nearby
- Fishing-rods available
- Rafting and Bungy Jumping
- 2 acres cottage garden
- Wineries
- Quilt gallery
- Restaurants 6 min.

Riverbank Cottage is situated above the banks of the Arrow River, and surrounded by deer farms, yet this beautiful secluded rural setting is only 15 minutes from downtown Queenstown. The house is set in 2 acres of established cottage gardens with magnificent views of Coronet Peak, the Remarkables and surrounding mountains.

DIRECTIONS: From Cromwell drive 3 1/2 km past Bungy sign, driveway on left. From Queenstown, 1 1/2 km past 'Crown – Range' road sign, driveway on right.

The Cottage: Country style accommodation with each bedroom having its own ensuite. Enjoy the guest lounge with beautiful views overlooking an extensive cottage garden, orchard and backdrop of mountains or relax in the shade of the courtyard in the height of summer. If you are interested in quilting and patchwork, put a little time aside to look at the dozens of quilts on display in our gallery, or stroll out to the garages, where there is always an interesting car under restoration. If you require any help about what you should do or see during your visit, we would like to assist, as we have lived in the area for the past 18 years. Our interests are quilting and patchwork, gardening, Ikebana, classic and antique cars.

VILLA SORGENFREI

11 Arrowtown/Lake Hayes Road, Queenstown
Ph (03) 442 1128. Fax (03) 442 1239
e-mail: *villa@xtra.co.nz*

Tariff : N.Z. Dollars		
	Double	$195-245
	Single	$165-185
	Child	$35

Bedrooms	Qty
Double	2
Twin	
Single	

Bed Size	Qty
Super King	2
King	
Queen	
Single	

Bathrooms	Qty
Ensuite	1
Private	1
Guest Share	
Family Share	

**Boutique Accommodation
Bed & Breakfast**

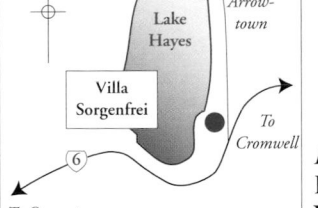

DIRECTIONS:
From Queenstown or Cromwell take
SH 6 to Lake Hayes. Turn onto the
Arrowtown/Lake Hayes Road,
take first turn left.

Features & Attractions

- *Beautiful lake, fishing, swimming*
- *Country peace close to Queenstown*
- *Multitude of outdoor activities*
- *Golf courses nearby*
- *Stacked stone house*
- *German spoken*
- *4 ski fields within region,
  or just holiday relaxation*

Dear Friends –
Found this lovely place called **Villa Sorgenfrei** at Lake Hayes. Just fifteen minutes from Queenstown or five minutes from Arrowtown. Played golf yesterday (choice of four golf courses), then into Queenstown. What a choice of restaurants and bars. Sure was nice to come back here though, to this **so** relaxing stacked stone house – transported us to another world – humm –. Today we'll go to the winery for lunch to build up courage for a Bungi Jump! Might check out historic Arrowtown and its interesting museum **or** better still, go fishing in the lake for those trout that keep waving to me (can see them from the breakfast table!). My god, there's so much to do and see in this area. Shame we didn't allow more time for here. When you come, just phone Micha and Klaus. Cheers.
(Wish you were here now.)

Lake Hayes - Queenstown YOUR HOSTS: Lee and Jaap Van Der Geest Ph: (03) 442 1107

THE TURRET

Rapid No 712, Lake Hayes, RD 1, Queenstown
Ph (03) 442 1107, Fax (03) 442 1160
Mobile 025-294 3464
e-mail: *theturret@xtra.co.nz*
http://www.theturret.co.nz

Tariff : N.Z. Dollars		
	Double	$135-195
	Single	$95
	Child	

Bedrooms	Qty
Double	2
Twin	1
Single	
Bed Size	**Qty**
Super King	
King	
Queen	2
Single	2
Bathrooms	**Qty**
Ensuite	2
Private	1
Guest Share	
Family Share	

 Bed & Breakfast Luxury Accommodation

Features & Attractions

- *French, German, Dutch spoken*
- *Close to 4 ski fields*
- *4 golf courses nearby*
- *Award winning garden*
- *Email access*
- *Stunning lake & mountain views*
- *Fishing & swimming in Lake*
- *French doors opening to terrace*

DIRECTIONS:
Overlooking Lake Hayes between Queenstown and Arrowtown on SH 6. Across the road from the Lake Hayes Pavillion.

While a five-star, homemade breakfast awaits you, from your room you watch a hot-air balloon float over Lake Hayes with Coronet Peak as a back-drop: the usual start of the day for guests at **The Turret**.

This distinctive lakeside retreat near Queenstown offers luxury accommodation, featuring hospitality, stunning lake and mountain views and all the comforts you come to expect to make your stay a memorable one.

The Turret is perfectly situated in the historic Arrow Basin, looking out over picturesque Lake Hayes onto Coronet Peak, skiers' paradise.

Three guest rooms are available, all overlooking the lake and the mountains beyond, with french doors opening onto the terrace and a stunning award-winning garden.

WILLOWBROOK

Malaghan Road, RD 1, Queenstown
Ph (03) 442 1773, Fax (03) 442 1773
Mobile 025-516 739
e-mail: *info@willowbrook.net.nz*
www.willowbook.net.nz

Tariff : N.Z. Dollars	
Double	$120-140
Single	$105-125
Child	'POA'

Bedrooms	Qty
Double	2
Twin	1
Single	

Bed Size	Qty
Super King	1
King	
Queen	1
Single	2

Bathrooms	Qty
Ensuite	2
Private	1
Guest Share	
Family Share	

**Guest House
Bed & Breakfast**

Features & Attractions

- *Peaceful rural location*
- *Guest lounge, 2 open fires*
- *Large garden with tennis court*
- *Door to ski lift - 15 min.*
- *Millbrook Resort - 3 min.*
- *Luxurious outdoor spa*

DIRECTIONS:
Willowbrook is on Malaghan Rd, the 'back road' between Queenstown and Arrowtown. Queenstown 15 min., Arrowtown 5 min., Millbrook Resort 3 min.

Willowbrook is a 1914 farm house at the foot of Coronet Peak in the beautiful Wakatipu Basin. The setting is rural, historical and distinctly peaceful, and with the attractions of Queenstown only 15 minutes away, **Willowbrook** can truly claim to offer the best of both worlds. The old homestead has been beautifully renovated. While the character of the original house has been retained, it now boasts such modern comforts as central heating, Sky TV and a luxurious spa pool. Guest rooms contain a bed (or beds) more comfortable than you would find in most hotels and are ensuite or have a private bathroom.

The front deck is an ideal spot to sit back and watch hanggliders drifting down from Coronet Peak. In the colder months, enjoying one of the open fires in the lounge, following an apres-ski spa, can be addictive. We have a tennis court and are within easy reach of four ski fields and three golf courses. An Anglo/Japanese couple with a wealth of cross cultural experiences, we are only too happy to help with local bookings and itineraries in general. Coming soon: Self-contained cottage.

YOUR HOSTS: **Glenys and Kevin Reynolds**   Ph: (03) 442 2194

THE OLD "FERRY HOTEL"
GUESTHOUSE (circa 1872)
Spence Road, Lower Shotover, Queenstown
Ph (03) 442 2194, Fax (03) 442 2190
e-mail: *info@ferry.co.nz*
www.ferry.co.nz

Tariff : N.Z. Dollars	
Double	$185
Single	$150
Child	POA

Bedrooms	Qty
Double	2
Twin	1
Single	
Bed Size	**Qty**
Super King	
King	1
Double	1
Single	2
Bathrooms	**Qty**
Ensuite	1
Private	1
Guest Share	
Family Share	

 Bed & Breakfast Guest House

VISA   MasterCard

Features & Attractions

- *Country kitchen for guests' use*
- *10 min. to Queenstown & Arrowtown*
- *Fishing advice & guide*
- *Central to ski fields & local attractions*
- *Genuine historic building*
- *Peaceful & relaxing location*
- *Photo display of Hotel's history*
- *Huge wood-burning fire*

Old World Elegance aptly describes this delightful Guest House – not just a place to stay but a feature of your holiday. Formerly a popular hotel for 100 years, the Guest House is a local landmark. Your hosts Kevin and Glenys have traced the hotel's history back to 1868 and in the process ascertained that they are the 25th owners of the Hotel. Kevin and Glenys, their daughter Clare and everyone's favourite, Chester the English springer spaniel, have separate accommodation which adjoins the Guest House, but are on hand at any time to help with tour bookings, advice and information. They are equally happy to sit and chat with guests who look for local information and companionship. Kevin can guide or advise you on all aspects of local fishing. Ferry Hotel Guest House has three bedrooms, one of them with an antique brass bed and character ensuite bathroom. There is a kitchen that Granny would have been proud of and a charming lounge-dining room, decked with historic photos, paintings and memorabilia, and kept warm by a roaring log wood-burner. Laundry facilities and a gas barbecue are available. Alfresco eating areas are situated in the English cottage garden. Kevin and Glenys enjoy helping you to make the most of your stay in Queenstown and look forward to meeting you.

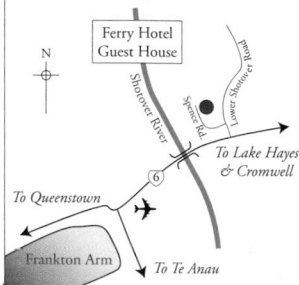

DIRECTIONS:
From SH 6 turn into
Lower Shotover Road – Blue B & B Sign,
follow left turn into Spence Road.

Tariff : N.Z. Dollars	
Double	$120
Single	$60
Child	neg.

BUSH CREEK HEALTH RETREAT

21 Bowen Street,
Queenstown
Ph (03) 442 7260, Fax (03) 442 7250

Bedrooms	Qty
Double	1
Twin	2
Single	1

Bed Size	Qty
Super King	
King	
Queen	1
Single	5

Bathrooms	Qty
Ensuite	
Private	
Guest Share	2
Family Share	

DIRECTIONS: From Queenstown follow the road to Coronet Peak Ski field. **Bush Creek Health Retreat** is sign posted.(Approx. 1km)

 Homestay - Bed & Breakfast
Specialized Health Retreat

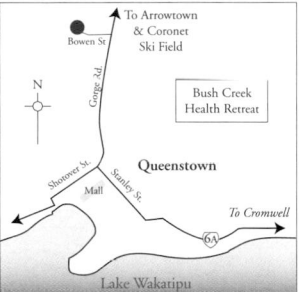

Features & Attractions

- *3 acres of natural paradise*
- *Organically grown food*
- *Internationally recognised Natural Healing Practitioner*
- *Renowned old-world garden*
- *Deep Tissue Massage Therapy*
- *Wholesome, nutritious meals*
- *Pure, natural spring water*

Advance booking is recommended.

Bush Creek is one of the longest established Health Retreats in New Zealand. It is set in three acres of natural paradise only ten minutes walk from the centre of Queenstown, your base for the majestic splendour of the Southern Alps, lakes and Fiords. The rooms are fully appointed with all the extras that provide the ultimate in comfort. Enjoy nutritious, organically grown and prepared food and pure natural spring water.

Ileen Mutch, who owns and operates **Bush Creek Health Retreat**, is an internationally recognised natural healing practitioner, one of the longest practising in this part of the globe. Still your soul and revitalize your energies in harmony with her renowned old-world garden, listening to songs of native birds and the cascading waterfall.

There is also Deep Tissue Massage Therapy available to you. Come and join the list of travellers that return again and again for their rejuvenating stay.

ANNA'S COTTAGE

67 Thompson Street, Queenstown
Ph (03) 442 8994, Fax (03) 441 8994
Mobile 025-626 2165

Features & Attractions

- *Breakfast available*
- *Quiet location*
- *Tranquil garden setting*
- *A few minutes to town centre*
- *Mountain views*
- *Cosy stacked stone cottage*

Double	$110	
Single	$95	
Child		

Self-contained Suites
Breakfast Available

Bedrooms	Qty
Double	2
Twin	
Single	
Bed Size	**Qty**
King	
Queen	2
Single	
Bathrooms	**Qty**
Ensuite	2
Private	
Guest Share	
Family Share	

A warm welcome to Anna's Cottage.
Myrna is a keen gardener and golfer and Ken has a love of fishing. Enjoy the peaceful garden setting and mountain views.

The cottage has full kitchen facilities and living room, combined washing machine and dryer. It is tastefully decorated throughout, the bedroom features sheridan linen.

Only a few minutes from the centre of Queenstown, with private drive and parking at the cottage. Attached to the end of our home is the Rose Suite, also self-contained, one queen bed with ensuite, small kitchen, TV and featuring sheridan linen. Washing mashine and dryer available.

We will help and offer advice on all Queenstown activities.

CAMPBELLS B&B

10 Wakatipu Heights, Queenstown
Ph (03) 442 9190, Fax (03) 442 4404
Mobile 021-116 8801
e-mail: *roosterretreat@xtra.co.nz*

Features & Attractions

- *Child friendly*
- *Tranquil garden setting*
- *Self-contained guest unit*
- *Panoramic views*
- *Generous breakfast*
- *Walk to town centre*

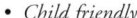

SC-Unit	$200	
Double	$100	
Single	$60	

Bed & Breakfast and
Self-contained Unit

Bedrooms	Qty
Double	2/3
or Twin	1
Single	
Bed Size	**Qty**
Super King	1
Queen	1
Double	1
Single	1
Bathrooms	**Qty**
Ensuite	
Private	1
Guest Share	1
Family Share	

Our 2 girls, 1 cat and 2 bantams welcome other children to share their playground with them. We have a tranquil home with off-street parking and a ½ acre garden to relax in. It has outstanding views of Lake Wakatipu, Queenstown and the surrounding mountains including the Remarkables.

Our fully self-contained cottage garden unit has proven immensely popular with guests – especially those with children! It includes a fully equipped kitchen and laundry. This allows you complete privacy or you can mix with us as you wish. A super king (or twin) room with private bathroom is in the house. Complimentary tea, coffee and laundry facilities. There are no stairs as all guest facilities are on ground level. Enjoy a generous continental breakfast with fresh baked bread and real coffee at your leisure.

Guests say "Excellent value for money".

DIRECTIONS: Turn off Frankton Rd. and up Suburb St. First right into Panorama Terrace, second on left into Wakatipu Heights.
(1.5 km north-east of town centre or 20 min. walk to town and $5 taxi back home - uphill).

THE HISTORIC STONE HOUSE
47 Hallenstein Street
Ph (03) 442 9812, Fax (03) 441 8293
Mobile 025-573 903
e-mail: *stone.house@xtra.co.nz*
www.stonehouse.co.nz

Features & Attractions

- *Outdoor Jacuzzi*
- *Historic ambience*
- *Fire-side drinks*
- *4 min. from downtown*
- *Tour-booking service*
- *Lake views*

Double	$250	
Single		
Child		

Boutique Bed & Breakfast Inn

Bedrooms	Qty
Double	4
Twin	
Single	
Bed Size	**Qty**
King	3
Queen/Double	1
Single	
Bathrooms	**Qty**
Ensuite	3
Private	1
Guest Share	
Family Share	

Originally built of local Otago stone in 1874, **The Stone House** has been restored to provide charming accommodation for travellers. We are a short walk from the main village of Queenstown, and also provide car parking. Guestrooms feature hairdryers, bathrobes, radio alarm and telephone. Each room has private bathroom facilities and beds are made up with feather duvets and pillows and crisp cotton sheets. Choose between king or queen bed, lake or garden view, ensuite shower or private bathtub. Breakfast is served overlooking Lake Wakatipu, and includes cooked choices such as pancakes or Eggs Benedict, as well as a Continental selection accompanied by freshly brewed coffee and tea. Soak up the alpine ambience in the outdoor hot tub, then meet Baz the cat and your fellow guests over a fire-side aperitif. We will help you choose the best restaurant to suit your mood, and provide advice on how to spend the next day in Queenstown, New Zealand's Adventure Playground.

DIRECTIONS: Coming from Frankton on SH 6A, after 7 km turn right into Dublin St., then left Hallenstein St. We are on your right.

PINESONG
58 Fitzpatrick Road (PO Box 312) Queenstown
Ph (03) 442 5607, Fax (03) 442 5697
Mobile 021-334 876
e-mail: *pinesong@queenstown.co.nz*
http://www.pinesong.co.nz

Features & Attractions

- *4 ski fields in region*
- *4 golf courses nearby*
- *360° mountain vistas*
- *10 min. from Queenstown*
- *Stack stone and cedar home*
- *Outdoor spa bathouse*

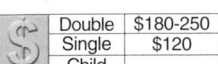

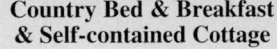

Double	$180-250	
Single	$120	
Child		

Country Bed & Breakfast & Self-contained Cottage

Bedrooms	Qty
Double	3
Twin	
Single	
Bed Size	**Qty**
King	2
Queen	1
Single	
Bathrooms	**Qty**
Ensuite	2
Private	1
Guest Share	
Family Share	

Pinesong is an Austrian style country retreat, nestled in 35 acres of rolling farmland surrounded by mountains. The main house provides 2 king-size ensuite bedrooms and adjacent in the Stables Cottage is the self-contained honeymoon suite with a four poster queen size bed, guest lounge/study for undisturbed reading or business. Each room contains TV, video, hairdryer, heated towel rail, phone.

A stroll through the orchard takes you to a large pergola where one can sit and take in the view over a glass of wine or wander a little further and relax in the spa bathhouse. Just 10 minutes from Queenstown, Arrowtown and the airport **Pinesong** is absolutely your best choice for a memorable holiday.

LARCH HILL HOMESTAY/B&B

16 Panners Way, Goldfields, Queenstown
Ph (03) 442 4811, Fax (03) 441 8882
e-mail: *information@larchhill.com*
www.larchhill.com

Tariff : N.Z. Dollars	
Double	$105-150
Single	$85-105
Child	neg.

Bedrooms	Qty
Double	3
Twin	1
Single	
Bed Size	Qty
Super King	1
King	1
Queen	1
King/Single	2
Bathrooms	Qty
Ensuite	2
Private	2
Guest Share	
Family Share	

 Homestay/Bed & breakfast Superb Accommodation

Features & Attractions

- *Magnificent scenery*
- *Tranquil setting*
- *Gourmet breakfast*
- *Italian & German spoken*
- *Dine with hosts option*
- *Golf courses & fishing nearby*
- *Adventure/itinerary planning*
- *Music, art and craft lovers*

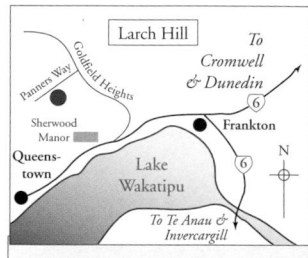

DIRECTIONS: From Frankton drive 2½ km on SH 6A towards Queenstown. At 'Sherwood Manor' turn right into Goldfields Heights. Panners Way is 2nd left, then 1st access on left.

Maria and Chris offer you a warm welcome to **Larch Hill** in beautiful Queenstown. **Larch Hill Homestay** is built on an elevated site overlooking the blue waters of Lake Wakatipu. It is surrounded by spectacular mountains which are snow-capped in winter. Larch Hill is only a 3 minute drive from the centre of Queenstown and in walking distance from the lake. Public transport passes the driveway. All rooms and sundeck overlook the lake and surrounding mountains. This home provides a feeling of relaxation. A restful theme flows through the bedrooms into the dining room with its library, opening to a sunny courtyard surrounded by cottage gardens. On arrival you are welcomed with fresh coffee and home-made cake. In winter a roaring log fire awaits your return from a day's skiing or sightseeing. Having worked as a chef, Maria provides three-course dinners by prior arrangement. Breakfast: continental, home-made bread and yoghurt and fresh fruit salad. We have pleasure in organising any Queenstown experience. We provide: Complimentary pick-up from Queenstown Airport or Bus Station. Fax and e-mail communications facilities.

TRELAWN PLACE

Gorge Road, Arthurs Point, Queenstown
Postal: PO Box 117, Queenstown
Ph/Fax (03) 442 9160, Mobile 025-224 2819
e-mail: *trelawn@ihug.co.nz*
www.trelawnb-b.co.nz

Tariff : N.Z. Dollars		
	Double	$180-250
	Single	
	Child	

Bedrooms	Qty
Double	5
Twin	1
Single	
Bed Size	**Qty**
Super King	1
King	2
Queen/Double	2
Single	
Bathrooms	**Qty**
Ensuite	5
Private	
Guest Share	
Family Share	

Bed & Breakfast and
Self-contained Accom.

DIRECTIONS:
Take SH 6A into Queenstown,
right at 2nd roundabout into Gorge Rd,
travel 4km towards Arthurs Point.
Trelawn Place is sign posted
beside gate on right.

Features & Attractions

- *Unique location beside the Shotover River*
- *Fantastic views of surrounding mountains*
- *Large private garden*
- *Five minutes from centre of Queenstown*

Sited dramatically above the Shotover River with gardens and lawns sweeping to the cliff edge, **Trelawn Place** is a superior country lodge only four kilometres from busy Queenstown. We have four comfortably appointed ensuite rooms, furnished with country chintz and antiques. Our guest sitting room has an open fire and a well stocked library. Outdoors you will find quiet sitting areas and shady vine-covered verandahs.

Generous cooked breakfast features home-made and grown produce. If you are missing your pets, a cat and friendly corgis will make you feel at home.

A forty eight hour cancellation policy applies.

Fly Fishing Guide. Michael guide is available for trout fishing trips in the area. We can also help with bookings for all other local activities.

Self-contained cottage. With its own fireside and roses framing the door, the two bedroom stone cottage is a honeymoon hideaway.

DRIFTWOOD

Kelvin Peninsula,
Postal Address: P.O.Box 2176, Wakatipu,
Ph (03) 442 7088, Fax(03) 442 7044
e-mail: *info@driftwood.net.nz*
www.driftwood.net.nz

Tariff : N.Z. Dollars		
	Double	$150-180
	Single	$100
	Studio	$180

Bedrooms	Qty
Double	4
Twin	1
Single	
Bed Size	**Qty**
Super King	1
King	1
Queen/Double	3
Single	2
Bathrooms	**Qty**
Ensuite	3
Private	2
Guest Share	
Family Share	

 Absolute Lakefront Self-contained Accommodation

Features & Attractions

- *Private access to Lake*
- *Large secluded garden*
- *Golf course 5 min. walk*
- *Kayaks, rowboat, swimming*
- *Fax, phone, e-mail*
- *Music, art. library, maps*
- *Homemade preserves, fresh coffee*
- *Sauna and outside bath*

Nestled in native bush beneath "The Remarkables" on the "wild side" of Kelvin Peninsula, **Driftwood** offers a secluded retreat right on the edge of Lake Wakatipu. Wake to bellbirds and sunrise on the mountains. Wander down through the garden to the lake where the view is breathtaking, the water clear and the beach deserted. Both Studio Apartments are finished in natural timber have queen bed, ensuite, logfire, TV, stereo, kitchen stocked with basic ingredients. Bed & Breakfast guests have the option to dine in their apartment, on the deck, in the house with their host, on the beach or in the garden. (Weekly rate for studio $1,000). The **Three Bedroom House**, elegant and comfortable, with king double and twin rooms, is also available for single party bookings or family groups – minimum 4

DIRECTIONS: Brochure with map available... or phone for easy directions. Bookings essential

nights, $400 night, $2400 week. We are widely travelled outdoor enthusiasts, who have lived locally for 30 years – happy to help you plan and book your daily expeditions. We appreciate good food and wine and can advise on Queenstown's many wonderful restaurants. Above all we want you to feel at home in the relaxed, casual atmosphere at **Driftwood**.

ATHOL TRAVELLERS REST

1155 Garston/Athol Highway 6 (PO Box 23, Athol),
Southland
Ph (03) 248 8995
e-mail: *ntribeathol@xtra.co.nz*

Features & Attractions

- *Brown trout fishing centre*
- *Centrally located for Southland*
- *Pick up point for tours*
- *Genuine hospitality*
- *Recently redecorated*
- *Dinner by arrangement*

	Double	$100-140
	Single	$80-100
	Child	$80-100

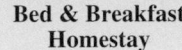

Bed & Breakfast Homestay

H

Bedrooms	Qty
Double	1
Twin	1
Single	
Bed Size	**Qty**
King	1
Queen	
King Single	2
Bathrooms	**Qty**
Ensuite	2
Private	
Guest Share	
Family Share	

Nestled in the centre of Northern Southland in the heart of the Brown Trout Fly Fishing Country is **Athol Travellers Rest**. Only 60 min. from Queenstown Airport and on the banks of the world famous Mataura River. **Athol Travellers Rest** is situated in a quaint little town with two local licenced cafés, gift shop, fishing tackle and licence shop, as well as an internationally recognised fishing guide if required. Described as a comfortable quality B&B Homestay. Friendly atmosphere and great home cooked breakfast to help make your day. Home cooked dinner also available **or** eat at one of the local licenced cafés across the road. Leave your car and take a bus trip to Milford or Doubtful Sound. Pick-up at the gate. Lake Wakatipu and Queenstown are approximately 1 hour away, Invercargill and Stewart Island a little further. A great place to make your Southland base. I will endeavour to make your stay with me a memorable one and will always welcome you back. Your Hostess Noaleen Tribe .

Old Stock Yards

MATAURA VALLEY STATION
850 Cainard Road (Rapid Number)
Garston, Southern Lakes
Postal: PO Box 2, Garston, Southland
Ph (03) 248 8552. Fax (03) 248 8552
e-mail: *matauravalley@xtra.co.nz*

Tariff : N.Z. Dollars		
	Double	$120-250
	Single	$100-180
	Child	$50-100

Bedrooms	Qty
Double	3
Twin	1
Single	1
Bed Size	**Qty**
Super King	
King	2
Queen/Double	1
Single	3
Bathrooms	**Qty**
Ensuite	2
Private	
Guest Share	1
Family Share	

**High Country Farmstay
Fishing Lodge**

Features & Attractions

- *Working farm*
- *19,000 acres*
- *Trout fishing river*
- *Glorious views and tranquillity*
- *10,000 sheep and 300 cattle*
- *Queenstown Airport 45 min.*
- *Kingston Flyer steam train*
- *Alpine walks & bird watching*

Welcome to our 19,000 acre high country sheep and cattle station.
Our sunny, comfortable homestead has glorious views overlooking the Mataura River, famous for brown trout fishing. Alpine tranquillity, only 45 minutes scenic drive from Queenstown's airport. Experience farm activities, walk alpine trails into high mountain pastures, take a 4-wheel drive tour or relax, enjoy the views, the garden and the skylarks. Paradise ducks nest on the creek, hawks soar, a New Zealand falcon may rest on the rooftop. Meet our pet lamb, two cats, the pig, 6 sheep dogs.

Self-contained lodge available – sleeps 4. Delicious three-course, farm-style meals, with fresh, organically grown vegetables, home baking and local wines. Day visitors welcome – includes lunch and farm tour. Aerial and 4-wheel drive trips by arrangement. Easy travel to Queenstown, the Southern Scenic Circuit, Milford and Doubtful Sounds. Tour bookings available. We are members of the HostLink group and aim to make your stay a special memory. Open October 20th – May 20th.

KOWHAI LODGE

5665 Highway 94, Post Office
Mossburn - Te Anau Highway
Ph (03) 248 6137, Fax(03) 248 6137
e-mail: *pjswann@xtra.co.nz*

Tariff : N.Z. Dollars	
Double	$100-150
Single	$90-100
Child	$15

Bedrooms	Qty
Double	1
Twin	1
Single	

Bed Size	Qty
Super King	
King	
Queen	1
Single	2

Bathrooms	Qty
Ensuite	
Private	1
Guest Share	
Family Share	

 Fishing & Hunting Lodge

Features & Attractions

- *Working sheep and deer farm*
- *Guiding available for hunting*
- *Mountain and rural views*
- *Central fishing location*
- *Close to amenities*
- *Horse riding available*

Our rustic 2 bedroom lodge features a hand-built stone chimney and large open fire, with comfortable beds and cosy atmosphere. Kowhai Lodge is surrounded by red deer, including a pet hind to hand feed!Mossburn, the Deer Capital of NZ, is centrally located, half way between Fiordland, Queenstown, Invercargill or The Catlins. The Oreti River boundary's the property for top fishing. Let us help you plan your stay, help us on the farm, ride our horses or enjoy the garden.
We also guide for fishing, hunting and tramping. Johnny has experience guiding safaris in Zimbabwe and at a hunting lodge in Scotland and wants to share his love of the New Zealand wilderness with you. Flexibility is our byword. Totally self-contained, the Lodge provides a central base to enjoy your break. We have two skifields within an hour's drive, return to a roaring fire and relax. Kowhai Lodge is 1 km west of the Mossburn township, on the left hand side of Highway 94 to Te Anau and Milford Sound. We look forward to meeting you and sharing our 100% pure New Zealand hospitality.

"TAPUA"

66 Wilderness Road (Rapid No), 2 RD,
The Key, Te Anau
Ph (03) 249 5805, Fax (03) 249 5805
Mobile 025-201 9109
e-mail: *Tapua.Cromb@xtra.co.nz*

Tariff : N.Z. Dollars	
Double	$110
Single	$70
Child	half price

Bedrooms	Qty
Double	1
Twin	1
Single	

Bed Size	Qty
Super King	
King	1
Queen	
Single	2

Bathrooms	Qty
Ensuite	
Private	
Guest Share	1
Family Share	

 Farmstay Bed & Breakfast

Features & Attractions

- *Working sheep farm*
- *3700 sheep - 100 cattle*
- *Trout fishing rivers*
- *Milford/Doubtful Sound trips*
- *Wonderful scenery*
- *Walking tracks, golf*

You are surrounded by "Million Dollar" views while enjoying the

DIRECTIONS:
Please phone for simple directions.

comfort of our large modern family home. Electric blankets/ wool underlays on all beds - heaters in bedrooms. Enjoy traditional farm-style meals, homemade preserves and jams. Evening meals by prior arrangement $25 pp. Children under 12, ¹/₂ price.

We are situated in a very handy position close to the main road, only 15 minutes from Te Anau or Manapouri, an excellent base for your sightseeing trips to magnificent Milford and Doubtful Sounds. We recommend a two night stay so you can enjoy a relaxing trip to the Sounds, as well as look over our 348 ha (870 acre) farm with 3700 sheep and approximately 100 cattle. Some of New Zealand's best fishing rivers within a few minutes drive, the finest walking tracks in the world, golf course etc. We are happy helping plan your day trips. Personal attention and service assured.
We have a cats. Smoke free home.

COSY KIWI BED & BREAKFAST
186 Milford Road, Te Anau
Ph (03) 249 7475. Fax (03) 249 8471
Postal: Po Box 172, Te Anau
e-mail: *cosykiwi@xtra.co.nz*

Features & Attractions
- *Wir sprechen deutsch*
- *Sumptuous breakfast buffet*
- *3 minute walk to centre*
- *Immaculately clean*
- *Trip booking and pick-up*
- *E-mail and fax facilities*

Bed & Breakfast Guest House

Double	$85-99
Single	$60-70
Child	$5-20

"Cosy" truly describes how you will feel within our warm, architecturally designed, modern Bed & Breakfast House. We provide privacy with comfort. Our quiet bedrooms are spacious, ensuited with top quality beds, TV, individual heating and double glazed windows. Enjoy a sumptuous buffet breakfast of home-made breads, topped with home-made jams, marmalade, fresh fruit salad, yoghurt, home-bottled fruits, brewed coffee, special teas and our legendary pancakes with maple syrup. We have a modern laundry, good off-street parking and luggage storage for track walkers. Our warm guest lounge provides excellent space to relax, chat and a computer to access e-mails.

Relax outside on our sun-terrace overlooking the ever changing moods of the Murchison Mountains or stroll into the town centre to highly recommended restaurants (3 min.) We can recommend and book any sightseeing trips around Fiordland.

Bedrooms	Qty
Double	4
Twin	3
Single	
Bed Size	**Qty**
King	2
Queen	4
Single	6
Bathrooms	**Qty**
Ensuite	7
Private	
Guest Share	
Family Share	

New Zealand Association of Farm & Home Hosts

This logo represents the leading organisation of Farm and Home Accommodation in New Zealand, namely Homestay, Bed & Breakfast, Farmstay and Countrystay. It assures you of a warm welcome in a private home where guests are treated as friends of the family and given personal care and time by the hosts, with meals available. Members' homes are inspected on a regular basis.

New Zealand Association
FARM & HOME
HOSTS

LITTLE BLUE HOUSE

14 Lakefront Drive, PO Box 50, Te Anau
Ph (03) 249 7739, Fax (03) 249 77 55
e-mail: *dawnlittlebluehouse@amcom.co.nz*

Features & Attractions

* Local knowledge
* Friendly homely atmosphere
* Therapeutic massage service

* Trip bookings and pick-up
* Opposite Fiordland Park -
  Information Centre

Double	$80	
Single	$60	
Child		

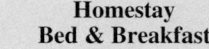
Homestay
Bed & Breakfast

Bedrooms	Qty
Double	2
Twin	
Single	
Bed Size	**Qty**
King	
Queen/Double	2
Single	2
Bathrooms	**Qty**
Ensuite	1
Private	
Guest Share	
Family Share	1

Welcome to our home, peacefully situated on the Te Anau lakefront, 10 minutes walk to the town centre, "and opposite the National Park Information Centre". Dawn is from a farming background, having worked with organic husbandary and still has a keen interest in that area. Ross is a Senior Ranger with the National Park. He also does Port lecturing on some cruise ships visiting the Fiordland coastline. Evening meals are available, $30 pp. Specialising in organic food and complimentary wines.

We have two rooms available.

Room 1: Has one queen bed and one single bed, with private toilet/bath ensuite.
Room 2: Has one queen bed and one single bed adjacent to a shared shower facility. Off-street parking, laundry service, no credit card facilities.

Therapeutic massage available $40 an hour. Bookings essential please.

SHAKESPEARE HOUSE

10 Dusky Street, PO Box 32, Te Anau
Ph (03) 249 7349. Fax (03) 249 7629
e-mail: *marg.shakespeare.house@xtra.co.nz*
http://ww.ubd.co.nz/shakespearehouse

Features & Attractions

* World Heritage Park
* All ground-floor units
* Courtesy car

* Milford & Doubtful Sound tours
* Continental & cooked breakfast
* Walking track, golfing, fishing

Guest House &
Self-contained Accom.

Double	$80-112
Single	$60-80
Child	0-15

DIRECTIONS: Drive north on Lake Front Drive, carry on along Te Anau Tce. Dusky Street is the last right turn before the boat harbour.

Fiordland – the "Walking Capital" of the world – is right on your doorstep when you stay at **Shakespeare House**. Marg and Jeff extend a warm welcome to you and offer personal attention in a homely atmosphere. We are situated in a quiet residential area, yet are within walking distance of shops, lake, restaurants and attractions. Our units have their own private facilities, are warm and comfortable with tea/coffee, TV and have the choice of king, double or twin beds. They open onto a sunny, relaxing conservatory where you may share your holiday experiences with other guests. We also have a two bedroom self-contained unit, which is popular with families or two couples travelling together. Our dining room catches the morning sun and has a lovely view of the mountains. Enjoy a substantial breakfast – either cooked from the menu or buffet-style continental. Good off-street parking, washing machine and dryers are available. We invite you to experience our hospitality and meet our cat 'Brothersoul'.

Bedrooms	Qty
Double	4
Twin/Triple	3
Quad	1
Bed Size	**Qty**
Super King	2
Queen/Double	4
King/Single	2
Bathrooms	**Qty**
Ensuite	8
Private	
Guest Share	
Family Share	

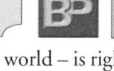

PERENUKA FARM

2 Sinclair Road, No.1 RD, Te Anau
Ph (03) 249 7841, Fax (03)249 7841
e-mail: *perenuka@xtra.co.nz*

Tariff : N.Z. Dollars	
Double	$95-105
Single	
Child	

Bedrooms	Qty
Double	2
Twin	
Single	
Bed Size	Qty
Super King	
King	
Queen	2
Single	1
Bathrooms	Qty
Ensuite	2
Private	
Guest Share	
Family Share	

Homestay
Bed & Breakfast

DIRECTIONS:
From Te Anau continue towards Milford
Sound for 5 km. Turn right into
Sinclair Road, then immediately
right again into our driveway.

Features & Attractions

- *Friendly hosts*
- *Tame sheep*
- *Farm walk*
- *Quiet and peaceful*
- *Magnificent views*
- *Privacy*
- *On road to Milford Sound*
- *Fiordland National Park*

Perenuka is a 750 acre working sheep and cattle farm. Our home and accommodation is high on a terrace which allows for fabulous panoramic views of the lake and mountains.

The spacious guest rooms are separate from the house, in a garden setting, for total privacy. Each room has high quality furnishings, firm beds with electric blankets, heaters, tea/coffee and other facilities to make your stay comfortable and warm.

We encourage guests to join us for breakfast and in the evenings for friendship.

Being situated on the edge of the beautiful Fiordland National Park provides a number of walking options, ranging from very short to 3 to 5 hours. If you want a spell from driving, we can highly recommend a private operator for a day trip to Milford Sound.

Te Anau (5 minutes drive) has many fine cafés and restaurants with a wide range of cuisine.

Perenuka is not suitable for children.

ETHRIDGE GARDENS

10 Sealy Street, Timaru
Ph (03) 684 4910, Fax (03) 684 4910
Mobile 025-365 365

Tariff : N.Z. Dollars	
Double	$120
Single	$90
Child	$30

Bedrooms	Qty
Double	1
Twin	1
Single	1
Bed Size	**Qty**
Super King	
King	
Queen	1
Single	1
Bathrooms	**Qty**
Ensuite	
Private	1
Guest Share	
Family Share	

Bed & Breakfast Homestay

Features & Attractions

- *Charter flights over Mt Cook & Alps*
- *Private gardens to visit*
- *Excellent fishing rivers*
- *5 ski fields within easy distance*
- *Bush walks*
- *Golf course nearby*
- *Christchurch 2 hours*
- *Queenstown 4 hours*

Ethridge Gardens is a beautiful character house built in 1911 and set in romantic English-style gardens. Iron gates and rose-covered archways lead through to exciting vistas. High brick walls divide the garden into rooms, each one differing in style, colour and design.

To stay here is to enjoy the very best in old-fashioned hospitality. Guests are welcome to relax in a large gracious sitting-room which opens onto the terrace and courtyard with its fountain and pond. Afternoon tea on arrival can be served indoors or in a rose-clad gazebo overlooking a delightful rose garden and heated swimming pool.

Tea, coffee, chocolates, robes and fresh flowers in the bedrooms. TV in the main bedroom. Delicious breakfasts, continental and traditional, available.

Excellent restaurants nearby. Wine and aperitifs with your hosts early evening if desired.

Nan is a renowned New Zealand gardener and Wynne is Mayor of Timaru with a wide knowledge of the region.

DIRECTIONS: Just north of Timaru township on SH 1, turn west into Wai-iti Rd. Travel 2km, then turn right into Sealy St. **Ethridge Gardens** is on left.

TOKARAHI HOMESTEAD

47 Dip Hill Road, Tokarahi, RD 12C, Oamaru
Ph (03) 431 2500. Fax (03) 431 2551
e-mail: tokarahi@xtra.co.nz
www.homestead.co.nz

Features & Attractions

- *Challenging golf course*
- *Gateway to Danseys Pass*
- *Fishing guides available*
- *Horse trekking available*

- *Maori rock drawings*
- *Centrally heated*
- *Fossil & geology trails*
- *Wheel-chair access*

Tariff : N.Z. Dollars	
Double	$170-250
Single	$113-188
Child	neg.

VISA · MasterCard · JCB · Diners Club · AMERICAN EXPRESS

Bedrooms	Qty
Double	4
Twin	
Single	

Bed Size	Qty
Super King	1
King	
Queen	3
Single	

Bathrooms	Qty
Ensuite	4
Private	
Guest Share	
Family Share	

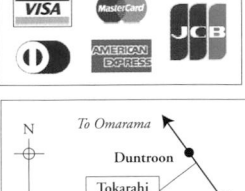

DIRECTIONS: South of Duntroon turn towards Danseys Pass, stay on Danseys Pass Rd for 11 km, then turn left at Dip Hill Road.

**Historic Homestead
Luxury Accommodation**

Described as a 'hidden treasure' **Tokarahi Homestead** (1878) is an authentic, completely restored Victorian limestone homestead. Many original features have been retained, including the unique, embossed imitation leather wallpaper in the entrance hall. Using imported period wallpapers and fabrics, we have created an atmosphere of past opulence, but with all the luxury features of today.

Relax and enjoy open fires, and elegant period surroundings. Soak in an antique clawfoot bath. Enjoy delicious food and good wines 'silver service style' at the big kauri table. View the Southern stars in clear, dark, skies through our telescope. Nothing is overlooked in providing guests with exceptional personal hospitality and a memorable experience of colonial grandeur, in a superb country setting. Oamaru, with its Victorian limestone architecture and Blue Penguin colony is only 35 minutes away.

Christchurch – 3½ hours............................Queenstown – 3hours
Dunedin – 1¾ hours..................................Mount Cook – 2 hours

 YOURHOSTS: **Stephanie and Norman Slater** Free Ph: 0800 003 319

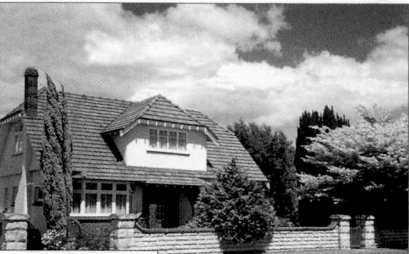

HIGHWAY HOUSE

43 Lynn Street, Oamaru
Ph (03) 437 1066, Fax (03) 437 1153
Mobile 025200 2976
e-mail: *cns@ihug.co.nz*

Features & Attractions

- *Historic Oamaru (stone)*
- *Harbour and blue penguins*
- *Idyllic rural scenery*
- *mais on parle français*
- *Essentially English residence*
- *Mais on parle français*

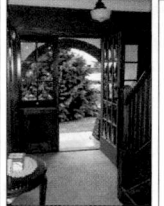

Boutique Bed & Breakfast

Double	$80-100
Single	$60-80
Child	

Stephanie and Norman welcome you. Our character residence, right on Thames Highway, the main road as you travel into town from the north, has been refurbished under the direction of Interior Designer, Deborah Still. There are beautiful and warm bedrooms, new bathroom facilities and a breakfast room which provides continuous coffee or tea. Off-street parking is available, adjoining our expansive garden. Kiwi "light" and/or full English breakfast is available. We can arrange a tour of historic places or nature sites or visits to sporting facilities, but at the least our courtesy car can collect you and even deliver you to dining establishments nearby. We have ourselves travelled extensively overseas. Let us assist you now with your holiday.

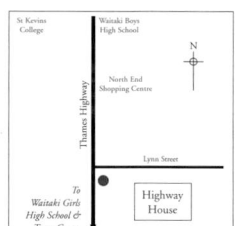

Bedrooms	Qty
Double	2
Twin	1
Single	
Bed Size	**Qty**
King	2
Queen	
Single	2
Bathrooms	**Qty**
Ensuite	
Private	
Guest Share	1
Family Share	1

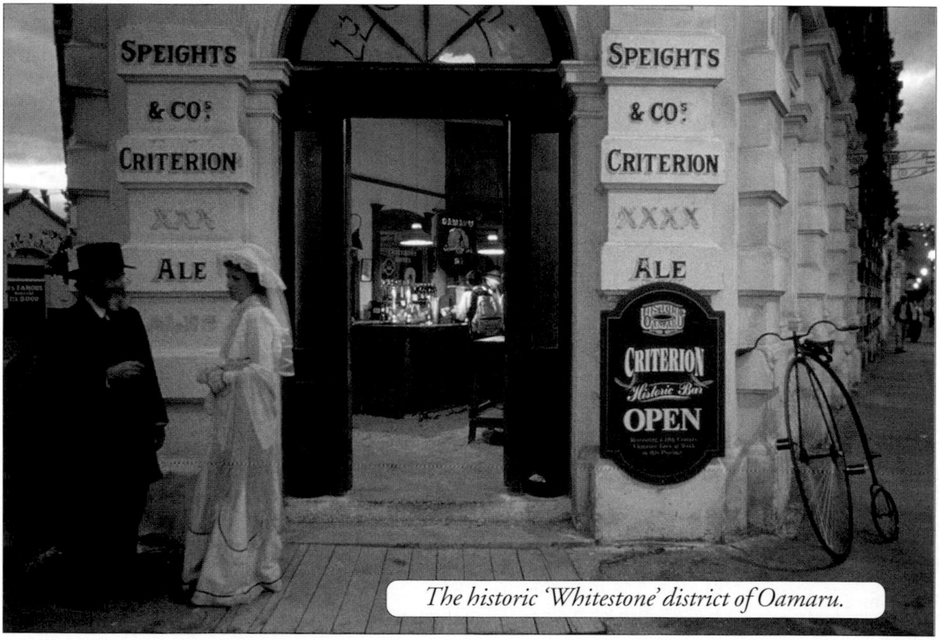

The historic 'Whitestone' district of Oamaru.

GLEN HAVEN BED & BREAKFAST

5 Forth Street,
Oamaru
North Otago
Ph (03) 437 0211, Fax (03) 437 0201

Features & Attractions

- BBQ area in quiet, peaceful garden
- Interesting Matchbox car collection
- Sample homemade Anzac biscuits
- Delightful public gardens
- "Oamaru Stone" quarry
- Historic buildings

	Double	$60-70
	Single	$45
	Child	neg.

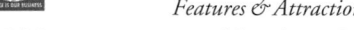

**B & B Homestay &
Semi Self-contained Unit**

DIRECTIONS: From north – 1st Street on right past Meadow Bank Dairy. From south – 1st street on left past Orana Park

Bedrooms	Qty
Double	2
Twin	
Single	
Bed Size	**Qty**
King	
Queen	2
Single	1
Bathrooms	**Qty**
Ensuite	1
Private	
Guest Share	
Family Share	1

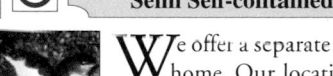

We offer a separate self-contained unit, as well as a bedroom in our home. Our location is north of the township, close to the main highway. The familiar blue B&B-sign makes finding us trouble free. A menu folder is available for a wide selection of local restaurants and eating establishments and we are within walking distance of dairies and takeaways. Having travelled extensively throughout New Zealand on our retirement in 1990, we are happy to provide budget accommodation for those wishing to enjoy the many pleasures our country provides. "Oamaru Stone" is unique to the area and a visit to the quarry is a must, followed by a tour of the town to admire the many grand buildings. The two penguin colonies are well worth looking at – nature at its best. After a walk in the Oamaru public gardens you will agree with us, that it is one of this country's most beautiful parks. Our motto for hospitality is "Your comfort – our pleasure".

GLEN FOULIS

39 Middle Ridge Road, Waianakarua
ORD 9, Oamaru
Ph (03) 439 5559, Fax (03) 439 5220
Mobile 021-940 777
e-mail: *hjm@wxc.net.nz*

Features & Attractions

- Biking, forest trails
- Country picnic trail
- Clear sparkling river
- Meals by arrangement
- Music and home theatre
- Yamaha Clavicord keyboard

	Double	$90
	Single	$55
	Child	$30

Country Homestead

Bedrooms	Qty
Double	1
Twin	1
Single	
Bed Size	**Qty**
Super King	1
Queen/Double	
Single	2
Bathrooms	**Qty**
Ensuite	
Private	
Guest Share	1
Family Share	1

Our hidden valley - called Waianakarua - is just off the Main South Highway to Dunedin. Twenty minutes south of Oamaru with its renowned attractions of penguins and beautiful buildings.

Glen Foulis, a modern homestead, elegantly styled with Oamaru Stone, surrounded by acres of green lawns, tall beech, birch, weeping willows, maples. It has underfloor heating and two efficient open fireplaces. French doors open out to expansive views and sunny terraces lined with roses and covered in wisteria. Native birdsong close by. If you plan more than one night here, we can show you hidden treasures of North Otago from our tough but comfortable 4-wheel drive.

We both work at Energy Efficiency businesses at home. Our two Golden Retrievers, McDuff and Adam delight in greeting your car. Mishka the ginger pussycat follows on behind. Cooked breakfast included with fresh eggs from our hens.

ATANUI

Heywards Point Road, No 1 RD
Port Chalmers, Dunedin
Ph (03) 482 1107, Fax (03) 482 1107
e-mail: *atanui@actrix.gen.nz*

Tariff : N.Z. Dollars	
Double	$100-120
Single	$80-100
Child	$40

Bedrooms	Qty
Double	1
Twin	1
Single	
Bed Size	**Qty**
Super King	
King	
Queen	1
Single	1
Bathrooms	**Qty**
Ensuite	1
Private	1
Guest Share	
Family Share	

 Farmstay with a spectacular view

Features & Attractions

- *Walking tracks and beaches*
- *Pet animals and spa*
- *30 minutes from Dunedin*
- *Spa bath*
- *Spectacular views*
- *Quiet and relaxing*
- *Dinner by arrangement. $25 per person*

We welcome you to our spacious renovated stone house, in a peaceful rural setting only 30 minutes from Dunedin.

From our home, which is heated throughout with radiators off the rayburn range, you can enjoy spectacular views looking out across the Otago Harbour.

Relax in the spa poolor feed our animals - emus, alpaccas, peacocks, pig and pet sheep. Walking tracks and beaches are close by.

Morning and afternoon teas with home baking are complimentary. Three course farm style meals are available by prior arrangement.

We invite you to experience our hospitality and meet our cats "Honey", "Penny" and "Meg".

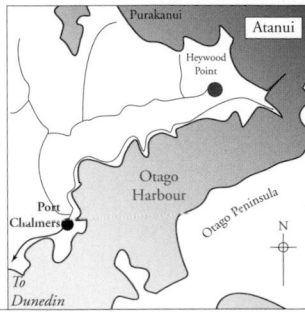

DIRECTIONS: From north turn left at Waitati, follow sign to Port Chalmers till crossroads. Turn left (No Exit) on to next junction take Heywards Point Road (metal road) 4 k on right. From south down to Port Chalmers highway 88, follow sign up the hill to Long Beach till Heyward Point Road (metal road) 4 k on right.

526 GEORGE STREET

526 George Street (PO Box 112), Dunedin
Ph (03) 477 3160, Fax (03) 477 2385
e-mail: *leviathan@xtra.co.nz*

Tariff : N.Z. Dollars		
	Double	$85-125
	Single	$60-95
	Child	

Bedrooms	Qty
Quad **or** Triple	6
Double **or** Twin	12
or Single	12
Bed Size	Qty
Super King	
King	
Queen	12
Single	12
Bathrooms	Qty
Ensuite	12
Private	
Guest Share	
Family Share	

          **Guest House**

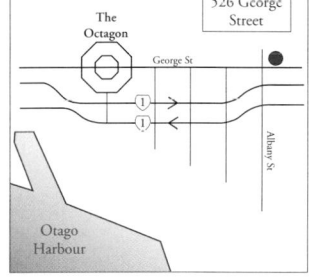

Features & Attractions

- *Downtown grand residence*
- *Adjacent University*
- *Adjacent museum*
- *Close to hospital*
- *Next to main shopping*
- *Disabled facilities*
- *Laundry, Internet access*
- *Full fire safety standard*

Welcome to 526 George Street This gracious residence built in 1907 by Dunedin Hospital's Surgeon, Doctor Roberts as his grand family home. It is next to the City's retail shops and well over 50 restaurants and cafés on George Street. It is on the flat, next to the Hocken Library, across the road from Otago Museum, across the Museum Reserve to the University of Otago and less than 400 metres from the hospital. Our house is particularly suited for guests who have a link with any of the tertiary institutions and the hospital. The disabled access and facilities enable ease of use for a wheel chair around the spacious ground floor and lovely grounds. Suites range from doubles to large family rooms, enabling the house to cater for many accommodation needs. The house is a drop off/pick up point for sightseeing tours. Tours include wildlife - Albatross, Yellow Eyed penguin, as well as Larnach's Castle and City Sights tours.

ALBATROSS INN

770 George Street, Dunedin
Ph (03) 477 2727 Fax (03) 477 2108
e-mail: *albatross.inn@xtra.co.nz*
http://www.albatross.inn.co.nz

Tariff : N.Z. Dollars	
Double	$85-125
Single	$65-85
Child	neg

Bedrooms	Qty
Double	8
Twin	5
Single	
Bed Size	Qty
King	
Queen	4
Double	3
Single	5
Bathrooms	Qty
Ensuite	8
Private	1
Guest Share	
Family Share	

 Guest House

Features & Attractions

- *Built early 1900's*
- *Main Street of Dunedin*
- *All wildlife and city tours pick-up & drop-off here*
- *Open fire, off-street parking*
- *Free internet and e-mail*
- *Close to restaurants, cafés, gardens, Olveston, Museum, University*

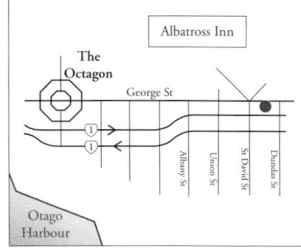

Welcome to Dunedin and Albatross Inn! Our beautiful late Victorian house is ideally located on the main street close to university, Gardens, museum, shops and restaurants.

Our attractive rooms have ensuite bathrooms, telephone, TV, radio, tea/coffee, warm duvets and electric blankets on modern beds. Extra firm beds upon request. Very quiet rooms at rear of house. Several rooms have kitchenette and fridge. We serve freshly baked bread and muffins, fresh fruit salad, yoghurt, juices, cereals, teas, freshly brewed coffee.

Nigel and Kerry are both Dunedin born and have an extensive knowledge of the city. All wildlife tours pick-up and drop-off here. We can recommend many great places to eat, most just a short walk down George Street. Nearby laundry, non-smoking, cot and highchair.

Winter special $69 Double – special conditions apply. Complimentary e-mail and Internet.
Our visitor book says: "The convenience of your location is wonderful, you can walk everywhere! Combined with a gorgeous house, such friendly hosts." Joe and Cathy Wallace, Georgia, USA

Brigantia House

60 Wallace Street, Maori Hill, Dunedin
Ph (03)474 1696, Fax (03) 474 5346
e-mail: *brigantia_house@hotmail.com*
http://www.bnbnz.com

Features & Attractions

- *Gracious, peaceful residence*
- *Ecologically friendly home*
- *Fully centrally heated*
- *Wholesome, healthy breakfast*
- *Native bush reserve adjacent*
- *5 European languages spoken*

	Double	$100-160
	Single	$80-100
	Child	neg.

**Charming
Bed & Breakfast**

Bedrooms	Qty
Double	2
Twin	1
Single	1
Bed Size	**Qty**
King	
Queen	5
Single	
Bathrooms	**Qty**
Ensuite	1
Private	1
Guest Share	1
Family Share	

Dear Guests, We have travelled to many countries around the globe and still remember the special things that made us feel welcome abroad - and to give you this feeling too, is our greatest pleasure. **Brigantia House** (ca.1900), a charming gentleman's residence, is located in a perfectly quiet neighbourhood, adjacent to a delightful native bush reserve. All rooms are centrally heated, the bedrooms are spacious and sunny. You have the choice between our richly appointed ensuite bedroom with four poster bed or one of the upstairs bedrooms with guest share facilities. It's only a 10 minute walk to the city centre and 5 minutes to Moana Pool and Olveston. The nearest gourmet restaurant is only 3 minutes away. We offer wholesome organic, vegetarian breakfast. Laundry is available. We are non-smokers. We share '**Brigantia**' with Hector and Apollo, our friendly dogs.

DIRECTIONS: Please phone for easy directions.

Castlewood

240 York Place, Dunedin, Otago
Ph (03) 477 0526. Fax (03) 477 0526
e-mail: *relax@castlewood.co.nz*
www.castlewood.co.nz

Features & Attractions

- *Gracious old-world charm*
- *Sumptuous continental breakfasts*
- *800m from Octagon & Olveston*
- *Sunny and peaceful*
- *Feather duvets*
- *Spa and sauna*

**Boutique Accomm.
Bed & Breakfast**

	Double	$100-145
	Single	$70
	Twin	$90

Bedrooms	Qty
Double	2
Twin	1
Single	1
Bed Size	**Qty**
King	
Queen	2
Single	2
Bathrooms	**Qty**
Ensuite	1
Private	1
Guest Share	1
Family Share	

Relax at **Castlewood** and experience the old-world charm of our graciously restored Tudor residence. Set on a hill above Dunedin, **Castlewood** offers expansive views and all-day sun, yet is only 800m (10 min. walk) from restaurants, live theatre, cafés, shops and attractions such as Olveston and the Dunedin Art Gallery. **Castlewood's** hospitality includes sumptuous continental breakfasts to make the start of your day a welcome experience. There is a sauna, spa bath and library for added relaxation. Both Peter and Donna are Dunedin-born and know New Zealand intimately. They provide useful and friendly advice on local attractions and having travelled internationally, appreciate the requirements of discerning travellers. Peter is an author and artist. His paintings are displayed throughout **Castlewood** for your enjoyment.

DIRECTIONS: From Octagon travel up Stewart St., turn left into Cargill St., then left into Arthur St. At the traffic lights **Castlewood** is diagonally opposite.

GOWRIE HOUSE

7 Gowry Place,
Roslyn, Dunedin
Ph (03) 477 2103. Fax (03) 471 9169
e-mail: *gowriehouse.bnb@xtra.co.nz*

Tariff : N.Z. Dollars	
Double	$100
Single	$60
Child	

Bedrooms	Qty
Double	1
Twin	1
Single	
Bed Size	**Qty**
Super King	
King	
Queen	1
Single	2
Bathrooms	**Qty**
Ensuite	
Private	
Guest Share	1
Family Share	

 **Boutique Accommodation
Bed & Breakfast**

Features & Attractions

- 5 min. drive from city
- Paved patio off double room
- Tea and coffee-making
  facilities in double room
- Warm & sunny bedrooms
- Otago Peninsula nearby
- 20-min. walk from city
- Peaceful surroundings

Gowrie House is in a quiet suburb on a sunny west-facing site with lovely rural views. It is only a 20-minute walk to the city, close to bus routes. The garden has a cosy cottage atmosphere, with all available space occupied by perennial and biennial flowers - regularly picked for rooms. The guests' bedrooms are warm and sunny. The bathroom is handily placed across the hall. All beds have electric blankets. The double room has access to the patio and cottage garden, where one can enjoy the floral fragances.

Otago Peninsula is easily accessible, as are bush walks and historic buildings. Your hosts will happily provide information about such popular attractions. Rod loves cricket, especially writing about it. Vivienne loves gardening, especially beautifying the setting within which Gowrie House cosily nestles.

DIRECTIONS:
Please phone for easy directions.

Advance booking is
recommended.

286

CILL CHAINNIGH

33 Littlebourne Road, Roslyn, Dunedin
Ph (03) 477 4963. Fax (03) 477 4965
Mobile 025-228 7840
e-mail: *wallie.waudby@xtra.co.nz*

Features & Attractions

- *Quiet, peaceful surroundings*
- *1km from centre of Dunedin*
- *Close to historic "Olveston"*
- *Tasty home-baking*
- *Close to Moana Pool Swimming Complex*

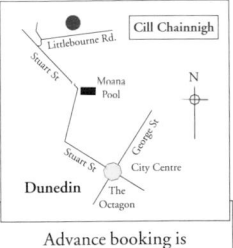

  Bed & Breakfast

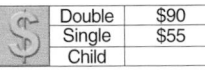

Double	$90
Single	$55
Child	

Bedrooms	Qty
Double	1
Twin	1
Single	
Bed Size	**Qty**
King	
Double	1
Single	2
Bathrooms	**Qty**
Ensuite	
Private	
Guest Share	1
Family Share	

Advance booking is recommended.

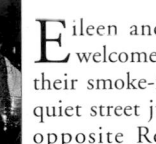

Eileen and Wallie would like to welcome visitors to Dunedin to their smoke-free home, situated in a quiet street just off Stuart Street and opposite Roberts Park. We have travelled extensively ourselves and understand how visitors feel when they arrive in a new town. Our home is in short walking distance to Dunedin's stately home "Olveston", the Moana Swimming Complex and just over one kilometre to the town centre. The guest bedrooms, situated on the top floor for privacy and quietness, are warm and sunny and as a backup all beds have an electric blanket. Tea and coffee making facilities are available to you. You are sure of a warm welcome and comfortable stay at **Cill Chainnigh**.

DEACONS COURT

342 High Street, Dunedin
Ph (03) 477 9053, Fax(03) 477 9058
e-mail: *deacons@es.co.nz*
www.deaconscourt.bizland.com

Features & Attractions

- *Spacious bedrooms*
- *Private facilities*
- *Generous cooked breakfast*
- *Close to city centre*
- *Large rose garden*
- *Historical home*

 **Bed & Breakfast Homestay**

Double	$110-120
Single	$70
Child	$20

Deacons Court is a charming, superior, spacious Victorian villa, 1 km walking distance from the city centre and on a bus route. Keith and Gail are mature, experienced travellers and B & B operators, who offer you friendly but unobtrusive hospitality in a quiet, secure haven.

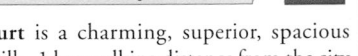

Guests can relax in our delightful, sheltered back garden and conservatory.

Our Rose Room has stunning views across the city to the harbour and sea, whilst our Garden Room overlooks the rose garden. All bedrooms are large with ensuite or private bathroom, heaters and electric blankets.

We provide full breakfast, 24 hour tea/coffee making facilities and laundry service. Ample parking is available. Family groups welcome. We have an unobtrusive cat.

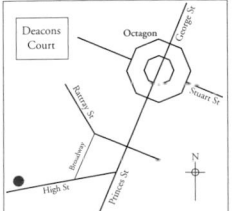

Bedrooms	Qty
Double/Twin	3
Twin	
Single	
Bed Size	**Qty**
King	1
Queen/Double	2
Single	3
Bathrooms	**Qty**
Ensuite	2
Private	1
Guest Share	
Family Share	

287

HERIOT HOUSE

26 Pitt Street, Dunedin
Ph (03) 477 7228, Mobile 025-274 4726
e-mail: *lcalvert@es.co.nz*

Tariff : N.Z. Dollars		
	Double	$100-140
	Single	
	Child	neg.

Bedrooms	Qty
Double	3
Twin	
Single	

Bed Size	Qty
Super King	
King	
Queen	3
Single	

Bathrooms	Qty
Ensuite	1
Private	
Guest Share	1
Family Share	

Elegant Bed & Breakfast Accommodation

Features & Attractions

- *Centrally located*
- *3 minutes stroll to cafés, bars and restaurants*
- *Off-street parking*

- *Quaint cottage garden*
- *Gracious Edwardian home*
- *Friendly, helpful hostess*
- *Sumptuous breakfast*

Louise welcomes you to stay in her gracious old home situated right in the heart of Dunedin. Only a casual stroll to shops and the local restaurants, bars and cafés. The quaint cottage garden has a pleasant charm that will draw you out of doors to inspect the treasures hidden from view.

All guest rooms are on the second floor with an area set aside in each room for those who prefer to relax in private. There is also a separate television room and a sitting room available for those who want a coffee and to chat.

You are sure of a warm, friendly and comfortable stay at **Heriot House**.

DIRECTIONS:
Travelling south on George St turn sharp right at Knox Church into Pitt St.

HULMES COURT BED & BREAKFAST

52 Tennyson Street, Dunedin, Otago
Ph (03) 477 5319, Fax(03) 477 5310
Mobile 025-351 075
e-mail: *normwood@earthlight.co.nz*
www.hulmes.co.nz

Tariff : N.Z. Dollars		
Double	$95-150	
Single	$60-150	
Child	enquire	

Bedrooms	Qty
Double/Twin	8
Twin	4
Single	1

Bed Size	Qty
Super King	
King	3
Queen	10
Single	4

Bathrooms	Qty
Ensuite	8
Private	
Guest Share	3
Family Share	

VISA, MasterCard, AMERICAN EXPRESS, Bankcard, Diners, JCB

Homestay - Bed & Breakfast

 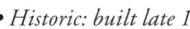

Features & Attractions

* Historic: built late 1860's
* Right in centre of Dunedin
* Off-street parking
* Complimentary laundry
* Close to restaurants
* Large drawing room, open fire
* Complimentary mountain bikes and Internet access

Hulmes Court B&B is two beautiful homes only a few minutes walk from the heart of town and the Visitor Centre. Tennyson Street is quiet and we have private gardens, trees, decks and sitting areas.

The **Victoria Hulmes Court** is one of the most historic homes in Dunedin. It was built in the 1860s by the first provincial surgeon Edward Hulme who helped found the Medical School.

Hulmes Too is a large Edwardian home built next to **Hulmes Court** on the grounds of the original estate. **Hulmes Court** has a variety of rooms which cater for all tastes from the economical cute single Rose Room at $60 per night to our grand ensuite rooms in **Hulmes Too** at $150 per night.

Your host Norman owns a variety of businesses and is interested in history, philosophy, geography and has stood for parliament twice. At the same time Norman at 34 and his staff are youthful, full of energy and travel widely. We provide complimentary laundry, internet and email, BBQ, mountain bikes and off-street parking.

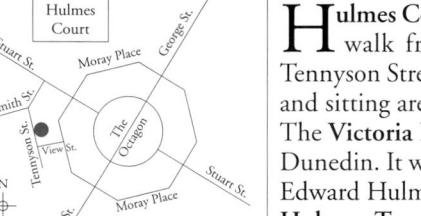

Dunedin City Centre

DIRECTIONS: Leaving the Octagon by Upper Stuart St. take the 2nd turning on the left into Smith St., then just 50m left again into Tennyson St.

PINE HEIGHTS RETREAT

431 Pine Hill Road, Pine Heights, Dunedin
Ph (03) 473 9558. Fax (03) 473 0247
e-mail: *pineheights@xtra.co.nz*
http://www.pineheights.co.nz

Tariff : N.Z. Dollars		
Double	$90
Single	$60
Child	neg.

Bedrooms	Qty
Double	1
Twin	1
Single	
Bed Size	**Qty**
Super King	
King	
Queen	1
Single	2
Bathrooms	**Qty**
Ensuite	
Private	
Guest Share	1
Family Share	

 **Homestay
with Norwegian Flair**

Features & Attractions

- *Tranquil, rural views*
- *Enjoyable native bird life*
- *Relaxing three-course dinner by arrangement*
- *Cosy, comfortable, peaceful*
- *Only 4.5 km to city centre*
- *Handy to University and Botanical Gardens*

DIRECTIONS: Please phone for simple directions and bookings.

Relax in the comfort of our cosy home set in a tranquil rural area, where native birds are frequent visitors. Enjoy our sheltered patio and cottage garden which we love.

Absorb the peacefulness of our surroundings. Sweeping views are shared by all living and bedroom areas. It's like living in the country yet only a few minutes by car from the city centre with public transport nearby. A courtesy car is available and we have ample off-street parking.

Flexible mealtimes allow time for sightseeing in our lovely city.

We enjoy meeting people and welcome you to share our home and informal lifestyle. Eli, who has lived in Dunedin for over 30 years, is Norwegian and offers a unique blend of Scandinavian and New Zealand hospitality.

Breakfast is full or continental with a wide range of choices, including fresh home-made bread and waffles. Our dinners, followed by Norwegian-style coffee are a speciality.

Children most welcome.

We will do our utmost to make your stay memorable and enjoyable.

THE STATION MASTER'S COTTAGE

300 York Place, Dunedin, Otago
Free Ph: 0800 327 333, Fax (03) 474 1300
Mobile 025-592 732

Tariff : N.Z. Dollars	
Double	$195
Single	$145
Extra person $100	

Bedrooms	Qty
Double	2
Twin	1
Single	

Bed Size	Qty
Super King	
King	
Queen	2
Single	2

Bathrooms	Qty
Ensuite	
Private	
Guest Share	1
Family Share	

     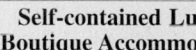

Self-contained Luxury Boutique Accommodation

Features & Attractions

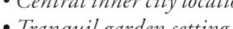

- *Central inner city location*
- *Tranquil garden setting*
- *Fine linen*
- *Peaceful and private*
- *Historic luxury cottage*
- *Self-contained and exclusive*
- *Romantically furnished*
- *Boutique accommodation*

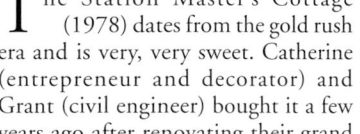

The Station Master's Cottage (1978) dates from the gold rush era and is very, very sweet. Catherine (entrepreneur and decorator) and Grant (civil engineer) bought it a few years ago after renovating their grand italianate villa next door. Catherine is a great fan of country living and has brought her considerable talents to bear on the project... so expect everything to be country chic. It looks deceptively small from the outside, but actually there are three bedrooms, a sitting room (a mix of old and new), a bathroom (with clawfoot bath) and a cosy yellow kitchen at the back which is well equipped with dishwasher, microwave, toaster, etc. Catherine has a happy knack of throwing together antiques and bric-a-brac to create something special. You can sit and admire the cottage garden from the verandah, full of roses and daisies. Just 10 minutes walk to the centre of town. And remember, the cottage will always be yours exclusively, you do not share with others.

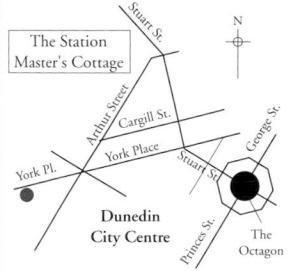

DIRECTIONS.
From the Octagon travel up Stuart St., turn left into Cargill St., then left to Arthur St. At the traffic signals travel up York Place to
"The Station Master's Cottage".

KINCAPLE
215 Highgate, Roslyn, Dunedin
Free Phone: 0800-269 384, pin 4774
Fax (03) 477 4380, Mobile 025-248 8968
e-mail: *kincaple@xtra.co.nz*

Features & Attractions

- Relaxed atmosphere
- 2 kilometres from city
- Coffee and tea facilities
- Friendly reception from family and their dog
- Your comfort our priority

Double	$85-120	
Single	$60-100	
Child	half / u12	

Homestay Bed & Breakfast

Bedrooms	Qty
Double	1
Twin	1
Single	

Bed Size	Qty
Super King	1
Queen	
Single	2

Bathrooms	Qty
Ensuite	1
Private	
Guest Share	1
Family Share	

Kincaple, built in 1903, is a gracious home set in a well established suburb. It has been our family home for 28 years, lies well to the sun and is surrounded by an attractive garden. There is off-street parking and the bus stops at the door. The Visitor Centre is 2 km and the Roslyn shops, Moana leisure and swimming pool and the Belleknowes Golf Club are all a short walk. The stately home, "Olveston", and the Otago Golf Club are 3 km distance.
Inside this smoke free environment are living rooms of generous proportions with open fires and central heating, excellent bedding and plenty of reading material.
We have a long haired dachshund.

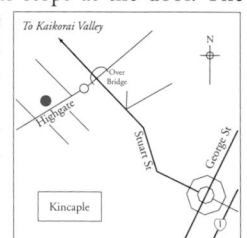

HARBOURSIDE BED & BREAKFAST
6 Kiwi Street, St Leonards,
Dunedin
Ph (03) 471 0690, Fax (03) 471 0063

Features & Attractions

- 7 minutes to city centre
- Overlooking harbour
- Children welcome
- Complimentary tea on arrival
- Home baking
- Dinner by arrangement

Double	$75-85	
Single	$45	
Child	$15 u/12	

Bed & Breakfast Homestay Spectacular Harbour Views

Bedrooms	Qty
Double	2
Twin	
Single	

Bed Size	Qty
Queen	1
Double	1
Single	3

Bathrooms	Qty
Ensuite	1
Private	
Guest Share	1
Family Share	

We are situated in a quiet suburb overlooking Otago Harbour and surrounding hills. Handy to all local attractions – Larnach Castle, Olveston, Albatross and Yellow Eyed Penguin Colonies, Harbour Cruises, Taieri Gorge Excursion Train. Bookings can be arranged. There are many lovely bush walks close to the city. Children very welcome (lots of preloved toys). We have a generous amount of living space for you to relax in after a busy day. Cooked breakfast is included and with a little notice we can arrange a 3 course meal. Courtesy pick-up from bus or train.

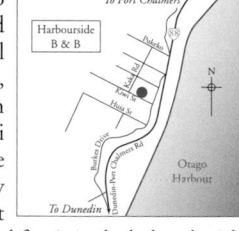

DIRECTIONS: Coming from Northern Motorway turn left towards Port Chalmers (SH88) from Anzac Ave. onto Ravensbourne Rd. After 5 km in St Leonards, turn left into Moa St, left into Kaka Road, straight ahead Kiwi Street.S

ALLOWAY

65 Every Street, Dunedin
Ph (03) 454 5384. Fax (03) 454 5364
e-mail: *alloway@xtra.co.nz*

Tariff : N.Z. Dollars	
Double	$95-120
Single	$85-115
Child	

Bedrooms	Qty
Double	2
Twin	1
Single	

Bed Size	Qty
Super King	
King	
Queen	2
Single	2

Bathrooms	Qty
Ensuite	
Private	
Guest Share	1
Family Share	

Homestay - Bed & Breakfast

DIRECTIONS:
Please phone for easy directions.
Advance booking is recommended.

Features & Attractions

- *Wildlife, Walking Tracks*
- *Taiaroa Head, Albatross Colony*
- *Disappearing Gun, Seal Colonies*
- *Rhododendrons*
- *Yellow-eyed Penguins*
- *Glenfalloch Gardens*
- *7 min. to Dunedin City*
- *Great Architecture*

We are situated on the gateway to the Otago Peninsula, which features wildlife, walking tracks, Taiaroa Head, Albatross Colony, Disappearing Gun, Seal Colonies, Yellow-eyed Penguins, Glenfalloch Gardens and much more. We are 7 minutes from the town centre. Our home is a modern interpretation of a traditional Scottish house and set in one acre of gardens and lawns, with indoor/outdoor living. Awaken to the sound of abundant bird-life in a quiet and secure neighbourhood. We serve delicious, healthy breakfasts. One luxury bedroom complete with one queen and one single bed, plus one luxury bedroom with one queen and one single bed. All rooms have tea making facilities, TV, heaters, electric blankets. Separate facilities with modern guest bathroom. Relax far from the madding crowd. Businesspeople welcome. All non smoking, no pets and not suitable for young children.

ARDGOWAN

218 Musselburgh Rise, Musselburgh,
Dunedin
Ph (03) 456 0411
e-mail: *kturner@southnet.co.nz*

Tariff : N.Z. Dollars	
Double	$100-160
Single	$70-100
Child	

Bedrooms	Qty
Double	3
Twin	1
Single	
Bed Size	**Qty**
Super King	2
King	
Queen	1
King Single	2
Bathrooms	**Qty**
Ensuite	2
Private	1
Guest Share	
Family Share	

**Quality
Bed & Breakfast**

Features & Attractions

- *Private guest lounge/kitchen*
- *Generous menu breakfast*
- *Wine tasting option*
- *Off-street parking*
- *Handy to Peninsula/City attractions*
- *Warm, friendly Edwardian home*
- *Large, spacious bedrooms*
- *Complimentary evening port/sherry*

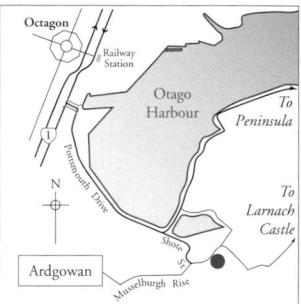

Ken and Margaret welcome you to their gracious Edwardian villa at the gateway to Otago Peninsula and just six minutes from central Dunedin. Our guests have their own private lounge and dining area with Sky television, stereo, books and magazines and a cosy gas log fire. The upstairs bedrooms are large and spacious. The **Endeavour** and **Arthurian Rooms** have super king beds and full ensuite facilities. Our queen room is tastefully decorated and has a private bathroom available. Our knowledge of local attractions and restaurants is at our guest's disposal. Otago Peninsula attractions include the Albatross Colony, Yellow-eyed Penguins, Portobello Marine Aquarium, Larnach Castle and the unique 'Blackbird' and 'Happy Hens' potteries. There are numerous short walks on the Peninsula. A complimentary daily paper and an evening port or sherry is offered. A tasting of Central Otago wine, with cheese board, is available by prior arrangement. We have laundry facilities and off-street parking for our guests.

HARBOUR LIGHTS HOMESTAY B&B

1 Wharfdale Street, Macandrew Bay, Dunedin
Ph (03) 476 1019, Fax (03) 476 1019
e-mail: *harbourlights@actrix.co.nz*

Tariff : N.Z. Dollars	
Double	$85
Single	$55
Child	neg.

Bedrooms	Qty
Double	2
Twin	
Single	1

Bed Size	Qty
Super King	
Queen	1
Double	1
Single	1

Bathrooms	Qty
Ensuite	
Private	
Guest Share	1
Family Share	

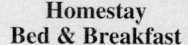

Homestay
Bed & Breakfast

Features & Attractions

- *On beautiful Otago Peninsula*
- *Superb day & night harbour views*
- *Close to Dunedin City – 11 km*
- *Taiaroa Head & Albatross Colony*
- *Yellow-eyed penguins & seals*
- *Armstrong Disappearing Gun*
- *Close to Glenfalloch Gardens*
- *Evening meals on request*

"What a view!" This is often the first remark of our guests upon arrival at **Harbour Lights Homestay,** but many have had a few pangs of regret at having to leave us. Many of our guests who have stayed here, now consider us as friends. We know how visitors feel upon arrival in unfamiliar surroundings as our travels have taken us to many parts of the world. So please accept a warm Scottish welcome. The guest rooms are on the upper level to maintain our guests' privacy. All rooms are equipped with heating and electric blankets and include tea

and coffee facilities. In the morning choose either continental or full cooked breakfast. Libby and Alex are looking forward to welcoming you to **Harbour Lights Homestay.**

Otago Peninsula

YOURHOST: **Nicole Kolig**   Ph: (03) 478 0911

CONEHENGE HOMESTEAD
1589 Highcliff Road, Dunedin
Ph (03) 478 0911
Mobile 021-675 413
e-mail: *kolig@ihug.co.nz*

Features & Attractions
- Central Peninsula position
- City & Wildlife colonies 25 min.
- Magnificent harbour & sea views
- German spoken
- Ceramic artist
- Electr. blankets/hairdryer

Double	$110
Single	$95
Child	

**Rural Retreat
Bed & Breakfast**

Bedrooms	Qty
Double	1
Twin	
Single	

Bed Size	Qty
King	1
Queen	
Single	

Bathrooms	Qty
Ensuite	1
Private	
Guest Share	
Family Share	

A warm welcome awaits you in our new homestead on Harbour Cone – it will be my pleasure to share this special environment with you. I am running a 35 hectare farm carrying beef cattle, sheep, and two utterly spoilt donkeys. Take the time to explore the many wildlife attractions such as the unique Royal Albatross Colony, the habitat of the rare Yellow Eyed Penguin, seals and all kinds of birds, sandy beaches, walking tracks, famous Larnach's Castle and many other places of interest. Your room offers you wonderful views over harbour and sea. It has its own private entrance, a tea kitchen with toaster, jug and complimentary tea and coffee. A continental breakfast with fruit and freshly baked croissants is brought to your room. In nearby Portobello Village you will find a licensed restaurant and a café with Internet facilities. I am a ceramic artist and my work is for sale.

DIRECTIONS: 1.5 km south of Portobello village.

Mosgiel - Dunedin

YOURHOSTS: **Margaret and Alan Dunbar**   Ph: (03) 489 6131

STRANALYTH GABLES
Rapid No 193, Riccarton Road,
RD 2, Mosgiel near Dunedin
Ph (03) 489 6131, Fax (03) 489 6131

Features & Attractions
- 10 min. Dunedin Airport
- Lambs, sheep & calves
- River rafting close by
- Dunedin City 15 minutes
- Good fishing & 3 golf courses
- 3-course evening meal available

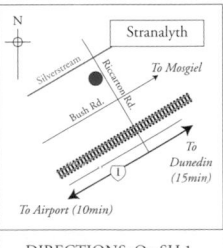

**Farmstay
Bed & Breakfast**

Double	$85
Single	$55
Child	half price

Bedrooms	Qty
Double	2
Twin	2
Single	

Bed Size	Qty
King	
Queen	2
Single	4

Bathrooms	Qty
Ensuite	
Private	1
Guest Share	1
Family Share	

Map showing Stranalyth, Silverstream, Riccarton Rd, Bush Rd, To Mosgiel, To Dunedin (15min), To Airport (10min)

DIRECTIONS: On SH 1, 20km south of Dunedin, turn right into Riccarton Road. **Stranalyth** is at Rapid No 193 on the left

Come and enjoy a country life-style with us on our 10-hectare property, where we fatten lambs and graze sheep and calves. We are semi-retired and have hosted tourists for 12 years. You are invited to share our warm and comfortable home and enjoy the spacious garden. Our farm is situated 10 min. drive from Dunedin Airport and 3 km off State Highway 1. Bus, airport or train transfers can be arranged. The small town of Mosgiel is 5 min., the city of Dunedin 15 min. drive away. The Taieri River, well known for its excellent fishing, tennis courts and 3 golf courses are close by. With prior notice we would take pleasure in providing you with a 3-course evening meal at $20 pp.
Arrive at **Stranalyth** as a tourist and leave as a friend.

ARGYLL FARMSTAY

Rapid No 246, Clutha River Road,
Clydevale No 4 RD, Balclutha
Ph (03) 415 9268, Fax (03) 415 9268
Mobile 025-318 241
e-mail: *argyllfm@ihug.co.nz*

Tariff : N.Z. Dollars	
Double	$80
Single	$45
Child	neg.

Bedrooms	Qty
Double	1
Twin	1
Single	

Bed Size	Qty
Super King	
King	
Queen	1
Single	2

Bathrooms	Qty
Ensuite	
Private	
Guest Share	1
Family Share	

 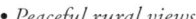 **Farmstay Bed & Breakfast**

Features & Attractions

- *Peaceful rural views*
- *Extra option of jet boat or fishing trip on Clutha River*
- *Experience farming life*
- *Homestyle 3 course meals avail.*
- *Swimming pool*
- *Experienced fishing guide*
- *Farm tour/deer, cattle, sheep*

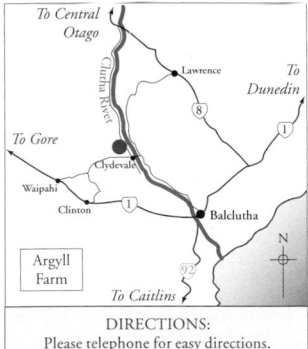

Trish and Alan welcome guests to our comfortable country home with large garden, swimming pool and beautiful views of green pasture and river flats.

We farm 530 acres, running 800 deer, 150 cattle and 1000 sheep. Guests would be welcome to tour our farm or join the family at their daily farming tasks.

Argyll Farm is situated on the banks of the Clutha River that provides guests with a unique opportunity to enjoy several recreational pastimes. We offer guests the extra option of a Jet Boat Ride or Fishing Trip on the Clutha River in our commercial boat Blue Mountain Jet.

Alan is an experienced fisherman who enjoys sharing his knowledge of our local rivers. We are centrally located for visitors travelling to the Catlins, Queenstown or Te Anau. We enjoy meeting people and we hope to make your stay a comfortable, relaxing and memorable experience.

DIRECTIONS:
Please telephone for easy directions.

🚫

BLACKHILLS FARMSTAY

192 Robertson Road, North Chatton, RD Gore
Postal: RD 3. Gore, Southland
Ph/Fax (03) 207 2865
Mobile 025-209 1563

Tariff : N.Z. Dollars	
Double	$80
Single	$40
Child	$20

Bedrooms	Qty
Double	1
Twin	1
Single	

Bed Size	Qty
Super King	
King/Twin	1
Queen	1
Single	

Bathrooms	Qty
Ensuite	
Private	
Guest Share	1
Family Share	1

 Farmstay / Bed & Breakfast

Features & Attractions

- *Superb views*
- *3-course dinner $25 pp*
- *Farm tour/sheep & cattle*
- *6 fishing rivers within 30 min.*
- *Sports facilities in Waikaka*
- *Your comfort, our concern*

Our sixty-year-old home – which has been renovated to give us a generous, comfortable living area – is situated on our 360 ha intensive sheep farm on a ridge above Waikaka River. You may have dinner with us, or if you prefer only bed and breakfast. A farm tour is avilable and as our family becomes more independent, we like to share time with guests. Venture off the main road and enjoy warm hospitality, superb views and the refreshment of a quiet rural visit.

DIRECTIONS: Turn off SH1 just north of Gore onto SH90. Turn left at Waikaka Valley corner, marked by church and windmill, follow sign posts to Waikaka until T-junction (approx. 10km). At T-junction turn left, then first right onto gravel – Nicolson Road. Proceed 4 km, veering right at each intersection. We live on Robertson Road, the last kilometre is a steep hill - just 20 min. from SH 1.

AFFLECK HOMESTAY

13 William Street, Gore, Southland
Ph/Fax (03) 208 9437,
Mobile 025-721 996
e-mail: *nolalex@ispnz.co.nz*

Features & Attractions

- *Warm home with attractive garden*
- *Dinner by arrangement*
- *Great fishing and golf close by*
- *Close to town centre*
- *Farm tour by arrangement*
- *Use of laundry*

Double	$80
Single	$40
Child	$20

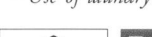

**Homestay
Bed & Breakfast**

Bedrooms	Qty
Double	1
Twin	1
Single	
Bed Size	**Qty**
King	
Double	1
Single	2
Bathrooms	**Qty**
Ensuite	
Private	1
Guest Share	1
Family Share	

We are involved in farming sheep, deer and cattle on the family farm, 15 minutes from Gore. Our home in Gore is 5 years old, close to the town centre, quiet and on a large private section.

Our interests include family, gardening, travel, cooking, cards and various community-based interests. We enjoy meeting people and both are of a friendly disposition.

Gore is ideally situated two hours from Queenstown and Dunedin, 1½ hours from Te Anau and Bluff. The rivers close by are world renowned for great trout fishing. Golf courses are not far away. Enjoy a visit to the unique Hokonui Moonshine Museum in the town. We have e-mail, fax and Internet facilities available, if required. Advance bookings recommended. We invite you to experience our hospitality.

HAWTHORNDEN INN

141 Waikaka Road, 5 RD, Gore
Southland
Ph (03) 207 1869, Fax (03) 207 1869
e-mail: *hawthorn.den@xtra.co.nz*

Features & Attractions

- *Character 1870's house*
- *Extensive gardens*
- *On working farm*
- *World class fishing rivers*
- *Central location*
- *Dinner by arrangement*

Double	$95-110
Single	$60-75
Child	neg.

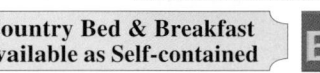

**Country Bed & Breakfast
Available as Self-contained**

Bedrooms	Qty
Double	2
Twin	1
Single	
Bed Size	**Qty**
King	1
Queen	1
Single	2
Bathrooms	**Qty**
Ensuite	
Private	
Guest Share	1
Family Share	

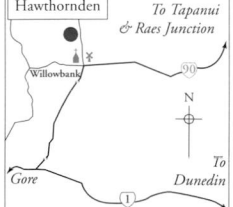

HawthornDen Inn is an 1870's farm homestead extensively renovated and dedicated to the sole use of its guests. The house is welcoming and comfortable with open fires, guest lounge and dining room, and bedrooms with garden views. House is surrounded by extensive gardens, in turn set in the rolling green hills of a working sheep farm.

We are ideally located halfway between Dunedin and Te Anau/ Queenstown and minutes from Gore. For the fisherman we are central to several world class fishing rivers or try on farm fishing in the smaller Waikaka Stream.

Continental breakfast included, with full breakfast and evening meals available. The kettle is always hot for tea and coffee with some of our home baking.

SMITH'S FARMSTAY
365 Wyndham-Mokoreta Rd, No. 2 RD, Wyndham, Southland
Ph (03) 206 4840, Fax (03) 206 4847
Mobile 025-286 6920
email: *beverly@smithsfarmstay.co.nz*
http://www.smithsfarmstay.co.nz

Tariff : N.Z. Dollars	
Double	$90-120
Single	$60
Child	neg.

Bedrooms	Qty
Double	2
Twin	2
Single	
Bed Size	**Qty**
Super King	1
King	
Queen	1
King Single	2
Bathrooms	**Qty**
Ensuite	1
Private	1
Guest Share	1
Family Share	

 Fisherman's Retreat - Farmstay

Features & Attractions
- *Genuine sheep farm experience*
- *Close to "Maple Glen" garden*
- *Hand knitted jerseys - pure NZ wool*
- *Beautiful "Catlins" area close by*
- *Trout fishing 5 km*
- *Quiet, peaceful surroundings*
- *Dinner by prior arrangement*
- *Garden and craft tours*

Beverly and Doug assure you of a warm welcome to their modern farm house and 260-hectare sheep farm.
We are situated on the hills above **Wyndham, only 3.65 km,** set in quiet and peaceful surroundings. The **Mataura, Mimihau and Wyndham Rivers,** renowned for **Brown Trout** are only a short 5 km away. Doug, a keen experienced fisherman, is only too happy to share his knowledge of these rivers with you. Beverly, a qualified nurse, enjoys cooking, floral art, gardening and hand knitting.
Each bedroom has a view and is tastefully furnished to meet your needs. Genuine home cooking. Special diets available on request.
You are most welcome to join us for the evening meal which is $30 pp. Children's rates negotiable. We love sharing **Christmas Day** with guests!!
Farm tour and feeding of the animals when in season. We have one friendly cat.
We enjoy meeting people and both are of a friendly disposition with a sense of humor.
Packed lunches, laundry facilities, fax and e-mail also available.

DIRECTIONS:
Drive to Wyndham: only 4km from Wyndham on the Wyndham Mokoreta Rd. Smith's Farmstay sign at gate.

300

LEYAVA LODGE

169 Roslyn Road, Roslyn Bush, RD 6, Invercargill
Ph (03) 230 4789 or (03) 218 4648
e-mail: *relax@leyavalodge.co.nz*
http://www.leyavalodge.co.nz

Tariff : N.Z. Dollars	
Double	$150
Single	
Child	

Bedrooms	Qty
Double	1
Twin	
Single	

Bed Size	Qty
Super King	
King	
Double	1
Single	

Bathrooms	Qty
Ensuite	1
Private	
Guest Share	
Family Share	

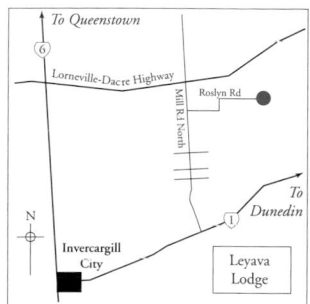

 Leyava Lodge Countrystay

Features & Attractions

- *Good 'kiwi' style country breakfast*
- *Coffee/tea, homebaking*
- *City & restaurants, 10 min. drive*
- *Dinner by arrangement*
- *Trout rivers within 30 minutes*
- *7 Golf courses – 20 minutes*
- *Delightful and varied gardens to visit*

If you desire a peaceful stopover in comfortable and pleasant surroundings close to Invercargill City, **Leyava Lodge** offers a beautiful double bedroom with ensuite facilities awaiting you – also an upstairs retreat with pool table, overlooking gardens and lush Southland countryside.

Our interests include harness horses, sports, photography, art and of course gardening. Shirley has a home studio and paints Southland and Central Otago landscapes. We would like to welcome you to our home.

E-mail facilities available.

Advance booking recommended.

SOUTHERN HOME HOSPITALITY

Rimu Rural No. 375
R.D.1, Invercargill, Southland
Ph/Fax (03) 230 4798
e-mail: *margalanthomson@actrix.co.nz*

Tariff : N.Z. Dollars	
Double	$90
Single	$65
Child	neg.

Bedrooms	Qty
Double	1
Twin	1
Single	
Bed Size	**Qty**
Super King	
King	
Queen	1
Single	2
Bathrooms	**Qty**
Ensuite	
Private	1
Guest Share	1
Family Share	

 Country Homestay

Features & Attractions

- *Warm hospitality*
- *Peaceful garden setting*
- *Fabulous meals*
- *Home-baking a speciality*
- *Gateway to Fiordland*
- *Excellent golf courses*
- *Invercargill City*
- *Famous trout fishing rivers*

Welcome to our warm and comfortable home surrounded by colourful gardens. We are semi-retired, graze cattle and sheep, enjoy meeting people, love to cook, home baking a speciality, all meals prepared from fresh produce and vegetables from our large garden. We are enthusiastic golfers, with many courses nearby. Invercargill City has historic buildings, lovely parks and gardens, interesting museum with live Tuatara, prehistoric lizard, Anderson Park, Art Gallery, famous trout fishing rivers within easy reach. Have dinner with us and share an evening of relaxation and friendship. "We look forward to having you visit us." – Margaret and Alan. Gateway to Catlins, Stewart Island, Fiordland and Queenstown.

DIRECTIONS: **From Invercargill** travel appr. 7 km towards Dunedin,
turn right at Clapham Rd. (towards large green building with red roof), turn left, then right
over railway line. Travel straight ahead for 4 km. A.J.Thomson is on mailbox – Rural No. 375.
From Dunedin turn left at Longbush Road South, turn right at crossroads - we are 1 km on right.

THE GROVE DEER FARM
154 Oteramika Road, RD 1, Invercargill
Ph (03) 216 6492 Fax (03) 216 6492
e-mail: *the_grove@xtra.co.nz*

Features & Attractions

- *Only 1 km from city boundary*
- *Ideal stopover - Southern/Scenic Route*
- *Good local knowledge*
- *Internet/e-mail access*
- *Close to all attractions*

Double	$90
Single	$50
Child	neg.

   **Country Farmstay Bed & Breakfast**

Bedrooms	Qty
Double	1
Twin	2
Single	
Bed Size	**Qty**
King	
Queen	1
Single	4
Bathrooms	**Qty**
Ensuite	
Private	
Guest Share	1
Family Share	1

E xperience Bed & Breakfast on a deer farm only 1 kilometre from the city boundary in a unique, quiet rural setting with homestyle welcome and atmosphere. Enjoy seeing deer and sheep on a complimentary tour of the farm. Connect with sea and air travel to Stewart Island or tour the Aluminium Smelter. Great trout fishing is easily accessible in Southern Lakes and rivers. Alex is a vintage car and machinery enthusiast and can arrange good viewing. Courtesy pick-up from airport and rail/bus terminals. Beach and golf courses nearby. Continental or cooked breakfast available. Attractive garden setting.

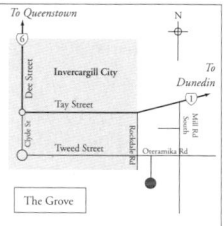

93 TOWACK HOMESTAY B & B
93 Towack Street, Riverton, Southland
Ph (03) 234 8732, Fax (03)234 8732
e-mail: *rbjmdore@actrix.co.nz*

Features & Attractions

- *Peaceful private garden setting*
- *Studio unit with spa bath*
- *Golf course & walking tracks*
- *Harbour & sea views*
- *Walk 5 minutes to restaurants and shops*

Double	$60-120
Single	
Child	

   **Homestay Bed & Breakfast**

Bedrooms	Qty
Double	3
Twin	
Single	
Bed Size	**Qty**
King	
Queen/Double	3
Single	
Bathrooms	**Qty**
Ensuite	1
Private	
Guest Share	1
Family Share	

DIRECTIONS:
Only 30 min. drive from Invercargill on the Southern Scenic Route. Drive over the bridge, turn left and look for the yellow 93 Towack B & B sign.

W e would like to welcome you to Riverton, a seaside retreat. Relax and enjoy our peaceful private garden setting with excellent river and harbour views.
We are within walking distance of the beach, bush walks, shops and cafés.
The house has three spacious downstairs bedrooms. The bathroom has a bath and separate shower. Upstairs is a private studio unit with spa bath and superb views. Handy facilities are available. If you are looking for a relaxing stay at the seaside, Riverton is the place to be.
We look forward to meeting you.

KEPPLESTONE-BY-THE-SEA

9 Surat Bay, Owaka, The Catlins
Ph (03) 415 8134. Fax (03) 415 8137
Mobile 025-676 7253
e-mail: *kepplestone@xtra.co.nz*

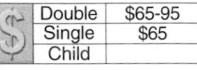

Features & Attractions

- Sandy beach & Hooker Sealions
- Close to penguins and falls
- Gourmet meals available
- Separate guest house
- Royal Spoonbills
- Special diets catered for

Beachstay
Bed & Breakfast

Double	$65-95
Single	$65
Child	

There are NO strangers here, only FRIENDS we have not met. Situated 100 m from beach, with hooker sealions basking there. Close to all The Catlins scenery, waterfalls, walks, Royal Spoonbills. Private yellow eyed penguin viewing and tours, with Catlins Natural Wonders. Delicious breakfasts, with lots of homemade goodies. Organically grown vegetables from our own garden, served with fabulous meals. Special diets catered for with every care taken. Chip and Putt course on property and golf course 3 kms. Proud to be members of HOSTLINK, your personalised guide to New Zealand.

DIRECTIONS:
Follow signs "towards" Pounawea, at golf course go "across" bridge and turn right to Newhaven and Surat Bay Road (3 kms metal) first house on left.

Bedrooms	Qty
Double	2
Twin	1
Single	
Bed Size	**Qty**
King/Single	1
Queen	1
Single	2
Bathrooms	**Qty**
Ensuite	2
Private	
Guest Share	
Family Share	1

Our Farm

BARRS FALLS

389 Barrs Falls Road, Owaka, Catlins
Ph (03) 415 8128, Fax (03) 415 8128

Features & Attractions

- Quiet, peaceful surroundings
- Handy to Catlins scenic spots
- Comfortable home
- Great sea and farm views
- Wildlife nearby
- Golf, bowling, fishing close

Farmstay
Bed & Breakfast

Double	$55-60
Single	$40
Child	$10

Bedrooms	Qty
Double	1
Twin	1
Single	
Bed Size	**Qty**
King	
Double	1
Single	2
Bathrooms	**Qty**
Ensuite	1
Private	
Guest Share	
Family Share	1

Our comfortable home is set in peaceful garden surroundings on our 385 hectare sheep and cattle farm, 5.5 km from Owaka. You will be able to take a leisurely stroll in the evening down to "Barrs Falls" waterfall in the reserve and enjoy the glow-worms and native bush and birds. A variety of wildlife is within easy travelling distance, for example 15-20 minutes to Nugget Point Lighthouse to view Hooker Sea Lions, seals and yellow-eyed penguins. Walking tracks, golf and bowling clubs and an excellent museum are added attractions. There are two dairies providing meals and takeaways, the local pub and the popular restaurant/bar the "Lumberjack". We hope you will join us in this beautiful unique area of New Zealand. Laundry, folding cot and high chair facilities available.

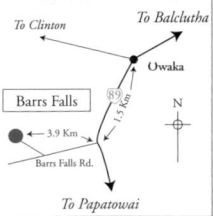

GORGE STREAM COTTAGE
2057 Tahakopa Valley Road, RD 2, Owaka
Tahakopa, Catlins Region
Ph/Fax (03) 418 0994, Mobile (025) 301 394
e-mail: *hosts@gorgestream.co.nz*
www.gorgestream.co.nz

Tariff : N.Z. Dollars	
Double	$225
Single	$175
Child	neg.

Bedrooms	Qty
Double	2
Twin	
Single	
Bed Size	**Qty**
Super King	2
King	
Queen	
Single	
Bathrooms	**Qty**
Ensuite	
Private	1
Guest Share	
Family Share	

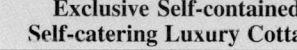
**Exclusive Self-contained
Self-catering Luxury Cottage**

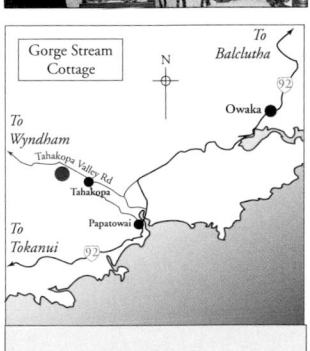

Features & Attractions
- *Hunting, fishing, mountain biking on site*
- *Thoroughly modern luxury interior*
- *Striking views in all directions*
- *Indonesian hand-carved teak wood furniture*
- *Ideal for the long stay*
- *Catlins activities nearby*
- *Secluded and private*
- *Off the beaten track*

Nestled in the heart of the Catlins and Tahakopa Valley and close to the beach, **Gorge Stream Cottage** is a luxurious cottage surrounded by beautiful gardens, pond, wildlife, river, stream and views to the native bush in every direction. Even though the cottage is off the beaten track, it is close to all the activities in the Catlins and an hour from Invercargill and Stewart Island. A partial list of activities in the Catlins: two golf courses, Catlins Woodstock, ocean fishing trips, four waterfalls, cliffs, beaches, surfing, tramping and walking paths, bird watching, dolphin watching, Catlins Coastal Rainforest Park, eco-tours by licensed guides, horse trekking on the cliffs and beaches, river fishing, Catlins Forest Park, Yellow-eyed penguins, New Zealand fur seals, Hooker sea lions, Elephant seal. The cottage office boasts modern communication with the outside world, e-mail, fax, internet, Sky TV satellite, as well as a fold-out sofa sleeping 2 people. Tariff includes all linens, full breakfast provisions and well stocked pantry for all cooking needs. Minimum two-night stay.

DIRECTIONS:
On Southern Scenic Route near Papatowai, turn north-west onto Tahakopa Road. and go 19 km.

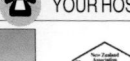

ALSTED FARMSTAY

173 Neill Road, Tokanui, No 1 RD
Ph (03) 246 8804, Fax (03) 246 8804

Features & Attractions

- Fabulous panoramic view
- Tranquil garden setting
- Handy to the beautiful Catlins
- Wake up to birdsong
- Dinner by arrangement
- Farm tour optional

Farmstay
Bed & Breakfast

Double	$95-100
Single	$55
Child	

Bedrooms	Qty
Double	1
Twin	1
Single	
Bed Size	**Qty**
King	
Queen	1
Single	2
Bathrooms	**Qty**
Ensuite	
Private	1
Guest Share	1
Family Share	

DIRECTIONS: Just off Southern Scenic Route at Tokanui. Turn at Neill Rd. 1km east of Tokanui. We are 2km uphill, rapid No 173

Welcome to our 350 hectare sheep and cattle farm. We offer a high standard of warm hospitality and comfort, relaxation, tasty home-cooking and a base from which to explore. Our home is centrally heated and has a log fire in winter. We are just off the popular Southern Scenic Route in a well sheltered garden setting overlooking farmland and Tokanui Village. From farm hills we have great views of Foveaux Strait towards Stewart Island and inland to the Takitimu Mountains. We are centrally located to the Catlins scenic area, petrified forest and hectors dolphins at Curio Bay, Waipapa Lighthouse and the rugged Southern Coast. With our family grown up, we enjoy our grandchildren, meeting people, various sports, travel and local history. We look forward to your stay in our piece of paradise.

 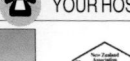
PORT OF CALL

Leask Bay Road, PO Box 143, Stewart Island
Ph (03) 219 1394, Fax (03) 219 1394
Mobile 025-244 4722
e-mail: info@portofcall.co.nz
www.portofcall.co.nz

Features & Attractions

- Stunning views
- Courtesy transfers
- New self-catering unit
- Birdlife and bush surroundings
- Sixth generation Island family
- Water taxi - customised trips

Boutique Coastal
Accommodation

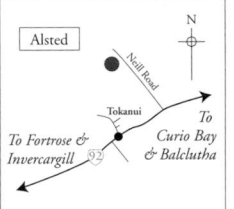

Double	$240
Single	$180
Child	

Bedrooms	Qty
Double/Twin	1
Triple	1
Single	
Bed Size	**Qty**
SuperKingTwin	1
Queen	1
Single	
Bathrooms	**Qty**
Ensuite	1
Private	1
Guest Share	
Family Share	

From its cliff top site, overlooking Halfmoon Bay and Foveaux Strait, is Port of Call, new home of hosts Philippa and Ian. Giving you the ultimate in home-away-from home accommodation for the discerning traveller. Surrounded by native bush attracting varied birdlife. Walk two minutes to Harrolds Bay or walk on to Acker's Point Light House. The walk into Halfmoon Bay is 15 to 20 minutes. Philippa and Ian run Water Taxi and Stewart Island Eco Guiding, Ian is a paua diver, having 20 years experience in waters surrounding Stewart Island. Being from an Island family he is happy to share his local knowledge and assist in planning daily excursions if needed. We have on the property two historic houses, sheep, goat, ducks, plus a very friendly family dog.
We are in our 30s with no children at home, enjoy travel and have a great love for the Island. Come and enjoy pure nature in a tranquil and relaxed environment.

The
Translated Travellers' Pages

Herzlich Willkommen!
ようこそ！
歡迎！

"Lernen Sie das wahre Neuseeland kennen - die Neuseeländer selbst"

Bed & Breakfast in Neuseeland heißt Sie herzlich willkommen!

Eine überaus große Auswahl an Übernachtungsmöglichkeiten erwartet Sie in der Welt von "Bed & Breakfast" (private Übernachtung inclusive Frühstück) - vom einfachen Landhaus bis zum stattlichen Familiensitz. Überall werden Sie auf freundliche, aufgeschlossene Neuseeländer treffen. Manche von ihnen haben die Tradition des Gastgebens im Lauf der Jahre zu einer regelrechten Kunst entwickelt, auf die sie besonders stolz sind. Sogenannte "Homestays", "Farmstays", Gastehäuser oder "Boutique"-Unterkünfte - sie alle fallen unter den Begriff "Bed & Breakfast". Hier lernen Sie das wahre Neuseeland kennen: die Neuseeländer selbst.

- Ob Lehrer, Farmer oder ein pensionierter Angestellter, ob Künstler, Obstbauer, Heilpraktiker oder Schriftsteller, die Palette ist reichhaltig. Zum angenehmen Abenteuer kann die Übernachtung beispielsweise in einer Fischerlodge oder auf einer Schafsfarm im Hochland werden. Warum lernen Sie nicht nebenbei ein wenig reiten oder weben oder fühlen Sie sich einfach wie zu Hause in einem "Homestay" oder "Countrystay" in der Stadt oder auf dem Land. Die Neuseeländer sind bekannt als warmherzige Gastgeber, Sie werden sich überall willkommen fühlen und unvergeßliche Reiseerinnerungen mit nach Hause bringen.

Was Sie erwarten können

Bed & Breakfast in Neuseeland ist bekannt für guten Service. Die Unterkünfte sind sauber, verfügen über bequeme Betten und bieten ein gutes, reichliches Frühstück an. Natürlich steht Ihr Wohlbefinden an erster Stelle. Ihre Gastgeber werden Ihnen gerne bei der Planung Ihrer weiteren Reise behilflich sein. Die Gastgeber wissen am besten darüber Bescheid, was die jeweilige Region zu bieten hat. Nutzen Sie diese unbezahlbaren Informationen aus erster Hand.

Was man von Ihnen erwartet

Ihre Gastgeber werden alles versuchen, Ihnen den Aufenthalt so angenehm wie möglich zu machen. Vergessen Sie jedoch bitte nicht, daß Sie in den meisten Fällen in Privathäusern zu Gast sein werden. Bedenken Sie auch die scheinbar unwichtigen Dinge. Es empfiehlt sich beispielsweise, um einen Hausschlüssel zu bitten, bevor Sie abends länger ausbleiben. Falls Sie ein Ferngespräch führen wollen, ist es besser, zuerst den Tarif abzuklären. Sagen Sie bitte auch so bald wie möglich Bescheid, wenn sich Ihre Ankunft verspäten sollte. Ein wenig Rücksichtnahme Ihrerseits wird so dazu beitragen, daß alle Beteiligten die Zeit auf eine angenehme Weise verbringen.

Praktische Hinweise

Besonders während der Sommersaison können Sie unnötige Enttäuschungen vermeiden, wenn Sie Ihre Unterkunft im voraus buchen. Es empfiehlt sich auch, die Gastgeber einen Tag vor Ihrer Ankunft anzurufen, um die Buchung zu bestätigen und die ungefähre Ankunftszeit mitzuteilen. Einige Bed & Breakfast Häuser bieten einen Abholdienst von Bus, Bahn oder Flughafen an - dieser Service ist oft im Preis mit eingeschlossen. Sagen Sie auch bitte rechtzeitig Bescheid, wenn Sie bei Ihren Gastgebern zusätzlich zur Übernachtung gerne ein warmes Abendessen hätten.

Bed & Breakfast Kategorien

Bed & Breakfast

Bed & Breakfast ist der Oberbegriff für alle Unterkunftsarten, die ein bequemes Bett, ein reichliches Frühstück und persönlichen Service im Preis einschließen. Während Ihres Aufenthalts werden Sie aufs Freundlichste von Ihren Gastgebern betreut.

Homestay

"Homestay" ist eine sehr beliebte Bed & Breakfast Variante. Sie wohnen in Privathäusern, die Gastgeber sind aufgeschlossen und freundlich und werden alles ihnen Mögliche tun, damit Sie sich "ganz wie zu Hause" fühlen nach dem Motto: "Sie kommen als Fremde und gehen als Freunde."

Countrystay

"Countrystays" sind Bed & Breakfast-Unterkünfte in ländlicher Umgebung. Sie wohnen meist in nächster Nähe von dem, was Sie am typischen Landleben so schätzen. Ob Sie wandern gehen wollen, angeln oder einfach nur die unbeschreibliche Natur pur genießen wollen, hier können Sie sich abseits vom Großstadtstreß in aller Ruhe erholen.

Farmstay

Wenn Sie echtes neuseeländisches Farmerleben hautnah genießen wollen, dann sind Sie im "Farmstay" gut aufgehoben. Üblicherweise können Sie bei der Farmtour mit auf die Weiden gehen und beim Füttern der Farmtiere mit dabei sein. Das Frühstück wird meistens mit der Familie zusammen eingenommen. Viele Farmstays bieten Vollverpflegung an.

 ## Guesthouse/Inn

"Guest Houses" sind meistens Häuser, die eine größere Zahl von Gästen beherbergen, aber trotzdem eine persönliche Note aufweisen. Manche haben mehrere Aufenthaltsräume und einen speziellen Frühstücksraum. "Guest Houses" bieten im allgemeinen kein warmes Abendessen an.

 ## Boutique Accommodation

Der Begriff "Boutique" soll Ihnen sagen, daß es sich hier um ganz besonders schöne Bed & Breakfast-Übernachtungsmöglichkeiten handelt: eine geschmackvolle Inneneinrichtung, stilvolle Architektur oder ein romantisches Ambiente. Die Gastgeber dieser Häuser legen größten Wert auf gepflegte Gastfreundschaft.

Luxury Accommodation

Die Luxusunterkünfte bieten eine hervorragende Ausstattung, exzellentes Essen und ganz besonderen Service. Oft sind diese Häuser architektonische Glanzstücke oder sie liegen in einzigartiger Umgebung. "Luxus" steht für außergewöhnliche Unterkunft und Gastfreundschaft.

 ## Self-contained Accommodation

Unterkünfte für Selbstversorger sind oft komplette Einliegerwohnungen oder einzeln stehende Häuschen mit eigenem Badezimmer und eigener Toilette und meistens mit Küche, Waschmaschine und Wäschetrockner. In manchen Fällen nehmen Sie das Frühstück zusammen mit der Gastfamilie ein. Es wird aber auch oftmals an die Haustür gebracht, oder Sie finden die Zutaten bereits in der Küche.

"Auf einen Blick"
Kontaktaufnahme
Wer sind die Gastgeber und wo wohnen sie? Wie kommen Sie schnell mit ihnen in Kontakt?

"Auf einen Blick"
Übernachtungspreis
Alle Preise gelten für eine Übernachtung. **Double** *ist der Preis für zwei Personen in einem Zimmer,* **Single** *der Preis für eine Person in einem Zimmer. In einigen Fällen ist zusammen mit der Buchung eine Anzahlung erforderlich. Frühstück ist im Preis mit inbegriffen (falls nicht ausdrücklich anders erwähnt).* **Alle Preise gelten in \$ NZ. Bitte lassen Sie sich die Preise von den Gastgebern bestätigen.**

"Auf einen Blick"
Symbole für Kategorien
Mit diesen einprägsamen Symbolen können Sie Ihre bevorzugte Unterkunftsmöglichkeit schnell ausfindig machen. Dieses System ist besonders hilfreich für Reisende, die die englische Sprache nicht fließend beherrschen.

"Auf einen Blick"
Kategoriestreifen
Die Gastgeber beschreiben ihre Kategorie in ihren eigenen Worten.

"Auf einen Blick"
Besondere Details
In Stichworten die attraktivsten Details der Unterkunft und der Sehenswürdikeiten in der Umgebung.

"Auf einen Blick"
Kleine Straßenkarte
Im weißen Kästchen finden Sie den Namen des Hauses; der rote Punkt zeigt Ihnen die genaue Position. Im grünen Kästchen finden Sie die Wegbeschreibung.

Klar und übersichtlich
Schnell zu finden: Adresse, Telefon- und Faxnummer, E-Mail und Internetadresse.

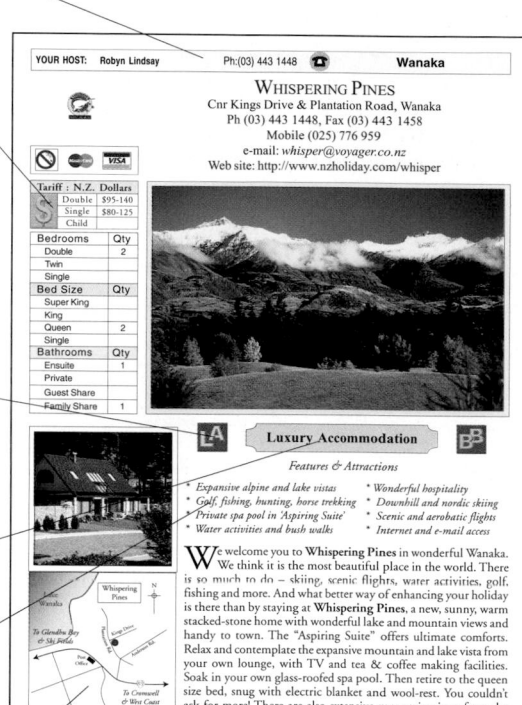

"Ein persönliches Willkommen"
Dieser Text, von den Gastgebern persönlich verfaßt, beschreibt deren Lebensstil und Interessen, die Art der Unterkunft und was Sie als Gast erwarten können.

 Nichtraucher

Abkürzungen
SH   – State Highway
h.p.   – halber Preis
N.A.   – nicht zutreffend
neg.   – nach Vereinbarung
Qty   – Anzahl
Tce   – Terrace

Direkt buchen - Extrakosten vermeiden

Wenn Sie die Buchung selbst vornehmen, haben Sie von Anfang an persönlichen Kontakt mit Ihren Bed & Breakfast-Gastgebern in Neuseeland und vermeiden unnötige Kosten.

Wie wird dieser Reiseführer benützt – Zimmerdetails

Gästezimmer

Double = Zimmer mit Bett für 2 Personen
Twin = Zimmer mit 2 Betten für 2 Personen
Single = Zimmer mit Bett für eine Person

Bad/WC

Ensuite = Bad/WC mit Zimmer verbunden
Private = Eigenes Bad/WC, aber separat
Guest/Family Share =Bad/WC wird von Gästen oder der Gastfamilie mitbenutzt.

Gästezimmer	Qty
Double	
Twin	
Single	

Bettgröße	Qty
Super King	
King	
Queen/Double	
(King-) /Single	

Bad/WC	Qty
Ensuite	
Private	
Guest Share	
Family Share	

Bettgrößen	
Super King	*180 x 200cm*
King	*165 x 200cm*
Queen	*150 x 200cm*
Double	*135 x 190cm*
Single	*90 x 190cm*
King Single	*90 x 200cm*

Kategorie Symbole

 Bed & Breakfast

 Boutique Accommodation

 Countrystay

 Farmstay

 Guest House / Inn

 Homestay

 Luxury Accommodation

 Self-contained Accom. & Cottages

Gängige Kreditkarten

 Amex – American Express

 Japanese Credit Card

 VISA

 Diners

 Bankcard

 MasterCard

 Maestro

Eftpos

Mitgliedschaft in folgenden Verbänden und Gesellschaften

 Historic Places Trust

 Hospitality Hosts

 New Zealand Association Farm & Home Hosts

 Superior Inns of New Zealand

 Auckland Home & Farmstay

 Heritage Inns of New Zealand

 Hostlink-Network of Fine Hosts

 New Zealand's Federation *of* Bed & Breakfast Hotels

 Dieses Symbol versichert Ihnen einen herzlichen Kiwi-Empfang und guten, aufmerksamen Service. "Kiwihost" ist Neuseelands preisgekröntes Dienst-am-Kunden "Trainingsprogramm". Dieses Zeichen soll Ihnen zeigen, daß wir Sie überall als Kunden schätzen.

ニュージーランドの家庭生活を実体験！

～ニュージーランド・B＆Bへのお誘い～

ニュージーランド人は、旅行者に対する心暖まる、フレンドリーなもてなしを誇りとする国民として知られています。この「ニュージーランド風のもてなし」をじかに体験できるのが、Bed & Breakfast（ベッド・アンド・ブレックファースト、B&B）です。これは一般のホテルとは一味ちがった、アット・ホームなサービスを身上とする宿泊施設の総称で、その具体的な中身はいろいろです。宿泊の場所でいうと、町中の一軒家・コッテージ・釣り場のロッジ・高原の牧場・乗馬や機織りの学校・お

城（！）といった具合に多岐にわたっています。実際の名称としては、 Guest House （ゲスト・ハウス）、 Inn（イン）、 Boutique Accommodation （ブティック・アコモデーション）、 Countrystay （カ

ントリーステイ）などがあります。また、安いものから高くて豪華なものまでありますので、予算に合わせて選ぶことが可能です。B&B のホスト（host, オーナー）は現役の教員・農家・芸術家・信仰療法家・作家、さらにはもと医師や弁護士など、実に多彩です。ホストの中には、単に話好き、という人から、専門的なサービスを提供する人まで、さまざまです。B&B は、「本物の」ニュージーランドを体験するのに恰好の機会といえます。ホストと、趣味や仕事の話などで盛り上がるのも楽しみのひとつではないでしょうか。

皆様の旅行が楽しく、思い出深いものとなりますように……

WHAT TO EXPECT

きれいな部屋、寝心地のよいベッド、おいしくて量もたっぷりの朝食、真心のこもったもてなし…ニュージーランドの Bed & Breakfast は、サービスの水準が高いことで知られています。さらに、ホストからは、その地域や周辺の見どころに関する詳しい「生の情報」を得ることができます。お客様の興味・関心をホストにお伝えください。ホストは皆様の旅行がすばらしいものとなる手助けができることを願っています。

― 宿泊者の心得

WHAT IS EXPECTED OF YOU

ホストは、お客様が楽しく思い出深いひとときを過ごすことができるよう、最大限の努力をしていますが、お客様の側にも配慮いただきたい点があります。それは、B＆Bは、基本的には「一般家庭」に泊まる、という形式をとっているという点です。ですから、ホストやその家族にたいする「ちょとした」気配りが大切です。たとえば、夜、帰りが遅くなる場合には、余裕をもって事前にその旨を伝えておき、「合鍵」を受け取っておくとか、電話を使用する際には、あらかじめ料金の確認をしておく、などです。こうした心遣いが、B＆Bでの滞在を成功させるカギなのです。

WHAT TO DO – HINTS

B&B 宿泊の貴重なチャンスを逃さないためには、予約するのが一番です。(特に真夏は込み合います。)予約されましたら、到着の前日にホストに予約の確認をし、到着予定時刻を伝えておくことをおすすめします。ホストの中には、coach (コーチ、長距離バス)・飛行機・列車の発着場からの無料送迎サービスを行っている人もいます。また、到着日の夕食を希望される場合には、前日または前前日に、その旨をホストに伝えておきましょう。

ベッド・アンド・ブレックファースト

一泊・朝食付きの宿の総称です。快適なベッドと、たっぷりの朝食、それにホストの暖かいおもてなしを存分にお楽しみください。

ホームステイ

ごく一般の家庭で、ホストによる身近なもてなしを受けながら宿泊するものです。ホストは人と出会うのが好きで、宿泊客をまるで自分の家にいるような、和やかな雰囲気にしてくれます。宿泊客の皆様が、初めて会った時には「見知らぬ他人」でも、別れるときには「親しい友人」となることを、ホストは心得ているのです。

カントリーステイ

Homestay と同様、一般の家庭に滞在するものです。Countrystay の特徴は、場所が「いなか」にある点です。都会とはちがった、ニュージーランドの一面をじかに体験できます。

ファームステイ

ニュージーランドの農業について理解を深めたい、という人には理想的な機会です。動物たちと身近に接しながら、農場での生活を経験していきます。牧場内のツアーを行っているところもあります。通常、朝食はホストの家族とともにとります。場所柄、近所にレストランなどがないため、多くのFarmstay では昼食や夕食も出されます。

Bed & Breakfast Categories

G ゲスト・ハウス

通常、規模が比較的大きく、他のB&B の施設に比べ、より多くの宿泊客を泊めることができる施設ですが、B&B ならではの、フレンドリーなもてなしは変わりません。複数のラウンジや、朝食室が用意されているところもあります。夕食は出されないのが普通です。

BA ブティック・アコモデーション

特色ある家屋を用いたB&B です。長い年月が醸し出す気品、優雅さ、ロマンス － Boutique Accommodation は、宿泊客の皆様をそうした雰囲気の中に包んでくれます。この雰囲気をいかに盛り上げるかが、ホストの腕のみせどころです。

LA ラクシャリー・アコモデーション

最高の立地条件のなかにある宿泊施設で、施設内外はさまざまな魅力でいっぱいです。豪華極まる設備や食事、それに群をぬいたハイ・クオリティーのサービスが特徴です。

SC セルフコンテインド・アコモデーション

宿泊者のための独立した入口・バスルーム・ラウンジを含むのが普通です。独立した台所や洗濯質室が用意されているところもあります。宿泊施設は、一軒家のなかの一区画として存在する場合と、別棟の建物として存在する場合とがあります。朝食はホストの家族とともにとる場合、宿泊施設まで届けられる場合、朝食の材料が宿泊所に用意されており、宿泊者が自分で用意する場合とさまざまです。

"at a glance"
イージー・コントロール・パネル
ホストの氏名・所在地・連絡先など。

"at a glance"
ここに表示されているのは、一泊あたりの料金です。**Double**（ダブル）は、一部屋を2名で使用した場合の料金です。**Single**（シングル）は、一部屋を1名で使用した場合の料金です。予約の際に deposit（ディポジット、料金の一部前払い）が必要なところもあります。特に明記のない場合、料金には朝食代が含まれています。**料金の表記は、すべて「NZ ドル」です。** 料金に関する詳しい内容は、直接ホストまでおたずねください。

"at a glance"
カテゴリー・シンボル
おさがしのB&Bのタイプがすぐに見つかるよう工夫されたマークです。お役立てください。

"at a glance"
カテゴリー・パネル
該当するB&Bのカテゴリーの、ホスト自身による定義・説明。

"at a glance"
フィーチャーズ＆アトラクションズ
宿泊施設およびその周辺のみどころのご紹介。

"at a glance"
ロケーション・マップ
宿泊施設の位置が赤丸で示されています。白のかこみの中に施設の名称が記されています。行き方の説明が追加で示されている場合もあります。

クリアー・アドレス・ディーテールズ
宿泊施設の所在地・電話番号・Fax番号・e-mailアドレス・インターネット・ホームページのアドレスといった、大切な情報はこちらをご覧ください。

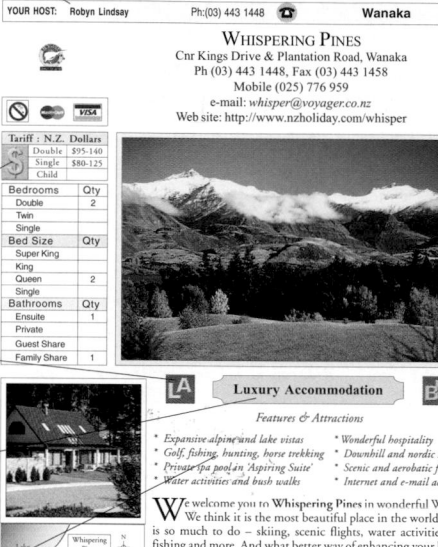

YOUR HOST: Robyn Lindsay　　Ph:(03) 443 1448　　Wanaka

WHISPERING PINES
Cnr Kings Drive & Plantation Road, Wanaka
Ph (03) 443 1448, Fax (03) 443 1458
Mobile (025) 776 959
e-mail: whisper@voyager.co.nz
Web site: http://www.nzholiday.com/whisper

Tariff : N.Z. Dollars	
Double	$95-140
Single	$80-125
Child	

Bedrooms	Qty
Double	2
Twin	
Single	

Bed Size	Qty
Super King	
King	
Queen	2
Single	

Bathrooms	Qty
Ensuite	1
Private	
Guest Share	
Family Share	1

Luxury Accommodation

Features & Attractions

* Expansive alpine and lake vistas
* Golf, fishing, hunting, horse trekking
* Private spa pool an 'Aspiring Suite'
* Water activities and bush walks
* Wonderful hospitality
* Downhill and nordic skiing
* Scenic and aerobatic flights
* Internet and e-mail access

We welcome you to **Whispering Pines** in wonderful Wanaka. We think it is the most beautiful place in the world. There is so much to do – skiing, scenic flights, water activities, golf, fishing and more. And what better way of enhancing your holiday is there than by staying at **Whispering Pines**, a new, sunny, warm stacked-stone home with wonderful lake and mountain views and handy to town. The "Aspiring Suite" offers ultimate comforts. Relax and contemplate the expansive mountain and lake vista from your own lounge, with TV and tea & coffee making facilities. Soak in your own glass-roofed spa pool. Then retire to the queen size bed, snug with electric blanket and wool-rest. You couldn't ask for more! There are also extensive mountain views from the large "Kings Room" with queen sized bed, electric blanket, woolrest, desk and chairs. Your host Robyn wants to "enrich your holiday" - she will do everything in her power to ensure a memorable and special stay for you at **Whispering Pines**.

DIRECTIONS: Coming from Cromwell just before Wanaka township turn right into Anderson Rd, left into Plantation Rd. Whispering Pines is on the right just past pine plantation.

パーソナル・ウォーム・ウェルカム
ホストから読者へのひとことです。宿泊施設の特徴や、ホストの人柄・ライフ・スタイルといったものを垣間見ることができます。

No Smoking

Cnr – Corner: コーナー「角」
h.p. – half price: ハーフ・プライス「半額」
N.A. – not applicable: ノット・アプリカブル「該当項目なし」
neg. – negotiable: ニゴーシャブル「交渉可」
Qty – Quantity: クウォンティティ「数量」
Tce – Terrace: テラス

宿泊予約申し込みは、B&Bのホストに直接なさいますと、ホストとそれだけ早くから知り合うことができ、また中間業者を通した場合にかかる、さまざまな手数料を省くことができるので有利です。

ガイドのてびき － 客室・設備に関する記述 について

Bedrooms

Double	= 二人用ベッドがある部屋
Twin	= 一人用ベッドが２つある部屋
Single	= 一人用ベッドが１つある部屋

Bathrooms

Ensuite	= 寝室に隣接
Private	= 各宿泊客専用
Guest Share/Family Share	= 他の宿泊客またはホストの家族と共用

Bedrooms	Qty
Double	
Twin	
Single	
Bed Size	**Qty**
Super King	
King	
Queen/Double	
(King-) Single	
Bathrooms	**Qty**
Ensuite	
Private	
Guest Share	
Family Share	

Bed Size	
Super King	*180 x 200cm*
King	*165 x 200cm*
Queen	*150 x 200cm*
Double	*135 x 190cm*
Single	*90 x 190cm*
King Single	*90 x 200cm*

ガイドのてびき － カテゴリー・シンボル

 Bed & Breakfast

 Guest House / Inn

 Boutique Accommodation

 Homestay

 Countrystay

 Luxury Accommodation

F Farmstay

 Self-contained Accom. & Cottages

ガイドのてびき － お支払可能なクレジット・カード について

 Amex – American Express

 Bankcard

 Japanese Credit Card

 MasterCard

VISA VISA

 Maestro

Diners

Eftpos

ガイドのてびき － B&B が提携している協会・団体について

 Historic Places Trust

 Auckland Home & Farmstay

 Hospitality Hosts

 Heritage Inns of New Zealand

 New Zealand Association Farm & Home Hosts

 Hostlink-Network of Fine Hosts

 Superior Inns of New Zealand

 New Zealand's Federation *of* Bed & Breakfast Hotels

 このマークは、ニュージーランド流の暖かく、フレンドリーで、質の高いサービスを保証するものです。Kiwi Host（キウイ・ホスト）は、我が国をリードする顧客サービス・トレーニング・プログラムです。

"體驗真正的紐西蘭—它的民族"

歡迎來到紐西蘭多樣化的旅店住宿簡介

紐西蘭的住宿，由小屋到別墅，從經濟單位到豪華大宅，您都會享受到在一個親切友善且好客的環境中居住。有多種不同的住宿方式：家庭住宿、農莊住宿、旅客之家、小客店、豪華旅店、鄉村住宿等等，他們一律提供給您一張溫暖的床以及香噴噴的西式早餐。這些都能讓您親身感受到紐西蘭的生活，認識居住在這裡的居民。您更可選擇嗜好與自己相似的家庭住

宿，例如：老師、農夫、退休的專業人士、園藝專家、畫家、作家等等，住宿在他們的家，彼此交換心得，同時可享受獨特真誠的招待，體驗在漁村、郊外綿羊、海外之家的生活。不管是旅館或多樣化的家庭住宿，除了種類多之外，還充滿了紐西蘭獨特的友善及好客，不論您選擇那一種住宿，您將都是一位貴賓，盡情享受生活，讓日後有個難忘的回憶。

介　紹

期望什麼？

在紐西蘭床鋪及早餐享有標準服務的聲譽，住客會有最清潔、舒適的床，多種選擇熱烘烘早餐，及主人樂意友善的招待。除此之外，主人也會給於您居住地區的詳細資料。他們樂意幫您安排您在本地的旅遊計劃。他們豐富的經驗能增添您居住的樂趣。

對您的期望？

主人家會爲您做任何的事，讓您享受一個難忘的停留。可是，請記得無論如何您只是一個客人。所以，請您注意一些事，例如，如果您晚歸的話，要向主人索取大門鎖匙，或當您要打長途、國內、本地電話時，應先詢問主人才可使用電話。請讓主人家知道您將夜歸。您處身置地的設想，會使您及主人都感到滿意。

給予您的建議

事先訂好一間房間，以避免屆時沒房間的失望，尤其在夏天時。除外，在您出發的前一天致電到主人家確定您訂好的房間及讓他們曉得您幾時會抵達。有些主人提供接送服務，如果您有需要的話。如果您需要他爲您準備午餐的話，也請您早一、兩天前通知主人。

床鋪及早餐系列

床鋪及早餐

床鋪及早餐是所有不同種類住所的代稱，供您選擇。除外，在您居住時間，主人更會給予您親切友善的招待，讓您有賓至如歸之感。

古典大屋

在床鋪及早餐系列中，古典大屋的建築物具有古典氣息、整齊美觀、寧靜浪漫，是適合喜歡這類型的您來居住，主人將這些建築物的特質保持得非常好，確保您最佳的享受。

鄉村居住

鄉村居住類似家庭住宿。您將居住於私人家庭中，慢慢地認識及接觸鄉村迷人的風景。許多鄉村住宿都靠近著名的旅遊風景區，能讓您最方便認識這些地方。

農場住宿

如果您選擇在農場居住，通常會由農場主人一家人接待您。如有需要，可為您安排參觀農場的行程，好讓您更加了解農場，您將跟農場主人一家人共同享用早餐；晚餐必須在事先通知，農場也將會為您準備，因為農場附近沒有餐館。

床鋪及早餐系列

G 旅客之家

旅客之家通常能容納較多的旅客。雖然如此,主人仍會給您友善親切的招待。旅客之家可能會有數間的客廳及餐廳。旅客之家不常提供晚餐給住客。

BA 家庭住宿

家庭住宿是最普遍的住宿方式,居住在溫暖、友善、好客的家庭中。主人喜歡認識不同的人,且樂意讓您有"家"的感覺,讓您曉得,您剛來的時候雖是一個陌生人,當您要離開時卻是以朋友的身份離開。

LA 豪華大宅

豪華大宅代表了一流的設備,上等的餐飲和超水準的服務,許多此類住宿都有各自的特色,給予您額外一流的享受,它們代表了優越的住宿。

SC 私人住宿

此居住方式,通常包括了,私人的走道、浴室及客廳。它可以是一個家庭中隔出來的一部份或是一整間小屋。早餐可在主人家享用,也可送到您的門口或餐室。

容易聯絡的範圍

您的旅店老闆；無論是何人，
身在何處，都能迅速與他們取
得聯絡。

明確的地址

明確的地址，應包括住宿的地址，電話
和傳真號碼，電子郵件地址與網址。

價目表

價目表上的金額，表示住宿一晚的住宿
費。雙人（ Double ）表示兩人合用一間
房間的價錢。當您預定房間時，您可能要
預付訂金。價目表上的價錢通常包括早
餐，除非有特別註明不提供早餐。全部價
錢都以紐幣計算。請與旅店老闆確定住宿
明細資料。

各種住宿的代表符號

設計這些容易辨認的符號，是為了方便您
預約訂房，對於不太熟悉英文的遊客們，
這是絕對有幫助的。

住宿種類

旅店老闆會為您詳細介紹住宿種類。

地區特色及焦點

您住宿的四周環境以及您住宿區域的特
色與焦點，都會為您列出。

區域地圖

您所住宿的地點，在地圖上將以
紅點標示。旅店的店名，也會在
地圖上刊出。通常為配合找尋，
也都有方向圖來確認正確方向。

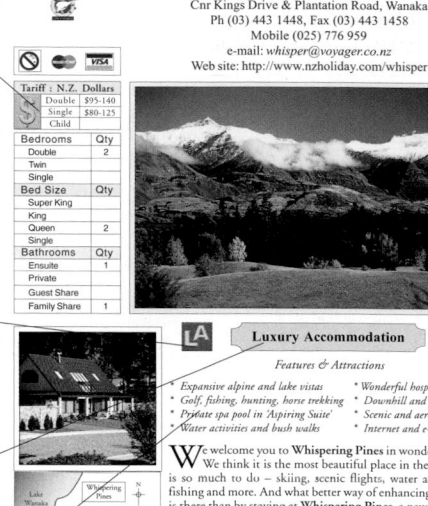

YOUR HOST:	Robyn Lindsay	Ph:(03) 443 1448		Wanaka

WHISPERING PINES
Cnr Kings Drive & Plantation Road, Wanaka
Ph (03) 443 1448, Fax (03) 443 1458
Mobile (025) 776 959
e-mail: *whisper@voyager.co.nz*
Web site: http://www.nzholiday.com/whisper

Tariff : N.Z. Dollars	
Double	$95-140
Single	$80-125
Child	

Bedrooms	Qty
Double	2
Twin	
Single	

Bed Size	Qty
Super King	
King	
Queen	2
Single	

Bathrooms	Qty
Ensuite	1
Private	
Guest Share	
Family Share	1

Luxury Accommodation

Features & Attractions

* Expansive alpine and lake vistas
* Golf, fishing, hunting, horse trekking
* Private spa pool in 'Aspiring Suite'
* Water activities and bush walks
* Wonderful hospitality
* Downhill and nordic skiing
* Scenic and aerobatic flights
* Internet and e-mail access

We welcome you to **Whispering Pines** in wonderful Wanaka. We think it is the most beautiful place in the world. There is so much to do – skiing, scenic flights, water activities, golf, fishing and more. And what better way of enhancing your holiday is there than by staying at **Whispering Pines**, a new, sunny, warm stacked-stone home with wonderful lake and mountain views and handy to town. The "Aspiring Suite" offers ultimate comforts. Relax and contemplate the expansive mountain and lake vista from your own lounge, with TV and tea & coffee making facilities. Soak in your own glass-roofed spa pool. Then retire to the queen size bed, snug with electric blanket and wool-rest. You couldn't ask for more! There are also extensive mountain views from the large "Kings Room" with queen sized bed, electric blanket, woolrest, desk and chairs. Your host Robyn wants to "enrich your holiday" - she will do everything in her power to ensure a memorable and special stay for you at **Whispering Pines**.

DIRECTIONS: Coming from Cromwell just before Wanaka township turn right into Anderson Rd, left into Plantation Rd. Whispering Pines is on the right just past pine plantation.

"一項特別及溫暖的歡迎"

通常歡迎詞是由旅店老闆親自設計。有關
店內設備以及獨特的住宿方式，都會有清
楚的說明。

 No Smoking

縮寫

Cnr—角落
h.p.—半價
N.A. —無此設備
Qty—可磋商
Tce—陽台

直接預約—省錢

與紐西蘭"床與早餐"
旅店系列的老闆直接預約住宿，
您從一開始就會省了許多
不必要的附加費用。

如何使用這本指南 ― 客房資料

房　間

Double ＝ 一或二張床提供兩人住宿的房間
Twin ＝ 提供二張床給兩人住宿的雙人房
Single ＝ 提供一張床給單人住宿的單人房

浴　室

Ensuite ＝浴室在您的房間內
Private ＝ 提供您個人專用的浴室
Guest Share/Family Share ＝公共浴室，必須與
　　其他家庭或住客共同使用。

Bedrooms	Qty
Double	
Twin	
Single	

Bed Size	Qty
Super King	
King	
Queen/Double	
(King-)Single	

Bathrooms	Qty
Ensuite	
Private	
Guest Share	
Family Share	

床的尺寸

Super King
180 x 200cm

King
165 x 200cm

Queen
150 x 200cm

Double
135 x 190cm

Single
90 x 190cm

King Single
90 x 200cm

如何使用這本指南 ― 代號種類

	Bed & Breakfast	G	Guest House / Inn
	Boutique Accommodation	H	Homestay
	Countrystay		Luxury Accommodation
	Farmstay		Self-contained Accom. & Cottages

如何使用這本指南 ― 旅店老闆接受信用卡付款

AMERICAN EXPRESS	Amex – American Express	Bankcard	Bankcard
JCB	Japanese Credit Card	MasterCard	MasterCard
VISA	VISA	Maestro	Maestro
Diners	Diners	eftpos	Eftpos

如何使用這本指南 ― 協會

	Historic Places Trust		Auckland Home & Farmstay
	Hospitality Hosts		Heritage Inns of New Zealand
	New Zealand Association Farm & Home Hosts		Hostlink-Network of Fine Hosts
	Superior Inns of New Zealand		New Zealand's Federation *of* Bed & Breakfast Hotels

 這個商標就是保證您是受本地人所歡迎的，以及獲得親切友善的服務。 Kiwi Host 是紐西蘭顧客服務訓練計畫的得獎者，我們確信我們對於您的重視，與您對於我們的肯定。

Special thanks to all of these friends who gave help and reassurance
when deadlines loomed and spirits were low:

Christine Buess, for production assistance.
Tim Cornelius, famous Dunedin graphic artist.
Joshua and Matthew Newman, photographers.
Julia Stroud, fastest typist in Dunedin.

Scanning by *Norm & Marion Alford at Scanning Services Port Chalmers, Dunedin,*
nitefly@clear.net.nz

Translations
German translation by *Uli Newman.*
Japanese translation by *Yoshi Isoyama at Transla NZ, PO Box 8069, Dunedin, New Zealand.*
isoyama@xtra.co.nz
Mandarin (Chinese) translation by *Stephen Liu at Asian Communication Company Ltd.,*
Dunedin, New Zealand.

Photographs:
Destination Northland. *Pgs 4, 24, 25; E-Mail: northland@xtra.co.nz*
"Hartridge Bed & Breakfast". *Pg 16 vintage car.*
New Zealand Post. *Pg 22 (envelopes), E-Mail: cschelp@nzpost.co.nz*
"Parua House". *Pg 9*
Tourism Rotorua. *Fly Leaf, E-Mail: marketing@tourism.rdc.govt.nz*
Tourism Wairarapa. *Pg 19; E-Mail: tourwai@xtra.co.nz*
West Coast Tourism. *Pg 24, E-Mail: tourismwc@minidata.co.nz*
"The Nikaus", Marlborough Sounds, *Pg.188*
University of Otago Photographic Services. *Pg 271*

Index of Listings (by Regions)

Index of Listings (by Regions)

Index of Listings (by Regions)

Index of Listings (by Regions)

Index of Listings (by Regions)

Index of Listings (by Regions)

Index of Listings (by Regions)

Index of Listings (by Regions)

TRAVEL*wise* Ltd.

Uli and Brian Newman at TRAVEL*wise* would appreciate your comments, good or otherwise.
Your ideas and suggestions will be used to further develope the TRAVELwise Guide.
So please, don't hesitate to send us your ideas, suggestions, complaints or compliments.

Comments

_____

_____

_____

_____

_____

_____

_____

_____

_____

_____

_____

_____

_____

TRAVEL*wise* Ltd.